Surveying Buildings

H S Staveley
FRICS, FCIOB, FRSH, FCIArb

P V Glover
FRICS, ACIArb

Butterworths
London Boston Durban Singapore Sydney Toronto Wellington

First published 1983

© P. V. Glover 1983

British Library Cataloguing in Publication Data

Staveley, H. S.
  1. Surveyors – Great Britain
  I. Title   II. Glover, P. V.
  692   TA549

ISBN 0-408-01309-5

Library of Congress Cataloguing in Publication Data

Staveley, H. S.
  Surveying buildings.
  Bibliography: p.
  Includes index.
  1. Building inspection.   I. Glover, P. V.
  II. Title.
  TH439.S7 1983   692   83-15107

ISBN 0-408-01309-5

Photoset by Butterworths Litho Preparation Department
Printed in Great Britain by Robert Hartnoll Ltd, Bodmin, Cornwall

Preface

The authors were prompted to produce this volume, on the procedures followed by surveyors in their inspection of buildings and the preparation of reports, when they found that there was no other work on the topic which was up-to-date and covered all the ground currently considered to be most relevant.

We hope that fellow practitioners will find the contents helpful to them in their day-to-day work, and that students will find the book instructive.

H S S
P V G

Acknowledgments

The authors gratefully acknowledge the assistance of: National Wesminster Home Loans Ltd who gave permission for the reproduction of their Inspection and Valuation Report form; Rentokil Laboratories who gave permission to reproduce photographs of selected wood borers and timber defects; and Nelson Hurst & Marsh Ltd, Lloyds brokers specialising in surveyors' professional indemnity insurance, who provided the relevant section in Chapter 19.

Contents

Introduction

This book has been written as a practical guide for surveyors and others who may be asked from time to time, or perhaps regularly, to survey buildings, and prepare reports. Although not primarily intended to be a textbook on building construction, it is aimed also at the advanced student who, although perhaps familiar with basic construction, lacks knowledge or experience in building performance. Since therefore the range of experience among readers will be quite broad, well-qualified and experienced surveyors will find that it has been necessary to cover some elementary matters before proceeding to more complex issues. The writers trust that older readers will bear with them while they cover this ground.

The preparation of reports on buildings is a very personal service and since no two surveyors and no two clients will be the same, the style and content of reports can vary considerably from case to case, from practice to practice and in different localities. Though the writers would not wish to try to impose complete uniformity, they have observed certain broad principles in preparing the advice which their book offers, and have paid particular regard to the recommendations laid down in the Practice Note 'Structural Surveys of Residential Property' (May 1981) issued by the Royal Institution of Chartered Surveyors (RICS). The intention of this Practice Note was to introduce some uniformity of procedure and to improve the general standard of reports on residential property prepared by chartered surveyors.

At a time when the professions are open to searching criticism and the public are becoming more litigation conscious, it is not surprising that claims against the professions from their clients are increasing in numbers and value. All professions are affected by this trend but there are few areas of activity where the potential for significant error giving rise to serious financial losses to the client can be as great as in the field of structural surveys, especially where the larger type of commercial and industrial structures are concerned.

As a result of the tendency for surveyors' reports to become longer and for clients to expect more from their surveyor, there has now arisen a demand for a more abbreviated form of report on residential property and for shorter pro-forma reports. Not only do the major building societies now send a copy of their report to the borrower but the RICS have published their own pro-forma reports for intending house-buyers, banks and borrowers in connection with mortgage valuations. In response to this trend, a chapter on the use of such reports has been included in this book with some guidance as to the procedures to be followed. Later chapters deal with commercial and industrial buildings, flats, new and older buildings, and leasehold property reports as well as reports for mortgage purposes.

Publications mentioned in the text are listed in the bibliography so that the source of additional information on a particular topic may readily be found.

Chapter 18 covering specimen reports has been included only for guidance as to the layout and wording which may be adopted in typical reports. The examples should be followed cautiously rather than slavishly. The intention of using standard report clauses is that they can make report drafting easier, whether or not a word processor is used, in that they allow the rapid drafting or dictation of those parts which are routine, permitting the surveyor more time to devote to the particular and specific problems of the building under review.

Obviously all possible steps should be taken to avoid wasting time on routine report drafting or dictation from notes since the surveyor's time is his most valuable resource and it must be used efficiently.

Finally, a comprehensive index has been provided with references to the sections concerned in the book and sources of additional information where known.

The nomenclature used in the book and in the reports is that which is the most simple and straightforward. In respect of the reports which the reader may prepare, the writers would recommend the use of simple, straightforward English. Technical expressions should be avoided altogether when writing to a client unless they are known to be understood by that client or are explained at the time. Similarly, the writers have used spellings which the clients would expect rather than those which some surveyors may prefer. For example, throughout the text 'sill' is used rather than the more traditional surveyors' 'cill', and we have also used 'lintel' as being more suitable than 'lintol' for the same reason. Clients seeing 'cill' and 'lintol' in a report assume that a spelling mistake has been made, thus making the accuracy of the report suspect in their minds.

During the course of preparing the book, a selection of files for properties inspected and reported upon over the previous ten years was studied. Considering the nature of the properties involved and the variety of clients, we had cause to reflect on what a very mixed bunch they were. One point standing out from this evidence was that despite the almost inexhaustible range of possible building defects which could arise, a great deal of building construction is still basically sound. Reports which dealt with minor defects in a routine manner were the rule rather than the exception, most buildings being structurally sound. In only about 5% of cases were the buildings in such poor repair or subject to such serious defects that the client was advised not to buy or lease them unless prepared for substantial expenditure to put things right.

The main question from clients was, 'Is this price (or rent) fair and reasonable?'. In order to answer this question, surveyors need knowledge of both building construction and property values in the locality because, at the end of the day, after everything has been said about the leaking roof, the damp, the furniture beetle and a multitude of other potential hazards, it is that simple question which has to be answered.

H. S. S.
P. V. G.

Chapter 1

The surveyor and his instructions

It is highly important to ordinary members of the lay public that a surveyor should use proper care to warn them regarding matters about which they should be warned over the construction or otherwise of a piece of property and that they should be told what are the facts.
Mr. Justice Hilberry – Rona v Pearce (1953)

The Oxford Dictionary defines a surveyor as, among other things, 'a person professionally engaged in surveying', and to survey as 'let the eyes pass over, take general view of, form general idea of the arrangement and chief features of, make or present survey of; examine condition of (building etc); determine boundaries, size, position, shape, contour, etc, of (land, coast, district, estate, etc);' whence surveying!

The primary purpose of a structural survey is to give an independent professional opinion on the structural condition of a property, but the word 'independent' as used here probably requires further explanation. Strictly speaking, the surveyor carrying out the structural survey cannot be wholly independent since he is acting on behalf of his client, the purchaser, whose interests he is serving. However, the main object of such a survey is to ensure that an opinion is given by someone who has no connection with the vendor or his agents. In the same vein, the surveyor acting for a building society cannot be regarded as wholly independent since of necessity he must consider the building society's interests before those of a prospective purchaser, and he is therefore more likely to 'play safe' in his expressed opinions. As far as the description 'professional' is concerned, then those who are best qualified to carry out such a survey must have had considerable experience in the performance of buildings and their components as well as their design and construction.

The survey

Since the end of the Second World War, the expression 'structural survey' has entered the vocabulary of those engaged in the property market and their advisers. This term, although not ideal, is now generally used throughout the United Kingdom, and surveyors, estate agents, solicitors and bank managers, as well as many members of the public engaged in buying and selling houses, have become familiar with the term and the nature of the service it embraces. A large proportion of the property-owning public have commissioned surveyors' reports on buildings they have occupied or are about to occupy.

A structural survey report provided by a surveyor when a house is likely to change hands is now a commonplace occurrence. While many houses are still sold without the benefit of such a report, in an increasing proportion of cases a structural survey *is* involved and evidence suggests that about 20% of house buyers now commission their own report.

It is interesting to reflect that the provision of this service to the general public is a recent development brought about by a rapid increase in house ownership since the Second World War and an increasing awareness among the public of the possible pitfalls involved in owning defective property or buildings needing expensive upkeep. The present-day consumer expects value for money, is more knowledgeable in respect of the building he occupies, and has standards higher than those of previous generations.

The surveying profession may fulfill two roles in undertaking structural surveys of houses. First, clients can be advised and, if necessary, they can also be warned. Sometimes a great deal of expense and heart-ache may be avoided for a client who secures a surveyor's report on a building suffering from important defects which, although not apparent to the untrained eye, are obvious to the surveyor. A second role which surveyors may rightly assume is that of front-line professionals who daily come into contact with the nation's building stock and by careful examination and considered advice, may assist in the better maintenance of that stock for the benefit of the community as a whole.

It is also interesting and salutary for the practising surveyor to consider procedures followed in other countries. The house-buying public in the United Kingdom is fortunate in having available a service which is unrivalled elsewhere. In many parts of the world, even in highly-developed countries, the provision of professionally-prepared reports of the type available in the UK is unknown. This is an important service which must be encouraged and, where necessary, improved, and competent, well-trained surveyors are essential for the maintenance of this service in the future.

The surveyor

Before undertaking structural surveys, the surveyor should be qualified both academically and by practical experience to a high standard, but there is at present no statutory requirement for him to be so. Anyone may set himself (or herself) up as a surveyor and accept instructions from the general public to undertake such surveys. Undesirable as this may seem, there is no obvious prospect of the situation changing in the foreseeable future, although an unqualified surveyor without a professional indemnity insurance policy is taking a very high risk. On the issue of academic qualification it must, however, be said that there are many members of the profession who have had little or no examination success in the formal sense but who are nevertheless well qualified by their long experience and detailed knowledge to prepare reports to the highest standard.

Similarly, there are younger professional members who embark upon their careers lacking practical knowledge, having only examination success to start them off. The decision as to whether or not a newly-qualified surveyor is ready to undertake this complex and difficult work is not easy to take. Preferably, an older, more experienced surveyor should be available to advise his younger colleague on the timing of this decision based upon some personal knowledge of that younger man and his professional skills.

In case the reader may be a young man or woman contemplating surveying as a career, or an older man or woman advising on career choice, the writers would mention briefly the features which would seem to them to be needed by an individual wishing to undertake this work. There are, of course, other branches of the surveying profession to which these comments may not necessarily apply.

First, a surveyor should have good command of the English language, the ability to express himself in reports with clarity and the ability to express himself to his clients with verbal conviction.

Secondly, the surveyor should have a practical turn of mind. He should be capable, to a reasonable extent, of understanding the processes of building construction and the working of services such as heating systems. He should be able to assimilate new ideas and building processes. It is helpful, although not essential, for him to be able to undertake simple building operations himself since in many situations a personal knowledge of basic carpentry, brickwork operations, concreting, electrical wiring and plumbing can be of inestimable value.

Thirdly, the surveyor should acquire a tactful and pleasant personality. When inspecting houses before purchase it will be necessary for him to visit a vendor's home in circumstances which may be stressful for the vendor or his wife and to spend a considerable time there often with the intention of finding faults. He should never underestimate the anxious anticipation which will precede his visit and the fact that the vendor assumes that each note taken indicates a defect found or that from his point of view the longer the time spent on the inspection, the worse will be the resulting report. The surveyor should explain what he is going to do and should first ask for permission to proceed.

The foregoing may seem trivial or even obvious to the reader, but it is surprising how often, in practice, one hears of surveyors who have been less than courteous, left unrepaired damage or engendered in the vendor a general feeling of hostility. The surveyor is an ambassador of his profession and his client and should never lose sight of this fact.

Equipment

The surveyor requires certain items of equipment for use during his survey, but what is considered necessary tends to vary from one firm to another. The following are items which the writers have always found helpful.

First, lighting is needed for roof spaces, under floors and other dark areas in order to ensure a thorough inspection of timbers and structure. It is recommended that a protected lamp-holder be carried with an extension lead so that mains-powered lighting can be used whenever mains electricity is available. There is no real substitute for mains-powered lighting for this purpose and a lead-light with 100 to 150-W bulb should be. A selection of electric socket adaptors can also prove useful.

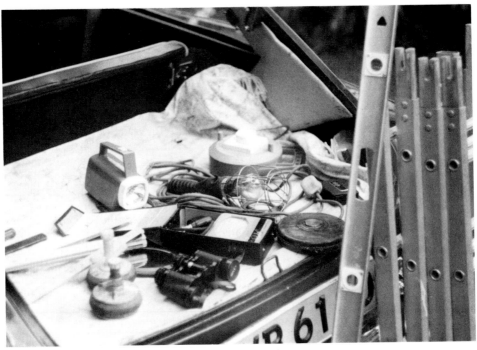

Figure 1.1 Typical set of equipment carried by a surveyor to inspect a simple low-rise building: folding wooden rule, torch, drain plugs, binoculars, moisture meter (probe type), lead lamp, extension lead, linen and steel tapes, long spirit level, surveyor's sectional ladder

Some lighting should also be carried for those situations where no mains electricity is provided. Powerful torches with spare batteries and bulbs are used by the writers. Lead-lights which run off 12-V car batteries are also used and may have advantages.

Tapes for taking dimensions are necessary. The writers use short steel tapes for taking dimensions in small rooms and of timber sizes, also a longer linen tape for longer distances. A folding wooden rule is useful for some purposes, for example it can be inserted between boards in a timber floor to check the depth of section of the floor joists.

Ladders are essential for gaining access to roof voids and external roofs. Lightweight aluminium ladders are recommended for this purpose and the writers use aluminium 'surveyors' ladders' which dismantle into four sections for fitting into a car boot.

Important attributes for any surveyor are that he has a reasonable head for heights and is sure-footed when engaged on inspections above floor level. A reasonable standard of fitness is also required since there will be many occasions when the surveyor himself, rather than an assistant, must look closely at a particular item. It may not be possible to stay at ground level and rely upon second-hand details taken by a helper. We hear that on one occasion a student was sent up a long extension ladder to the roof of a block of flats, not, as he discovered later, because his valued opinions were required but in order to test his resistance to vertigo. Access to roof voids, the roofs themselves and underfloor areas often require strenuous acrobatic feats.

Any surveyor should have available at least one good moisture meter for testing woodwork, plasterwork and other areas for dampness. The meter dial should be checked by shorting out the probes on each occasion before the instrument is used, and it should also be zeroed to ensure that it is functioning correctly and that the batteries are not expended. It is important that an instrument with failing or flat batteries should not be used since its readings will then be inaccurate and unreliable.

Various tools and other useful items which can be carried in the car boot include a pair of wellington boots, a spade for taking subsoil samples, assorted drain plugs, and manhole cover-lifting keys, together with a hammer and cold chisel for tight covers. Mirrors, too, are very useful. A small mirror can be used to look along underground drains between manholes and to check for tree-root intrusion, stepped fractures in the pipework and other obstructions. Mirrors are also invaluable for providing a wide view under floors and in other areas difficult of access. A good quality long spirit level for checking walls and floors is invaluable, as is a plumb-line. A pair of binoculars should be used for gaining a clearer view from ground level of roof details and upper storeys.

The following equipment, then, is recommended.

Wellington boots	Plumb line
Moisture meter	Protected lampholder for lead
Binoculars	Folding wooden rule
Clip board	Spade
Torch	Long spirit level
Linen tape	Tool box and assorted tools
Short level	Sectional aluminium ladder
Briefcase	Manhole keys
Extension lead	Claw hammer
Electric socket adaptors	Screwdriver
Drain plug	Notebook
Hand mirror	Hand tape recorder
Steel tape	

Instructions

A surveyor may be asked to prepare a structural survey report on a house for an intending purchaser, and this service may sometimes include a valuation of that house. He may be asked to prepare a pro-forma report for a bank, building society, insurance company or other lender, and this will undoubtedly include a valuation for mortgage purposes, probably also the provision of an estimate of the reinstatement cost involved in rebuilding the property for insurance purposes. The surveyor may be asked to inspect a house and provide the RICS 'House-Buyer's Report and Valuation' where a valuation is included automatically as part of the service. Where the survey report is being prepared for the purchaser of the freehold or the prospective lessee of a commercial property, then in many cases this is likely to include a valuation. It will be appreciated that the question of value is often fundamental to the advice being given. A client should know whether the price or rent being asked is fair, having regard to the implications of any matters raised in the surveyor's report.

In order to be able to advise in this way, the surveyor should be familiar with property values in the locality concerned. It can be dangerous for a surveyor to accept instructions to value property either in an unfamiliar locality or of a type with which he is not normally professionally involved. There will be exceptional cases, of course, where a client will ask a specific surveyor, in whose judgment he trusts, to travel some distance and report on a property for him, and it would seem quite reasonable for such instructions to be accepted provided that the client understands the implications and the possible limitations, points which should be confirmed in the surveyor's letter of acceptance of the instructions.

Again, there are many specialised types of property such as hotels, licensed premises, garages and others where special markets exist and where specialist firms of surveyors might best be consulted on questions of value. Where the building construction itself and the subsoils may be unfamiliar, it would not seem unreasonable for a surveyor to accept instructions provided that the position is explained and the fee is adequate to cover the additional research which will be necessary.

The RICS Practice Note 'Structural Surveys of Residential Property' recommends that before he takes instructions the surveyor discusses his client's requirements with him and advises on the type of survey needed. In some cases time should be spent with the client assessing his needs. It is considered essential, in the interests of both client and surveyor, that when instructions are given, the surveyor should write to his client to acknowledge their receipt and to confirm their details. In respect of structural surveys of houses, the RICS recommend that if possible this be achieved by a covering letter and a short pre-printed booklet describing in detail the extent and limitations of the proposed survey, a system already adopted by some larger surveying practices. At this stage the surveyor should also agree either the fee or the method of assessing the fee (i.e. if an hourly or other rate for professional time is to be charged).

There may be occasions where verbal instructions can be accepted from regular clients already familiar with the procedure and this will normally apply in the case of pro-forma reports for institutional or company clients who will already understand what is involved. The RICS recommendations need apply only to surveys or valuations for members of the public with whom the surveyor is dealing for the first time.

The Practice Note recommends that with respect to surveys of residential property the following matters be confirmed in writing by the surveyor to his client:

(1) The nature of the instructions. If something less than a structural survey is to be carried out it is important that the extent of the obligations being assumed by the surveyor are understood and agreed to by the client. Many surveyors decline to take instructions for anything less than a full survey for an intending purchaser, save in most unusual circumstances.

However, there will be many instances where a partial survey of some specific aspect of a building may be undertaken for an owner occupying his own property, perhaps concerned about some specific defect in, say, a roof or a particular floor. Where such a report is prepared for an owner, the letter confirming instructions will make clear the limitations of the advice given.

(2) When the survey is likely to be carried out. Contact should first be made through the vendor or his agent with the occupier of the premises to be surveyed and arrangements made for the inspection to be carried out at a

convenient time and date. The occupier should be informed of what is involved in the survey and the extent to which he will probably be inconvenienced. He must be told how long the survey might take and how many people are likely to be present, particularly if specialists are involved in testing and inspecting the services.

(3) The surveyor's intentions regarding:
   (a) The extent of the inspection of the main structure.
   (b) The extent of the inspection of outbuildings and grounds.
   (c) The amount of structural exposure to be carried out.
   (d) The limitations of inspection where surfaces are covered (e.g. by fitted carpets).
   (e) The extent to which furniture will have to be moved.
   (f) Any limitation of liability in the form of a general exclusion clause which will appear in the subsequent report.
   (g) The extent of enquiries to be made of local and statutory authorities.
   (h) The extent to which the survey includes the testing of services.
   (i) The fee payable and method of assessment.
   (j) Whether or not valuations are included. Estimates of reinstatement costs and the costs of recommended works and any limitations and reservations applicable to such works.

In most cases similar points will need to be confirmed when accepting instructions to prepare reports on commercial and industrial premises since the liability is the same and the scope for structural exposure may be more limited due to the nature of the occupation of the premises.

The Practice Note also recommends that appointments made with the vendor should be confirmed in writing with a note of the length of time likely to be involved and the extent to which the surveyor proposes to lift floor coverings, expose the structure or test services. This will not always be necessary. Frequently the surveyor will have to inspect empty buildings to which access will be gained by keys borrowed from estate agents. A letter to the vendor in these circumstances would be inappropriate. If no special exposure work or tests of services are to be undertaken then the survey of an empty building may proceed without any written exchange with the vendor or his agents but otherwise prior consent for opening up or testing should be obtained.

To record his observations the surveyor may take written notes on a clipboard or he may rely upon portable dictation or dictation to an assistant, as explained later in this chapter. The results of the inspection are confidential to the client unless that client wishes to reveal them. It is therefore necessary to observe discretion when taking notes as comments overheard by the vendor may be misconstrued. On no account should the surveyor discuss his findings with the vendor either during the course of his inspection or afterwards. Neither should he permit the vendor access to his notes.

Organisation

The surveyor's practice requires office premises and staff to be organised so as to provide all necessary assistance to surveyors in the field. Such organisation varies considerably from practice to practice, which range from small one-man firms to major multi-partner practices needing specialist management. Very often the one-man firms can offer a better service since a structural survey is a highly personal matter between client and surveyor which, in any event, can be carried out effectively by only one person.

It is suggested that the surveyors' practice should have a library kept up-to-date with all the relevant technical publications as they are published. The Building Research Establishment (BRE) publishes quarterly its *BRE News* as well as digests, information papers and technical papers.

The *Registered House-Builders' Handbook* is essential where new housing is to be reported upon. The writers have found it helpful to retain sections dealing with the previous types of certificate which were issued by the National House-Building Council (NHBC) prior to the current type, since procedures under previous certificates are different from those currently applicable. Older technical requirements where these have been superseded should be retained in order to be able to comment upon houses which are not now new but which are still subject to NHBC protection. Although basic NHBC requirements have not changed, a number of important detailed practice notes have been added to deal with certain specific problems.

A set of Ordnance Survey maps should be kept covering the district in which the practice operates. These can be invaluable by indicating old quarries, mine shafts, gravel workings and suchlike features as well as by providing information on local watercourses which can sometimes indicate where underground water may be present. At the base of a valley, the contours could indicate whether or not a constricted flood plain exists which in exceptional circumstances might pose a flood risk. The geological survey maps also indicate subsoil types and possible areas of fill material where gravel or other workings may exist, and a set of such maps covering the practice area is recommended.

Bomb maps are also available showing where known explosive devices fell in some localities during the Second World War. Occasionally important evidence of structural bomb damage may be confirmed from such maps. Information on bomb damage may also be obtained from the Greater London Council (for the London area) and the Imperial War Museum. The records are not complete but the authors have found them to be helpful on occasions.

Having completed the physical side of the survey, the surveyor returns to his office to draft the report. The writers recommend that this be done using a standard procedure, with a standard set of headings and layout and that some of the report may be compiled using specimen clauses to permit more rapid dictation or drafting and eliminate as much as possible of the time involved in the more routine parts of the report. The surveyor may then devote his time to those parts of the report which are individual and most important to the specific client. In the case of reports dictated on site, the experienced surveyor will be able to save a great deal of his time and consequently his client's money!

A suitable atmosphere is needed when a report has to be drafted and it is important to be able to work free from interruption and distraction with all the information needed readily to hand. It is also recommended, wherever possible, that each individual deals with one report at a time and completes the drafting of that report before commencing another. No matter how comprehensive the notes, there will often be points relevant to the report which arise from memory and it is clearly essential that the property under review should not become confused with another. Again, in the case of reports dictated directly on site, there is less likelihood of missing anything of importance as each item is then described while it is actually being inspected.

Clients

Having considered the means by which the surveyor takes instructions and undertakes to provide reports, it is necessary to consider the clients for whom he will be acting. The relationship between the surveyor and his client is a contractual relationship on the basis of which a service is provided and payment for that service is made. A relationship also exists between the surveyor and his client and may exist between the surveyor and third parties under the law of tort.

The report may be read and relied upon by third parties and if the surveyor wishes to avoid third party liability under the law of tort, a specific disclaimer to this effect should be inserted in that report. A particular danger arises when a report and valuation are being used by the client to raise a loan on the security in circumstances where that valuation may have been provided for some other purpose or where the surveyor should have included other or different advice had he known the use to which the report would be put. Cases have even been known of current market valuations being used by ill-advised clients for fire insurance purposes. Another hazard is that a report for a property owner which is related only to some particular aspect of construction, and is therefore not a complete report, may be used by that owner to further the sale of the property at a later date, and would perhaps be relied upon by a subsequent purchaser. In the case of commercial or industrial premises, a specific client running a particular type of business could obtain a report which could later be used by the proprietor of quite a different type of business for whom additional or different advice ought to have been necessary.

As a general rule it is recommended that a specific disclaimer against any liability to third parties be inserted prominently in all reports, although this may not of itself provide complete protection against third party claims. (See Chapter 19).

In the case of clients requiring reports on residential property, we have encountered a number of unusual cases where special treatment was called for. One such case is that of the disabled client who may be unable physically to make a proper inspection himself and who has particular needs for specific doorway widths and ramps for wheelchairs. It is advisable to spend some time ascertaining the specific needs of such a client and to cover those needs in the report.

Reports for blind clients have been prepared on the basis that the report would be read out to them and it is then necessary to reconcile two conflicting needs. A blind client needs a reasonably brief report which is very much to the point since it is otherwise most difficult to assimilate all the information when the report is read aloud. He also needs some description of all those matters which the sighted client will already know about and we have found that a considerable challenge arises in providing such a service.

Elderly clients might be warned about design which may be unsympathetic to their needs and a point should be made of closely checking staircase balustrading and handrails, also tight staircase winders which, although not now permitted under the Building Regulations, may be common in older buildings. Clients having young children should also be warned about this type of hazard and also the potential danger where there are large sheets of ordinary-quality glass in glazed doorways and patio doors.

On occasion, clients will consider buying a building with a view to a change of use, making alterations or carrying out extensions. They should be warned that planning permission may be needed for the proposal they have in mind and that the granting of planning permission can never be regarded as a foregone conclusion. We can recall a number of cases where the planning officer enthusiastically discused a proposal which was later rejected by the planning committee. This frequency of this occurrence is roughly equal to the number of cases where planning officers are distinctly gloomy about the prospects for a proposal which is later approved without difficulty.

Passing of plans under London building acts or Building Regulations may also be necessary and could present problems which should be mentioned in the report.

If permission to undertake alterations to or to change the use of a property is essential to the viability of the purchase, then the client should be advised to postpone any exchange of contracts until the outcome of applications for such changes is known and the certificates are in hand.

Clients buying a freehold building with a view to undertaking alterations may require permission under the terms of restrictive title covenants in addition to local and national statutory requirements. This applies especially to residential developments in the higher price brackets where estate covenants exist which could restrict considerably the alterations or changes of use which may be allowed.

For clients taking an existing or new lease and contemplating undertaking alterations or improvements to the premises, the consent of the freeholder and any intermediate leaseholder will generally be needed. In some cases there are certain steps which a lessee may take to safeguard his position and to secure an entitlement to compensation in respect of business premises. If the surveyor is aware of the proposals the client has in mind, he could provide helpful advice, not only on the physical and financial problems involved in undertaking the works, but also on the legal implications.

When it is known that the property to be surveyed has been altered or extended in the past, or its use has been changed, the client may wish to know whether such works had the necessary local authority approvals and any other consents. If not, he should be informed as to the implications which may arise. In the case of residential property, it is often found that small extensions or internal structural alterations have been undertaken, perhaps in an amateur fashion and without any consent being granted under the London building acts or Building Regulations. Occasionally a clear breach of regulations may be found and the question arises as to whether or not the local authority may wish to take action. In the vast majority of cases no action would be taken since the local authority are unlikely to know of the breach unless their attention is called to it. Building Regulations enforcement proceedings against a property owner will not normally be taken after a period of a year has elapsed from the commission of the breach save in unusual circumstances.

Clear breaches of Building Regulations or London building acts which appear in recently completed works should be noted and the details be given to the clients who may then take legal advice. In general most breaches will constitute defects which the surveyor will, in any event, discuss in his report, but occasionally such breaches could be purely technical and acceptable to the client such as, for example, natural lighting or ventilation requirements, low ceiling heights and the like. These are then merely to be pointed out to the client who may decide what, if anything, he wishes to do about them.

The possibility of enforcement proceedings being taken against a property owner under the Town and Country Planning Acts could arise in respect of unauthorised buildings, extensions or changes of use. Generally, buildings completed for four years or more are immune to such proceedings. Changes of use, however, need to have been established before 1 January 1964 to be immune, and if a surveyor is aware of buildings or changes of use which could be of doubtful legality, this may be a matter which the surveyor, the client and the client's solicitor should consider. The surveyor is the professional adviser who will actually spend time at the property concerned, whereas the solicitor will rarely see the property and any relevant information which the surveyor can provide is usually keenly appreciated.

Fees

The basis upon which the surveyor's fees will be calculated should be agreed in advance with the client. The RICS Practice Note states that this is one of a number of essential matters which should be confirmed with the client for structural surveys of residential property. It would also be necessary for surveys of other types of property except where the work is being undertaken for a client for whom the surveyor regularly acts on an agreed basis, or where a service is provided for prospective mortgagees or other clients and an agreed scale of charges applies.

During the course of the preparation of this book, the authors investigated a limited sample of procedures used by the other surveyors in assessing fees. In some practices the fees for residential surveys are assessed at a rate per room of accommodation and in others a scale proportionate to the proposed purchase price. In each case there was some variation having regard to the age of the property. At most times it was found that the charge was related to the amount of professional time involved in the inspection and the researching for the report, the account then being on an hourly basis.

Having considered the variations which are possible, the authors concluded that the fairest means of assessing fees would be on the basis of a charge at an agreed rate per hour of professional time taken, plus disbursements at cost. In taking instructions, it should be possible to explain to the client the approximate amount of professional time which would be involved on a specific survey having regard to the value, the size and age of the structure and the specific instructions of the client.

There are no fixed scales of charges for structural surveys. Scale 31 of the scales of professional charges published by the RICS simply states that 'A fee by arrangement according to circumstances' should be charged. In so far as a structural survey is being undertaken together with a valuation, then it is suggested that it should be possible for the overall cost to be reduced to the client so that a fee based upon a valuation scale, plus the additional professional time taken to prepare the extra structrual information, might apply. Although some surveyors have compiled their own scale rate of fees for structural surveys based on a percentage of the offer price of the property, this can be patently unfair against one party or the other. Take, for instance, the examples of a cottage with a very low offer price and minimal accommodation but in very poor order and requiring a considerable amout of time spent on the survey compared with a large expensive house in exceptionally good condition. The former could quite well prove more expensive in terms of time than the latter.

Increasingly, surveyors will find that they are instructed to prepare a valuation for a prospective mortgagee and at the same time carry out a structural survey for the prospective mortgagor. In such circumstances a reduced overall fee should normally apply as compared with the aggregate of the fees which would apply if the matters were dealt with separately. It is recommended that particular care then be taken to establish at the outset exactly who will be liable for which fee and to bill accordingly.

Traditionally, professional men render accounts after services have been given and often quite a little while later, especially in the case of regular and retained clients. However, having regard to the possibility of bad debts arising, especially when residential property is being surveyed, an account may be rendered with the report in cases where the client was not previously known to the surveyor. Steps should then be taken to recover fees as promptly as possible in such cases. If a client does not buy the house but moves elsewhere, it may be difficult to trace him in order to recover overdue charges.

All surveyors' offices therefore should have a firm procedure for following up outstanding accounts and recovering fees as promptly as possible, and such matters should not be allowed to drift.

In some situations it may be necessary to ask for a payment on account in advance for building surveying or other services, but in the writers' experience and that of the sample of surveyors with whom this was discussed, such action is rarely taken.

As a last resort, a client can be sued for non-payment of fees through the County Court procedure for small claims. The amount of fees for most structural surveys on a domestic scale would come within the limits set for County Court claims but it should be emphasised that this procedure should not be contemplated unless it is a 'one-off' client whom you know to be deliberately perverse. In these circumstances, such claims are not normally defended but it is a risk one has to take and although easy to make the application, if the defendant decides to counterclaim this could prove to be a most expensive and time-consuming matter, not to mention the bad publicity involved. Further details may be obtained from a booklet *Small Claims in the County Court* published by HMSO.

Preliminaries

Notes required during the course of the survey may be taken in writing on A4 or similarly-sized paper attached to a clipboard. This enables reasonably-sized sketches to be included. These notes, together with any correspondence relating to the matter and a copy of the final report, may be bound together durably in a permanent file and retained indefinitely in the surveyor's filing system, suitably referenced for identification should this be needed in the future. Alternatively, a 'notebook' tape recorder of the Grundig or Philips type may be used on site and the survey either typed straight off or in double-spaced draft form through a transcriber in the office. This method is particularly suitable where unoccupied buildings are being surveyed but otherwise the greatest care over confidentiality should be taken. Only very experienced surveyors should use this method and then preferably in conjunction with an *aide memoire* checklist.

Having regard to the potential legal liabilities involved in this type of work and that actions in tort might be taken against a negligent surveyor some considerable time later, it is felt that it would be unwise to destroy old files relating to structural reports. Apart from the question of legal liability, which should never arise in a well-run professional practice, there is also the fact that at some time a surveyor may find himself inspecting the same house again for some other purpose, perhaps on re-sale or to prepare design drawings for alterations. An original file in such circumstances could prove invaluable.

One of the well-known features of office life is that immediately old files are destroyed, perhaps having collected dust for many years, invariably something occurs which could have been dealt with better by recourse to the destroyed information. In larger professional practices, shortage of space may require microfilming of important old files so that the information contained may be retained in a more compact yet accessible form.

An office record system should include cross-references to all old files so that these are identified by the address, the client's name and the nature of the subject matter. In the future it would then be possible to look up old reports prepared for properties in the same area or in respect of the same building; also reports prepared for the same client over the years can then be compared and reports of an unusual nature may be compared with similar previous records. For example, in cases where, say, garages, public houses or ecclesiastical buildings are occasionally inspected, reference may be made to files for properties of a similar type in order to compare the approach adopted in the past.

In so far as the office records system deals with property values and building costs, these may also be recorded by reference to property type, size and characteristics, then cross-referenced to the main filing system. Since property valuation is essentially the art of comparing one property with another, accurate records of prices and rents for properties in the surveyor's area are essential if valuation opinions are to be soundly based.

In order to deal adequately with the full range of instructions likely to be received, a surveyor should be able to call upon assistance from other specialists and trades as required. It is helpful if continuing relationships be fostered with specialists and some trades with this in mind. A local firm of consulting engineers will be needed from time to time, a jobbing builder with long extension ladders and tools for undertaking exposure work will be necessary to assist with certain types of inspection, and a plumber and electrician will be competent to test the drains and electrical systems. A good specialist heating engineer who is able to prepare reports on heating systems is an added bonus, especially if he also tests and reports upon air conditioning units.

Having organised his office and his equipment and taken instructions from his client, the surveyor must brace himself to proceed with the survey. He will find many varied matters of interest every time he leaves his office and considerable challenges to his knowledge in many cases. The work will rarely be routine or boring and will often be enjoyable and rewarding, particularly if the advice given can be helpful and the clients who receive it may be grateful, especially if the report enables the clients to ensure that the purchase price is fair.

Up to this point, not yet even having undertaken the survey, the reader may have been led to believe that a living which is largely dependent upon structural surveys is too hazardous to contemplate. However, if one has a good working knowledge of design and construction, sticks to facts in the report, ignores hearsay and does not venture too many opinions, then structural surveys can help to make a rewarding career for the surveyor. Every single building is different, each has its own individual atmosphere and character and there is no better way of appreciating the love and craftsmanship which over the years has gone into so much of our architectural heritage.

Chapter 2

House surveys

We do not want a structural survey. If you can just have a quick look at the house to make sure that it is structurally sound, that will be fine.
Extract from client's letter of instructions

Inspection procedures

A surveyor should follow a definite procedure when inspecting a property. This procedure will vary from one practitioner to another, but in the writers' view, it is preferable in most cases to begin inside the building at the top and finish outside at the bottom.

For example, the procedure for a conventional two-storey dwelling-house might be:

(1) A preliminary inspection of the whole property to familiarise the surveyor with type and layout.
(2) A detailed inspection of the main roof-space and any subsidiary roof voids which are accessible.
(3) A room-by-room inspection at each floor level starting from the topmost floor.
(4) Inspection of accessible basements, cellars and sub-floor areas.
(5) An examination of the roof structure and coverings from ground level, using binoculars if necessary, and from ladders or through roof voids where accessible.
(6) An examination of the elevations, including structure and finishes.
(7) Inspection of the site boundaries, outbuildings and surroundings.
(8) Examination and testing of the drains.

Detailed procedures

The detailed procedures under each of the preceding sections are as follows:

(1) Preliminaries

The surveyor notes the general character and description of the property, i.e. whether detached, semi-detached, terraced, end-of-terrace, flat, bungalow, two-storey house, three-storey or other. If semi-detached, note if this is a left-hand or right-hand unit, and if terraced or linked to other units the overall length of the terrace should be stated.

The foundations serve a detached structure in isolation and that structure will not normally require provision for movement unless it is very large. Conversely, a long terrace has to be seen as a structural whole and the surveyor must consider whether the entire terrace has been designed to resist the forces to which it will be subject, including possible differential ground and thermal movements. Many examples of terraces of older houses will be encountered, some very long indeed and constructed without any provision for movement. In such circumstances his inspection should include the elevations of the whole terrace, not just the particular subject property.

Figure 2.1 When surveying a house it is wise to look carefully at the elevations. The distinct slope of the sill and lintel of this Victorian fenestration tells a story of past structural movement below ground (Middlesex 1982)

The surveyor must note the general lie of the land and the gradient on which the building stands. If the gradient is abnormal he will then be placed on his guard over the possibility of ground movements or landslips and the consequent need for a structural check on the foundation design. Houses built on sloping sites generally suffer more from problems of this type than those built on level sites, and in his subsequent inspection the surveyor will be looking for signs of past structural movements in such circumstances.

Reference may be made to the geological survey map for the area in which the property is located prior to the inspection and this will indicate the likely subsoil conditions. Again, caution is advised if the subsoil indicated on the geological survey map is shrinkable clay, or if worked-out gravel pits or old quarry workings are shown indicating possible unsuitable fill material or made ground. The surveyor will then be aware of the various subsoil conditions in his locality and their characteristics and will approach the survey armed with this information.

An important feature of any survey is to ascertain the age of the structure to be inspected. In most cases the surveyor will know on arrival roughly how old the property is from a first glance. If this is not the case, he should study the property and those nearby, then ask the vendor, appreciating that he may not be a reliable source of information. The age of the building is most material in deciding the advice to give on a wide range of problems, particularly on pitched and flat roof coverings which have well-defined life spans, as well as the brickwork or stonework, the timbers used, and finishes such as lath-and-plaster ceilings, all of which can vary in life span and quality according to the period during which the building was erected.

(2) The roof voids

The type of roof covering and its condition should be fully described. It may help to draw a sketch plan of the roof and make a note of the size and span of major timber members. At this stage the surveyor will also inspect the ceilings, any ceiling insulation, party walls and gable walls which may be present, and electrical or plumbing services in the roof-space. The detailing around and behind any chimney stacks which may be seen from within the roof should be carefully examined.

It is recommended that a high proportion of the survey time be devoted to the inspection inside the roof since in this way a great deal can be learned about the building. Here one can usually work quietly and undisturbed, except that occasionally a vendor has been known to make use of the surveyor's ladder to carry out his own inspection or even to more items of storage in or out!

Extreme care should be taken in negotiating the ceiling joists if the floor of the roof-space is unboarded. A foot through the vendor's ceiling can cause considerable embarrassment and he will probably assume that the surveyor is a novice. Good illumination is essential, not only for the surveyor to carry out his examination properly but also for his own safety and that of the property under survey.

One of the writers found to his cost that a leg through an early 19th Century lath-and-plaster ceiling is very difficult to extract as, like a shark's jaws, the harder one pulls the tighter the grip of the broken laths becomes.

(3) Room-by-room inspection

It may first be helpful to take the dimensions in each room. A note is then made of the condition of the ceilings, walls and floors. Doors and windows should be tested by opening and closing and any distorted openings and door architraves noted with sloping floors and ceilings or walls which are out of plumb. Fixtures, fittings, fixed appliances, electrical points and other matters of interest should be described.

One of the writers first prepares a sketch plan of each floor level, marking all openings and the locations of power and lighting points, radiators and the like. Such sketch plans, subsequently retained on the file, often prove invaluable in later discussions with clients, particularly when future alterations may be contemplated. If electrical or lighting points are few and far between the client should know about this and he may well not have noticed himself.

Comparison of room dimensions at each level can indicate which are the load-bearing walls and which the partitions which then may be eccentrically loaded on floors. The adequacy of floor construction for spans and loads may then be checked.

(4) Basements, cellars and sub-floor areas

It is always a matter for self-congratulation when the surveyor finds a cellar access under the stairs in an older house, especially if the cellar area disclosed corresponds with most of the ground-floor space. All manner of interesting discoveries about the structure may be made in cellars. Sub-floor ventilation, damp-proof courses, ground-floor timbers, main wall construction, and some of the services may often be capable of close study. As with the main roof void, it is recommended that some time be spent examining conditions in cellar areas and basements. Remember that many of the faults in a building originate, more often than not, at roof or below-ground levels.

Care should be taken to check the condition of the cellar steps since if these are timber and in contact with damp masonry, rot and beetle attack may be expected and defective stair treads may result, particularly if the cellar is disused. Collapse on use has sometimes been known to occur under these conditions.

(5) The roofs

The numbers of chimney flues to each stack should be noted and a check made to trace these through to their fireplaces to confirm if any flues are disused. Redundant flues require ventilated caps or hooded spigots at the top and ventilation at the base in order to keep them dry and prevent condensation forming inside. The general condition of chimney stack flaunching, pointing, brickwork, rendering an oversailing should be noted. The type and condition of the detail at the base of stacks should also be noted, especially behind stacks, and the condition of lead or zinc flashings and soakers or cement fillets described. Tile fillets or cement mortar fillets with no soakers beneath are often unsatisfactory since they tend to pull away from the sides of the stacks in time due to movement in the roof timbers. When this happens, water running down the face of the stacks penetrates directly behind the fillets and causes internal dampness.

The roof covering must be examined, paying particular attention to slipped, cracked or laminated tiles and slates and other signs of deterioration. The condition of hip and ridge tiles is checked, paying particular attention to the bedding mortar which will often be found to be soft and loose. Generally this should not be re-pointed if it is in poor condition but the tiles lifted and re-bedded in new mortar. The condition of valleys is important, particularly secret valleys which may become blocked with leaves and debris.

In older buildings such as Victorian or Edwardian villas and terraced cottages, projecting fire walls may be encountered, rising above the roof line above the party walls. The detailing of these is often poor. The advisability of good flashings and soakers, rather than cement fillets, as for stacks, also applies to this type of parapet construction. A particular check of these should always be made, especially on fire-stop walls, as the coping stones have an alarming tendency to slip off with consequent danger to occupants and perhaps the general public.

A careful inspection of flat roofs, including the feel of such roofs underfoot, is essential. Soft areas of decking, blistering due to trapped vapour, surface cracking to asphalt and built-up felt and other indications of trouble to come should be recorded. The first steps on to a flat roof should be taken carefully since there is a possibility of soft and rotten decking which could be in danger of collapse.

(6) The elevations

A sketch of each elevation may be drawn indicating any specific points of interest. If fractures are present in the walls it is advisable to sketch in all fracture lines roughly, showing starting and finishing points and widths at various points so that a total picture of any structural damage may be given. It is much easier to draw fractures than to describe them in notes, although they will also have to be identified by description in the written report.

Figure 2.2 Note should be taken of the location and size of any fractures found in elevations since often local crack damage is not associated with movements below ground. In the case illustrated the damage was due to thermal movements in lintel construction within the wall (Hertfordshire 1982)

One should stand back and look for any marks or strains on the walls caused by leaking overflows, gutters and downpipes and then mark these points on the sketch. A cross-check made on the internal notes will often show that dampness had been found at the corresponding location inside, especially in older, solid-wall construction.

Many surveyors use photography at this stage and an instant-print type of camera will provide an immediate photographic record of the elevations. These are available for immediate reference on return to the office, whereas conventional photography suffers the drawback of a delay before prints are returned, by which time the report will have been drafted. Unfortunately, fractures do not show up well on photographs when illumination is poor and instant cameras provide only one print.

Inspection of the elevations should include probing of pointing, rendering, brickwork and any cracks or fractures, also examination and probing of exterior woodwork, especially lower window and door frames and exposed fascias. Projecting balcony construction, exposed porches and bays call for particular attention. The elevations should be examined from a distance for signs of past structural distortions or distress and checked, using a spirit level on sills and brickwork courses where appropriate. In older buildings, especially those built with soft mortars, it will be found that considerable structural distortion is able to occur without cracking or fractures becoming apparent.

(7) The site and surroundings

The surveyor studies the general condition of the boundaries and any outbuildings and his comments on these may be framed in accordance with his client's instructions. He could agree with his client at the outset that he will not comment in detail on boundary fences and outbuildings and that the client should satisfy himself regarding these items. Often, from the client's point of view, there seems little to be gained in paying a surveyor for his time needed to inspect and report upon fences, gates, garden sheds, greenhouses and the like. In such cases, and only when the client agrees, a general exclusion clause may be inserted in reports advising clients to inspect these matters themselves in the light of their own particular requirements. The surveyor can then devote his time exclusively to the main building and its structural condition. However, particularly in larger, older buildings, permanent outbuildings and extensive masonry boundary walls can form a significant expenditure potential and should then be included in the survey.

At some stage in the report the client should be advised to consult his solicitor regarding the question of liability for boundaries since a boundary fence may or may not be the responsibility of the owner of a particular property, or may be a party fence, depending upon circumstances. This is a matter which should normally be deduced from a study of the title plan and convenants, if available.

As far as the surroundings are concerned, it is suggested that the surveyor checks for any indications of possible neighbouring future development or redevelopment, including road schemes. While the purpose of the survey is not strictly intended to reveal such matters, it is often helpful to comment where appropriate and then to suggest that a client consults his solicitor. Solicitors, for their part, would normally be most grateful for such comments which they can follow up since they will rarely have inspected the properties to be conveyed. If the highway is unmade or is a private road; if the highway is a public road which is narrow or lacking footpaths; these facts could be significant since they may indicate a widening scheme in the future, and in the case of private roads there could be a capital road charge liability in the future if the road were to be made up and adopted.

Should the surveyor notice building works on adjoining land this could be significant. A client may then be advised to investigate the nature of the works proposed, especially having regard to overlooking or to a use which could adversely affect the value of the property he is about to purchase. Such matters would not always come directly to the attention of the client's solicitor in the normal replies to searches and a specific enquiry may be required to unearth the facts if the solicitor is placed on his guard by the surveyor. Similarly, vacant land adjoining the property under review may be destined for development and this possibility would then need further investigation.

(8) Drains

It is debatable whether the testing of drains should be an automatic procedure to be followed in all cases or whether the surveyor should inspect the house and examine the drains with a view to providing a supplementary drains test report later, if required. The writers favour the latter procedure.

There are several reasons why initial drain tests may be difficult to undertake. There may be little or no manhole access to the system or the drains could be in such poor condition that any testing under pressure could only cause damage. The drainage system may be part of a long private sewer, the joint liability of all property owners connected thereto. This could require extensive testing some distance from the subject property, perhaps demanding entry within adjoining curtilages. Obviously, if the surveyor were to take a plumber with him in such circumstances, considerable wasted time and an abortive visit could result if tests were not able to be carried out.

We therefore suggest that the surveyor should begin by lifting all accessible manhole covers to check the drain flow and inspect between manholes, using a mirror. He would then make suitable initial comments in the report giving the client an opportunity to commission a supplementary drains test report if needed. This method has a secondary advantages for both surveyor and client since on the basis of the preliminary inspection, the surveyor should be able to assess the extra charges involved in providing such a supplementary report.

Naturally, if pipes are cracked, the falls poor or the drain flow sluggish, such matters can be commented upon initially and suitable advice given.

Manhole covers are frequently damaged, and invariably the older cast-iron covers will be rusted, sometimes solidly rusted to the frame and very difficult to remove without dislodging the frame. If all the covers are rusted solid from years of disuse this does at least indicate that the drains have not required rodding in the recent past.

Clean benching, brickwork and rendering to the inside manhole walls might indicate either that no recent stoppage has occurred or that the chamber has been flushed out after an obstruction. If the drains have blocked in the past and not been hosed out, then water marks and staining to the benching and walls may be found and should place the surveyor on his guard regarding the general drain flow. Blockages can of course occur in a system for quite innocent reasons and may not necessarily indicate a fault in the design or construction of the drainage system.

Occasionally the drains may be completely obstructed. In such circumstances any further inspections would normally be abandoned and the client advised that the system should be cleared, all chambers hosed out and a further visit arranged to prepare a supplementary report. In the first instance it is for the vendor to arrange such matters and the surveyor or his plumber should not be expected to have to deal with drains which are in a blocked or insanitary condition.

It is worth mentioning here that the surveyor and his staff dealing with inspections and tests of drains should take precautions against infection, especially if they have open cuts or abrasions. A periodic tetanus injection is advised in order to maintain immunity. Facilities for washing should be ensured after dealing with drains, handling drain plugs, inflatable bags and other equipment.

100 typical house defects

A list of the one hundred defects which, from the authors' experience, are most likely to be encountered is given below. This list is, of course, not intended to be exhaustive but should be of interest. (See also Chapter 7).

1 Settlement of solid concrete ground floors due to unsuitable or unconsolidated fill material in post-1945 housing. Indicated by gaps beneath skirting boards and dishing to floor slabs.

2 Common furniture beetle (*anobium punctatum*) in roof timbers, floors, staircases and plywood panelling, mostly in pre-1940 housing.
3 Wet-rot (*coniophora puteana*) or dry-rot (*serpula lacrymans*) attack to floors under WC pans due to leaks in trap and flush pipe seals.
4 Wet-rot or dry-rot attack to kitchen or utility room floors due to leaking washing machines or sink traps.
5 Shelling wall plaster in post-1945 houses built hurriedly in wet conditions and plastered on wet blockwork.
6 Failure of lath-and-plaster ceilings in pre-1930 houses, requiring new ceilings.
7 Lamination of machine-made clay roof tiles in pre-1940 houses.
8 Rusting nails to slate roof fixings and failure of slates in pre-1925 houses.
9 Unevenness, dishing and flexing of fully-spanned timber ground floors in modern houses due to excessive warping of joists and chipboard deckings and building down to minimum calculated standards.
10 Leaking built-up mineral felt roofs in post-1945 housing and extensions, often causing wet-rot or dry-rot to timber decking and joists beneath.
11 Inadequately braced roof strutting in conventional purlin timber roofs.
12 Parallelogrammatic movements to roof truss systems which lack diagonal restraint.
13 Rising dampness due to pre-1920 damp-proof courses of felt or slates perishing.
14 Damp penetration due to external bridging of damp-proof courses by soil and paving.
15 Damp penetration due to bridging of damp-proof courses by rubble and debris underneath suspended timber ground floors.
16 Damp penetration due to leaking gutters or blocked rainwater pipes leaking at the collars.
17 Damp penetration due to running overflow pipes.
18 Dampness in solid floors and internal walls due to leaks in embedded central heating pipework.
19 Soft and damp wall plaster due to rain penetration through unrendered solid walls or rendered walls in poor condition.
20 Cracking and movement of block partitions in post-1945 houses where these rest eccentrically on suspended floor construction lacking floor stiffening.
21 Distortion of door architraves in post-1945 houses on upper floors due to the bedding down of eccentrically-loaded partitions.
22 Distortion of door architraves and floors at upper levels in post-1945 houses due to inadequately-supported point loads of copper cylinders, and shrinkage caused by the heat of cylinders.
23 Asbestos cement gutters and rainwater pipes becoming porous with age.
24 Guttering blocked, leaking and broken due to lack of maintenance.
25 Lack of effective ceiling insulation in roof voids.
26 Insufficiently rigid platforms for mounting tanks in roof voids.
27 Galvanised steel hot and cold water tanks rusting.
28 Header tank overflows run into main water tanks.
29 Roof 'spread' due to insufficient collars in conventional roof structures.
30 Foundation settlements due to subsoil erosion from leaking drains.
31 Foundation settlements due to shrinkage of clay soils in the presence of vegetation and certain trees (e.g. poplar).
32 Structural damage due to ground heave on clay soils where buildings have been erected on sites involving the removal of trees.

33 Dampness to solid floor slabs due to punctured polythene membranes in post-1945 houses and extensions.

34 Rusting through of pressed-steel radiators in post-1945 small-bore heating systems.

35 Displacement of lead flashings where there is insufficient depth of chase.

36 Porches pulling away from main buildings due to shallow foundations.

37 Integral garages with inadequate protection against spread of fire into the main building.

38 Loose staircase balustrading, or balustrading and handrails removed making staircases dangerous.

39 Large sheets of ordinary-quality glass in glazed doors causing a hazard to young children.

40 Loose bedding mortar to hip and ridge tiles.

41 Loose and frost-damaged rendering, especially pebbledash and spar-dash.

42 Wet-rot to post-1945 painted softwood window frames and sills, especially to the lowest members; also frequently in porches, conservatories and other extensions.

43 Wet-rot to timber garage doors and door posts.

44 Wet-rot to exposed roof fascia boards.

45 Dry-rot to timber floors and skirting boards adjoining damp walls in pre-1920 houses.

46 Cracked lavatory basins and WC pans.

47 Poor caulking to edges of acrylic baths causing dampness behind bath, especially if shower attachment is used.

48 Poor caulking around shower trays causing damp penetration into walls and floors.

49 Damp penetration around base of, and especially behind, chimney stacks.

50 Leaning chimney stacks requiring rebuilding.

51 Mixed copper and lead plumbing systems causing galvanic corrosion to header tanks.

52 Structural settlement due to building on inadequate ground.

53 Sarking felt overlapped wrongly on roof slopes with lower felt overlapping higher felt.

54 Feed and expansion pipes to header tanks connected wrongly so that header tanks contain hot water and cause condensation in the roof void.

55 Unlagged tanks and plumbing in roof voids.

56 Uncovered tanks in roof voids causing condensation, and dead birds and other contaminants found in tanks.

57 Thatched roofs attacked by squirrels, mice and birds due to lack of protective wire netting.

58 Theft of leadwork from roofs causing leakages.

59 Storm drains blocked due to lack of maintenance and inadequate soakaways.

60 Leaking service pipework when laid at insufficient depth under driveways.

61 Electrical wiring in dangerous condition, possibly including amateur extensions.

62 Insufficient sub-floor ventilation to suspended timber ground floors where sub-floor vents accidentally or deliberately blocked off.

63 Obstructed wall cavities causing bridging and dampness.

64 Leaks from boxed internal soil/vent waste-pipe systems.

65 Condensation damage to decorations and plasterwork in the absence of adequate heating and ventilation.

66 Wet-rot or dry-rot attack to suspended timber ground floor wallplates where in contact with damp masonry.
67 Rot attack to timber lintels and wallplates built into solid exterior walls to elevations facing the prevailing weather or subject to damp penetration from leaking gutters and overflows.
68 Furniture beetle introduced into roof timbers from artefacts stored in lofts.
69 Dampness to inner skin of cavity walls due to incorrect detailing of damp-proof courses, especially when facing the prevailing weather.
70 Water hammer and dripping taps due to perished, worn or incorrect tap washers.
71 Gas leaks, particularly around gas meters and boilers.
72 Drains blocked due to fractured or displaced pipework causing a build-up of solid material.
73 Roof leaks from valleys due to blockage by leaves or other obstructions. Splits to the valley linings often causing rot attack to roof timbers and decking under.
74 Frost attack to common brickwork used in exposed locations on parapets, copings, garden and retaining walls without suitable tanking and weathering and where special-quality brickwork should have been used.
75 Amateur or 'cowboy' loft conversion, with inadequate provisions for escape from fire, fire-resistance and insufficient floor strength.
76 Domestic extensions built without permission or constructed as non-habitable rooms and then converted without permission into habitable rooms having inadequate ceiling heights and/or thermal insulation.
77 Condensation inside sealed double-glazing units due to failure of seal or poor manufacture.
78 Rusting to steel casement windows causing warping, loosening of window stays and catches and cracked glazing.
79 Inadequate bearings for or encasement of steelwork when used for internal alterations or extensions.
80 Warping to interior and exterior joinery, especially thin-section glazed timber doors, hardwood entrance doors and architraves.
81 Chimneys used for gas- or oil-fired boilers without linings causing deterioration to internal wall finishes.
82 Unauthorised changes of use or structural alterations to leasehold property where lessor's consent should have been obtained.
83 Weeping radiator valves causing damp patches to carpets and floors, rust staining to exposed pipes and fittings, and deterioration of floor timbers.
84 Foul drains not airtight due to cracked and ill-fitting manholes with worn covers and frames.
85 Chimney flues used as ducts for electric cable or other services but not sealed.
86 Ventilation blocked or not provided for conventional flue gas appliances.
87 Baths installed without necessary drainage fall to waste outlet causing ponding of water and staining to bath.
88 Poorly fixed or unsafe pull-down ladders to lofts.
89 Incorrect or insufficient weathering and throating to sills and overhangs.
90 Loose parapet copings and coping stones to fire walls in danger of being dislodged.
91 Company stopcocks and gas cocks in front gardens obscured by soil or paving and inaccessible in an emergency. Manhole covers similarly covered with paving or soil.

92 Insufficient ventilation to single-stack soil/vent pipe systems and connecting drainwork.
93 uPVC gutter systems with loose or missing seals, incorrect falls or insufficient brackets causing leaks, sagging and overflows.
94 Over-spanned floor joists in older buildings, often caused when internal walls beneath are removed.
95 Removal of interior walls or chimney work resulting in unsatisfactory slenderness ratio especially when lime mortar is used in walls.
96 Chimney breasts removed at lower levels leaving oversailing breasts at higher levels above with insufficient support.
97 Provision of open-riser staircases, spiral staircases and open stairs without handrails or balustrades in conversion of older buildings and in contravention of building regulations.
98 Use of inadequately fire-resistant materials in ceiling construction.
99 Failure to comply with regulations in respect of flat conversion schemes, especially protected means of escape from upper flats in the event of fire.
100 Lack of suitable intervening ventilated lobby between kitchen and bathroom or WC in converted flats.

Chapter 3

Foundations

Therefore, whosoever heareth these sayings of mine, and doeth them, I will liken him to a wise man which built his house upon a rock....And every one that heareth these sayings of mine, and doeth them not, shall be likened unto a foolish man, which built his house upon the sand.
St. Matthew VII 24–27

Modern foundation design for simple low-rise domestic structures requires a knowledge of underlying subsoil conditions and loads likely to be imposed upon that subsoil. Foundation design is the province of the specialist consulting engineers and while it is considered essential for any surveyor undertaking structural surveys to have a full understanding of the principles involved, he should be willing to refer to a consulting engineer any doubtful or difficult cases needing further investigation.

We have found it helpful to foster a continuing relationship with a consulting engineer's practice. Once such a relationship is established assistance is available, often at short notice, with structural calculations or scrutinising plans and details of an existing building under review.

Design

Modern foundations are normally of one of the following types; shallow strip; deep strip; pad-and-beam; pile-and-beam; or raft. Each type has advantages and disadvantages and will be suitable for some conditions and unsuitable for others. It should be borne in mind that builders generally use the most economical foundation which will satisfy the local authority or current district surveyor, and that fashions in foundation design change. A foundation thought to be suitable for the purpose when laid may later be found less appropriate with the benefit of hind-sight. When the surveyor is aware of details of the foundation design, he should include in his report any comments on that design in the light of current knowledge.

Older buildings often have foundations which fall short of modern standards and are often found to be technically inadequate when checked by calculation. Buildings erected before modern cement concretes became generally available often had very little foundations at all. Common 19th Century practice, especially in rural areas, was to provide shallow trenches with a bed of hoggin and to begin the brickwork with two courses of superimposed stepped footings perhaps 500 mm or

Plaster

Unrendered brickwork

Quarry tiles

Slate dpc

Oversite concrete 75 mm

Figure 3.1 Late Victorian foundation, circa 1900

Stepped footings

Shallow concrete strip 500 to 750 mm below ground

so below ground level, using soft bricks and soft lime mortars (*Fig. 3.1*). It is surprising how well many buildings erected in this way have stood the test of time but it is sad to reflect that many modern structures, professionally designed and reputably supervised, have suffered foundation failures necessitating expensive repair.

The surveyor will often inspect foundations exposed for this purpose. He will be surprised to see how sometimes they differ from any original plans and how often the overall depth of the base of foundations is shallower than the design, or prudence, would have required. This will often indicate poor supervision during the course of the works.

A surveyor will not normally be expected to expose the foundations for inspection in a typical structural survey. The Practice Note does not require this, it merely states that 'Wall foundations should only be exposed (by the surveyor or an appointed contractor) in cases where structural defects indicate problems below ground, after prior approval'.

The results of a foundation inspection may be relayed to the client in the form of a supplementary report, if necessary, and if the client should commission it. In some cases the surveyor may be able to arrange for inspection pits to be dug and the results reported. In other cases, especially where abnormal ground conditions may be present, the surveyor should undertake foundation investigations in conjunction with a consulting or geotechnical engineer, particularly if the results of trial bores and recommendations need to be conveyed to the client.

The surveyor must not be afraid of stating his views on a foundation when this is inspected and he is sure of his ground (in both senses), neither should he be reluctant to refer to a specialist where this seems necessary in the client's interests.

The Building Regulations lay down in Section D3 the following standard for foundations:

Foundations must (a) safely transfer all dead, imposed and wind loads to the ground without settlement or other movement which would impair the stability of, or cause damage to, the building or any adjoining building or works; (b) be taken down below frost damage or soil movement levels; (c) be resistant to attacks by sulphates or other deleterious matters in the subsoil.

Figure 3.2 Typical 1930 domestic foundation

It is suggested that the foundations of any structure inspected and reported upon by the surveyor should be judged by this standard and if this is not met or there is doubt, he should discuss this in his report and set out the implications clearly.

In England and Wales a depth of 450 mm is sufficient to place foundations below the level of frost damage in the most extreme conditions for which provision might reasonably be expected to be made. In practice it is felt that a greater depth than this is generally advisable because of the likelihood that ground conditions at the surface on a site may vary, and areas of topsoil or old excavations could be found which would make the bases of shallow foundation trenches subject to variations in bearing capacity. Accordingly we would generally regard 900 mm as being more suitable. Any foundation shallower than this must be regarded as being less than ideal unless the bearing is a hard rock formation, or similar base, of undisputed strength and regularity.

Subsoils

Care is required on chalk soils to ensure that the foundations are at least below the minimum for frost damage since chalks can be subject to considerable frost heave close to the surface.

Despite Biblical claims to the contrary, sandy soils make good foundation bases in many cases, although high-frequency vibrations in the range of 500 to 2500 impulses per minute can cause serious settlement problems, a point unlikely to arise with residential structures unless near to machinery. This factor should be borne in mind when dealing with industrial structures, particularly in the case of changes of use involving machinery.

On shrinkable clay soils a foundation depth of 1200 mm is recommended which would be below the level of seasonal change on level sites in the absence of vegetation. On sloping sites rather greater depths are required, especially on south-facing slopes where the ground will drain and dry out readily during periods of dry weather.

The presence of trees or bushes on shrinkable clay sites causes a particular problem for surveyors advising a prospective purchaser. The standard against which the property should be judged should be that set out in the appropriate British Standard. (BS 5837:1980 'Code of Practice for Trees in Relation to Construction'). This British Standard states, 'Where the presence of shrinkable clay has been established and where roots have been found or are anticipated in the future, it is advisable to take precautionary measures in the design of the building's foundation (in accordance with CP 2004:1972 and CP 101:1972). Alternatively, consideration should be given to designing the superstructure to accommodate any foundation movement that might be induced by clay shrinkage. Where a subsoil investigation has not been carried out, an approximate rule-of-thumb guide is that on shrinkable clay, if risk of damage is to be minimised, special precautionary measures with foundations or superstructure should be considered where the height or anticipated height of the tree exceeds its distance from the building'.

One should pause for a moment to consider the full implications of BS 5837. In most cases the property being inspected, whether residential, commercial or industrial in character, is unlikely to have special foundations of the type anticipated, unless it is quite modern. Generally a short-bored pile-and-beam foundation, or pad-and-beam, or occasionally a raft design, would be used to accommodate the seasonal ground movements on induced on clay sites tree roots. (A sketch section through a pile-and-beam foundation is shown in *Fig. 3.3*). It follows that for most older structures on clay sites a traditional shallow foundation design may be assumed, and that if trees are present whose height at maturity will exceed their distance from the walls of the structure, then the structure is at risk from shrinkage of the clay subsoil and damaging foundation movements would be possible during a dry summer.

Accordingly the surveyor should make a note of the locations of all trees and bushes near the building being inspected and record their distances from the main walls, and that he identify the species of tree involved, confirming whether or not the subsoil may be shrinkable. It should also be confirmed whether specific trees or bushes may be within the curtilage of the property under review, or in adjoining curtilages.

The surveyor should then comment and warn the client as necessary in the light of current knowledge. Three separate situations may arise. A building with shallow foundations on shrinkable clay may have trees within the curtilage closer to the structure than their mature height. In similar circumstances there may be such trees but they may be located in an adjoining curtilage under other ownership. Possibly there may be trees within the curtilage of the subject property which, while well back from the property concerned, could be a threat to an adjoining structure and thus give rise to a legal liability in the future.

If trees are closer to the building than the recommended distances, and within the curtilage, some action in the nature of removal, crowning, pollarding or simply

Flooring-grade chipboard

Fully-spanned timber floor

Loosely-laid polythene membrane (optional)

Slip plane

Ventilated sub-floor area, vents at 1.5-m centres

100 mm oversite concrete

Polystyrene packing

Reinforced ground beam

Short bored pile

Figure 3.3 Modern short bored pile foundation for domestic and other buildings. Common 1980 foundation

subjecting to a period of observation and future pruning, may be advisable depending upon the circumstances.

If trees in other ownership are closer than would be recommended then the surveyor could advise his client to write to the owners of these trees pointing out that their root systems could be hazardous to the property he is acquiring and suggesting that further advice be taken in the light of the fact that by virtue of the laws of nuisance the owner of a tree is liable in law for damage caused by its roots extracting moisture from the subsoil under adjoining structures. (See *Bunclark* v *Hertfordshire County Council* (1977) 243 EG 455 reported in *Estates Gazette*, 30 July, 1977).

Conversely, in a situation where trees within the curtilage of the property being acquired could pose a threat to adjoining structures, then the client should be warned of his own potential liability under the law of nuisance in case this should become significant in future years.

Certain species of tree are really unsuitable in a garden setting on shrinkable clay soil, particularly poplars, willows and elm, and if these are found they should be regarded with a critical eye. Poplar roots can extend for distances of up to twice the height of the tree in search of moisture. We have also found ash trees to have searching root systems and a particular liking for entering cracked drains and disturbing paving, quite apart from their possible effects on shallow foundations.

It is recommended that surveyors practising in localities where shrinkage clays are found should familiarise themselves with the various aspects of this particular problem and that they should be able to identify any species of tree encountered during their work where this seems necessary. The writers have found *Trees in Britain, Europe and North America* by Roger Phillips (Pan Books) to be a most useful guide to tree identification throughout the seasons.

One factor which can commonly cause problems with older foundations is subsoil erosion caused by cracked or leaking drains, or leaking water pipes. Unfortunately, storm drains and gullies to older property were rarely constructed well and soakaways will often have become blocked after the passage of time so that a point-discharge of water into the subsoil immediately adjoining the main walls will often occur. This can be damaging, especially to foundations on light sandy or silty soils which erode easily. Clients should be warned of the importance of maintaining both foulwater and stormwater gullies and drains in good order and to avoid any point-discharges of water into the subsoil adjoining the main walls.

Good building practice is to maintain foulwater drains in a watertight condition in normal use and to lay storm drains watertight for a distance of 3 m from any

Figure 3.4 This vertical fracture follows a bonding line between original and newer brickwork, commonly a point of weakness. Sealed movement joints to accommodate small differential movements, and initial consolidation of new work, can, in suitable cases, be recommended as an alternative to fully-bonding (Middlesex 1982)

structure. After this distance, storm drains may be laid as open-jointed land drains if required, and may run to soakaways if alternative stormwater sewers are unavailable and the soil is suitably porous.

Clients will rarely give a thought to what happens to the storm and foulwater discharges from their property and their significance unless these points are described and their importance to the structure is discussed. In practice, lack of access to storm drains will often preclude any description of the actual system by the surveyor.

Assessment of damage

Foundation defects requiring a specific remedy are those which cause serious distortion or separation in the structure on a scale which would be unacceptable to a reasonable occupier. Specific remedies would deal with foundations which are (a) not deep enough, or (b) not wide enough, or (c) not firm enough, for the particular subsoil conditions involved. The traditional remedy for such defects would be to underpin foundations in such a way as to make the overall structural support to the footings either deeper, wider or firmer as needed.

Figure 3.5 Another point of limited resistance to tension. The arch structure rests on shallow foundations in clay subject to seasonal movements, and is articulating relative to the main structure (Middlesex 1982)

First one must consider those cases where such work would be unnecessary or premature. A number of specialist underpinning contractors exist who undertake traditional or system methods using interrupted foundations of various types. Such contractors will be commercially-orientated and will wish to emphasise the advantages of underpinning using their own particular system. A surveyor will need to consider whether or not it is necessarily in his client's best interests to refer a problem to such a contractor rather than to a professionally-independent consulting engineer.

The first matter to be considered would be available evidence of actual past and present damage to the structure under review, having regard to age and all circumstances. Initially, any above-ground damage would need to be assessed, for example, cracks in walls (inside and outside), evidence of distortion to window and door openings, sloping floors and irregular ceilings. The BRE current paper 'Foundations for Low-rise Buildings', CP 61/78, and 'Assessment of Damage in Low-rise Buildings' in *BRE Digest* 251, make certain recommendations for the assessment of crack damage as follows:

Category 1   *Degree:* Very slight
Fine cracks up to 1 mm wide which can be treated during normal decoration.
Category 2   *Degree:* Slight
Cracks up to 5 mm wide, some external repointing may be required to ensure weather-tightness. Doors and windows may stick slightly.
Category 3   *Degree:* Moderate
Cracks between 5 and 15 mm wide, or a number of cracks up to 3 mm wide. Cracks require opening up and stitch-bonding by a mason, with repointing to exterior brickwork. Doors and windows sticking. Service pipes may fracture. Weather-tightness often impaired.
Category 4   *Degree:* Severe
Cracks between 15 and 25 mm wide, but also depending upon numbers of cracks. Extensive repairs needed to sections of walls. Window and door frames distorted, floors sloping, walls leaning or bulging. Some loss of bearing to beams. Service pipes disrupted.
Category 5   *Degree:* Very Severe
Usually 25 mm or more but depending on number of cracks. Requires major repair involving partial or complete rebuilding. Beams loose bearings. Walls lean badly and need shoring. Window glass cracks. Danger of instability.

Damage of Categories 1 and 2 proportions would not generally of itself justify any specific remedy, and a cosmetic repair should be sufficient. Categories 1 and 2 damage in circumstances where other adverse features of the structure or site exist may, however, be a foretaste of more serious problems to come. Most major structural fractures start with a hairline crack.

Category 3 damage could require a specific remedy depending upon the circumstances. Certainly such damage would require periodic monitoring in order to confirm whether or not the structural movement is continuous and worsening.

Categories 4 and 5 damage will probably require a specific remedy in addition to above-ground repairs. There is a likely need for some type of underpinning in these cases.

It should be mentioned at this stage that some settlement in certain structures is quite normal, being due either to the initial consolidation of the building after construction or to long-term consolidation over the life-cycle. A BRE current paper, 'Settlement of a Brick Dwellinghouse on Heavy Clay 1951–1973', CP 37/74, on this topic covered a 20-year history of settlement in the narrow strip foundations of a typical house in Hemel Hempstead, Hertfordshire. This settlement was found to continue fairly steadily for the whole period (without causing any cracking to the walls) at rates of between 0.12 and 0.39 mm/year, with angular distortion of the foundations to 0.1%. More-brittle wall surfaces, especially surfaces with a smooth stucco, would have cracked as a result of such angular distortion causing Categories 1 or 2 damage, but of itself this would not have been significant.

The question of which category in which to place a specific observed area of damage is very much a matter of judgment. A large number of narrow cracks may,

Plaster

Insulation block

Facing brick

Vinyl-asbestos tiles

dpc

100 mm concrete

Damp-proof membrane (polythene)

Hardcore fill

Cavity fill

Concrete strip
foundation
900 mm minimum from
ground level

Figure 3.6 Typical 1970 domestic
foundation

in some cases, be more significant than a few larger ones. The recommendations for categorising damage can be no more than a guide, and each property and area of damage has to be individually assessed on its merits. Having decided initially on the extent of the damage, advice must then be given.

There are three possible situations with which the surveyor may have to deal. First, he may be acting for an intending purchaser and in this circumstance the client will have the choice of either buying the property or not buying it. If he decides to buy he will probably have to do so within a reasonably short space of time, therefore there will be no opportunity for an extended period of observation. If there is any doubt about the significance of structural damage, it is clearly better *not* to buy the property and to look elsewhere. If then having had all the possibilities explained to him the client still wishes to buy, it is suggested that some adjustment of the purchase price might be recommended having regard to (a) the maximum likely cost of remedying the most severe defect likely to exist, and (b) the probability that such a remedy may be required having regard to the results of whatever investigations the client is prepared to undertake prior to buying.

The second situation occurs when the surveyor is consulted by an owner who is worried by signs of structural distress in his property. Advice given might then be (a) to do nothing, or (b) to subject the structure above ground to an extended period of observation using tell-tales and other indicators, or (c), in Categories 4 and 5 cases, to undertake temporary shoring and carry out trial excavations to determine the facts with a view to a subsequent specific remedy such as underpinning.

The third situation which can arise is where a building is inspected for a prospective mortgagee and signs of structural distress are found. In this situation the amount of the mortgage advance proposed, in relation to the current market value, should be taken into account and a view expressed on the client's behalf of structural repair costs which could arise in relation to the probability of such repairs being needed and to the percentage advance involved. In many cases of lower percentage advances it would be reasonable to make such an advance on the security of a building suffering Categories 1, 2 or 3 damage. Categories 4 or 5 damage would require further investigation unless the mortgage advance was very low indeed. In addition to advising mortgagees in such circumstances the surveyor would be bound to bring such a situation to the attention of the borrower if he is to have a copy of the report, and the borrower should be advised to take further advice before proceeding, irrespective of the outcome of the mortgage application.

A further point worthy of note in connection with structural damage due to subsidence, landslip or ground heave (normal insured risks in many residential property policies) is that such a cover applies only to damage arising after the policy came into force. It follows that an existing building owner may be covered for such risks in respect of damage apparent in his building but that if he sells, the purchaser may *not* be covered if signs of damage were apparent before the sale. Once a purchaser has commissioned a surveyor's report which has described structural damage he may be placed in a different position to recover subsequent costs under his insurance policy. In such a situation it may be that the vendor could make a claim and agree the extent of remedial works required prior to any sale. A purchaser should not assume that, because he is insuring against such matters, minor cracks reported by his surveyor need not concern him since the very fact that the surveyor has reported the damage may have undermined the basis of any later claim.

Remedies

Damage caused by the action of tree roots and proved to be due solely to the presence of trees and no other cause should not normally require underground repair. It should be sufficient to recommend that the offending trees be removed and that the site be given a number of wet winters to stabilise before the damage is made good by stitch-bonding cracked brickwork, repairing pointing and making good rendered surfaces in the normal way. If the offending trees cannot be removed, because they are either protected by tree preservation orders or in other ownership, then deeper foundation bases may be required to accommodate present and future root activity. An interrupted foundation should be used to ensure that expansion and shrinkage rates in the subsoil are the same on all sides of the foundation at different times of the year. If trees are a contributory cause of damage but the foundations are also inadequate for other reasons then an underground repair may be necessary in addition to the removal, pollarding or crowning of offending trees.

Traditional underpinning, which is an expensive and labour-intensive process, comprises the provision of an additional foundation below the existing foundation. This may be achieved by alternately excavating bases, usually $1\,\text{m}^3$ in extent, around the perimeter of the structure and under the internal load-bearing walls. Each base is cast incorporating steel reinforcement married into adjoining alternate bases so that a complete continuous foundation is provided under the existing foundation to whatever dimensions are specified. When the bases have hardened, the space between new and old foundations is filled by dry-packing with a hard cement mortar. During the course of such underpinning, allowances have to be

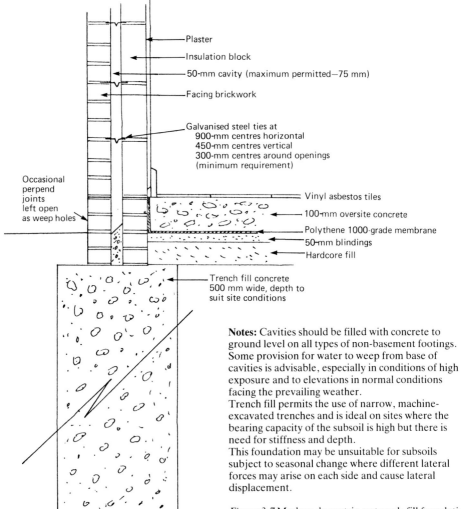

Plaster

Insulation block

50-mm cavity (maximum permitted—75 mm)

Facing brickwork

Galvanised steel ties at
900-mm centres horizontal
450-mm centres vertical
300-mm centres around openings
(minimum requirement)

Occasional
perpend
joints
left open
as weep holes

Vinyl asbestos tiles

100-mm oversite concrete

Polythene 1000-grade membrane

50-mm blindings

Hardcore fill

Trench fill concrete
500 mm wide, depth to
suit site conditions

Notes: Cavities should be filled with concrete to ground level on all types of non-basement footings. Some provision for water to weep from base of cavities is advisable, especially in conditions of high exposure and to elevations in normal conditions facing the prevailing weather.
Trench fill permits the use of narrow, machine-excavated trenches and is ideal on sites where the bearing capacity of the subsoil is high but there is need for stiffness and depth.
This foundation may be unsuitable for subsoils subject to seasonal change where different lateral forces may arise on each side and cause lateral displacement.

Figure 3.7 Modern deep strip or trench-fill foundation

made for diverting and repairing any services encountered. After the work is finished, a suitable period is allowed for consolidation of the structure on the new foundation, and then any cosmetic repairs, masonry repairs and levelling up are completed.

As a general rule such underpinning will be applied equally to all bearing walls, otherwise a danger of structural movement between those parts of the building which have been underpinned, and those parts which have not, arises. This may not apply on a sloping site where the underpinning depth may step up with the site slope and remain in the same stratum of subsoil.

Special difficulty arises with semi-detached or terraced structures in multi-ownership since if the general rule mentioned is to apply, the whole structure or terrace would need underpinning. In such situations a degree of engineering judgment is required and it may be necessary to undertake partial underpinning only. If so, it is recommended that the depth of the underpinning bases be graduated down from the point where non-underpinned walls end to avoid a sudden marked change in overall foundation depth at any specific point. If party walls have to be underpinned, hopefully this will be by agreement since although a party wall can be physically underpinned from one side only, the bases themselves will be trespassing beneath and adjoining ownership and permission is then needed. There is also a risk that partial underpinning of, say, a semi-detached house and the party wall will result in any future stresses being transferred to the adjoining house. This could cause movement relative to the party wall with consequential damage. Before advising on such works legal advice should be taken as to the implications and means by which the adjoining owner might be warned about the proposed works.

As an alternative to the traditional underpinning described, a number of specialist contractors now employ special systems to provide greater depths using a system of pads and beams. Pads are cast at corners and within the structure at the main point-loads to considerable depths if necessary. The pads are then linked by narrow reinforced ground beams cast directly under the original foundations. Such systems reduce the overall amount of excavation necessary and provide interrupted foundations which could be recommended on certain types of shrinkable clay, especially if live tree roots are present in close proximity.

If a surveyor is asked to deal with underpinning he should be satisfied that it is necessary in the circumstances that the shoring and other temporary support works will be adequate and that the procedure for casting a new foundation will not subject the structure, or any adjoining structure, to additional distress.

Generally, with traditional underpinning, bases should be cast leaving at least two equivalent areas of support between so that bases 1, 4 and 7 would be cast, allowed to harden, dry-packed completely and the packing set. Then bases 2, 5 and 8 might be excavated similarly, followed by bases 3, 6 and 9. In soft ground even greater spacing of excavations may be required to avoid further structural damage. In all cases excavations should be open for the least possible time since some subsoils deteriorate when exposed. All excavations should be adequately planked and strutted at all stages of the work to avoid lateral displacement of the adjacent subsoil.

The bottom of any underpinning excavation should be carefully checked to ensure that it is sound, level and dry before concrete placement begins.

If it is suspected that the structure under review has been underpinned in the past, the reasons for this should be ascertained and details obtained if possible. Nowadays, underpinning works require local authority consent under the Building Regulations and most recent works should appear in their records. Before 1976, such work was regarded as outside the scope of the Building Regulations or bye laws and normally went unreported to the local authority.

Drains and foundations

During the course of the survey it may be found that drains pass beneath foundations and floors or a shallow drain may pass through the walls below ground level and beneath the floors.

Certain precautions have to be taken when building over drains. Occasionally, a structure may have been built over drains originally and this will be found in many terraced Victorian and Edwardian houses with private drains running under the buildings from rear to front. Often, extensions to an existing building will have been erected over the drains at a later stage and this will commonly be found in small, single-storey domestic extensions.

Hopefully a manhole may be found on each side of the structure where the drain passes beneath and it should be possible to test the drain for leakage and to inspect the pipework for distortion using a mirror. Such drainwork should be laid with a compressible layer above and immediately over the pipework and with suitable lintels used to carry strip foundations or footings over the pipes without imposing a point-load. Modern uPVC underground drain systems are sufficiently flexible to cope with slight distortion without damage but older virtrified earthenware pipework is brittle and could fracture under compression caused by foundations.

One important point which should be considered in drainwork and shallow foundations is the relative depths of the original excavations where these would have been made side by side. It is not uncommon to find that the invert level of drainwork is deeper than the base of strip foundations. If the two excavations proceeded together at the time the building was erected, or if the drains were laid later and if the excavations have been in close proximity, then there would have been a danger of lateral displacement of the subsoil into the lower excavation following the work and during the period of back-fill consolidation. This could have an adverse effect on the subsoil bearing the weight of the adjoining foundation, and the effects may last for some years causing settlements in the structure adjoining the drains until finally the subsoil will have fully consolidated to a point where further movement will not be significant.

It is therefore recommended that invert depths of all drainwork near walls of buildings be checked where possible and especially if that drainwork runs alongside walls. Deep invert levels adjoining structures built with shallow foundations may indicate that subsoil consolidation around the back-filling could be taking place with adverse effects on that structure.

Mining and filled ground

Some surveyors practise in mining areas which are either active or worked out. In localities subject to mining subsidence it may be necessary to employ specialist advice before reporting on buildings, and it is recommended that the surveyor's library should include all available information in the form of plans and maps showing areas subject to mining where these are known. Coal-mining areas are mainly affected by this problem but there are many other types of mining and some areas have a mining history which goes back to the Middle Ages and beyond. In such situations the local knowledge of the surveyor may prove invaluable.

In areas having a chalk subsoil old chalk-mine workings may exist and the chalk itself may be subject to the sudden unexpected appearance of deep swallow holes either connected with workings or due to subterranean collapse caused by groundwater erosion. There is no effective way in which a surveyor carrying out a normal survey can forecast such events. The only protection available for the property owner against such eventualities would be to carry the normal subsidence and landslip insurance cover.

In some localities chalk pits, gravel pits, sand pits and worked-out quarries may be encountered where materials have been removed and the workings filled using either hardcore or compressible fill material. Buildings erected on bad ground where unsuitable fill material has been used, or where suitable material has not fully consolidated, are often found to be subject to movement. This type of structural movement can be highly damaging, occasionaly requiring the demolition of the building and often necessitating a special underpinning scheme making piles (or deep pads) to take foundation loads below the level of the fill. Because of the pressures to build on existing urban sites or reclaimed industrial land, the numbers of serious defects attributed to building on made ground appear to have increased in recent years.

An Ordnance Survey map of the area sometimes indicates old mines and workings, especially on $\frac{1}{1250}$ and $\frac{1}{2500}$ scales. This can be a useful source of information, also the geological survey map may show where such workings have taken place. Old maps of the area sometimes show detail which no longer appears on modern maps and the writers have found the old Ordnance Survey county series of large scale maps to be useful, sometimes in showing conditions on a particular site before it was developed. Many of the older county series maps date from the last century. The old $\frac{1}{2500}$ scale maps are often very accurate and informative.

The final comments regarding foundations and the problems which can arise due to foundation defects are intended to redress the balance to some extent since the vast majority of foundations will perform satisfactorily throughout the life of a building notwithstanding the apparently inexhaustible range of foundation problems which could, in theory, arise.

A great deal of superficial damage to buildings, such as some cracking, is minor and due to normal long-term consolidation of the structure or minor differential settlement. This must be regarded as normal, especially in older buildings. Some damage may be wrongly diagnosed as due to foundation movements when other and more prosaic causes may be responsible, especially in the case of widely-based structures where thermal movements may be expected and in recently-completed buildings where normal shrinkages, bedding down of partition walls and the like, will produce considerable cracking which may be quite unrelated to conditions below ground.

Serious damage is that which may be diagnosed as progressive and which will require a structural repair in order to arrest further movement. Most cracking is minor and not progressive. In the case of progressive movement there will normally be indications of the cause and this will often be obvious to one who has a knowledge of local soil conditions and the presence or otherwise of mining or made ground in the locality.

Chapter 4

Walls

Now the wolf, having blown down the house made of straw and....having blown down the
house made of sticks...., came to the house made of bricks with the third little pig inside.
'Little pig, little pig', he said, 'May I come in?' 'By the hairs on my chinny chin chin', said
the third little pig, 'You may not come in'. 'Then', said the wolf, 'I shall huff and I shall
puff and I shall blow your house down....So he huffed and he puffed....but he could not
blow down the house....because it was built of bricks.
The Three Little Pigs, Anon.

During a survey the thicknesses, lengths and locations of the walls around and
within the building should be noted, including any abutting or connecting walls
which are part of adjoining premises or boundaries. Those walls which are
load-bearing walls and those which are non-load-bearing walls can then be
distinguished one from another.

In simple two-storey dwelling house construction, as in the ubiquitous
between-the-Wars semi-detached, there is usually a central spine wall which
supports not only its own weight but also the loading from floor and ceiling joists
which span front-to-rear in the structure, and perhaps the strutting to roof purlins.
Openings may have been formed in such a wall and a check on the adequacy or
otherwise of remaining piers and bearings is recommended if two living rooms have
now been formed into a 'through-lounge'. It must be borne in mind that 150 mm of
bearing is desirable for most short steel sections and that in a 225-mm solid brick
party wall only 112 mm of bearing is technically available each side of the centre
line. Often there arises a temptation to dispense with piers with the result that the
bearing for rolled-steel joists in through-lounge conversions is often inadequate.

With a dimensioned sketch plan of the room layout on each floor one can easily
see which walls rise continuously within the building and which rest eccentrically on
the floors. In the inter-War structure already mentioned it is likely that at least one
main spine wall is provided and that some other walls are eccentrically-loaded on
the floors using a double-joist for support if the joist runs are parallel to the wall, or
a sole plate fixed over the boarding if the wall is at right-angles to the joist runs.

In post-War construction a greater use was made of fully-spanned roof trusses
and trussed rafters so that often all the partitions to first floor rooms rest on floors
and do not correspond to the location of ground-floor walls. Such partitions may be
timber-framed, consisting of studs and noggins clad in plasterboard and therefore
imposing fairly minimal loads, or they may be of blockwork resting on sole plates

on a boarded or chipboard floor, imposing some point loads on the floors. Sometimes considerable deflection will occur when partition walls of this type rest on the floor construction. A particular watch needs to be kept for such signs, especially in modern speculative construction. If the partitions do not rest centrally over the double joists beneath, or if joists have been omitted, or if a series of point loads coincide, then deflection, twisting and leaning of partition walls will occur and the solutions, though simple in theory, in practice often involve considerable disruption to the occupants.

The effects of joinery shrinkage in floors can be seen in deflection of partition walls resting on those floors, and in any event timber floors will tend to deflect downwards progressively with age. If, when the surveyor examines the architraves to doorways on the landing of a house incorporating this type of partitioning, he notices some slope to the tops of those architraves, he will know that movement has occurred. Generally in these cases downward slopes away from the main spine wall towards the partitions will be apparent.

Within normal tolerances such sloping door architraves and minor plaster cracking over doorways may be regarded as normal and an opportunity should be taken to give the client some reassurance that the cause is downward deflection of the supporting floor construction and not something more fundamental lower down in the building.

Point loads of copper cylinders and airing cupboards often contribute to this type of movement in partition walls and door architraves, both from the heat generated causing shrinkage, and the weights imposed. Good building practice should provide for two 100 mm × 50 mm timber bearers under copper cylinders to give at least 50 mm of clearance from the floor with the bearers spanning at least two, and preferably three, floor joists. The National House-Building Council requires such a 50-mm clearance in all new construction in order to meet their standards. The surveyor should check the hot water cylinder bearings. If the cylinder rests near or over a supporting wall beneath then the bearing may not be significant, but if it lies mid-way over a ceiling span to the floor beneath this may be important. Similar considerations also relate to the platforms on which cold water cisterns and header tanks are mounted since they may affect the ceiling construction beneath.

In dealing with older houses of up to Victorian or Edwardian times the importance of taking full notes showing the arrangment of the walls and their construction is even greater since there are many examples of such buildings where internal walls to upper storeys are all timber-framed stud partitions having very little resistance to tension at the points of contact with the main outer walls. The surveyor should then consider whether the outer walls are too slender and lacking in lateral restraint or buttressing to an extent where a danger of structural movement arises. He should then examine such walls carefully for signs of bulging and leaning, especially at tall gable ends and other similarly sensitive points.

Frequently, tie bars with S-plates or X-plates have been employed to restrain outer walls in older buildings either as a precaution or where separation has begun. If possible the condition of the tie bars, which often run under the floors or over the ceiling joists in the roof space, should be checked. If these are old the mild steel may have rusted and their effectiveness could be lost.

Tie bars and similar means of holding together old buildings which may lack any internal restraint and may be built in soft lime mortar must be regarded as unsatisfactory by comparison with a better initial standard of overall construction. Nevertheless, once the surveyor has warned his client of the limitations of the bars and the inherent drawbacks of a building which needed them in the first place, they have often been found to serve their purpose well. Their use is still advised on occasions where this seems sensible and having regard to the depth of the client's pocket at the time.

Figure 4.1 Red facing brickwork with black ash mortar; note the lamination of brickwork, especially on the coping course (South Wales 1982)

A cautionary sign arises when it is found that chimney breasts have been removed from existing structures. Chimney breasts often add very valuable stiffness to both old and modern walls, and the writers are normally opposed to their removal unless a careful check on the surroundings indicates quite clearly that the remaining construction will be unaffected, having regard to the slenderness ratios of remaining walls and the nature of the mortars used and therefore their resistance to tensile forces.

Slenderness ratio

Slenderness ratio is a useful concept to use in assessing the structural stability of buildings under review. It is recommended that the standard to apply is as laid down in the Building Regulations. Regulation D15 and Schedule 7 of the Regulations refer to structural works of bricks, blocks or plain concrete, and using Schedule 7 it is not necessary to calculate loads or wall thicknesses required, the rules of the Schedule being sufficient as a check on the stability of the construction.

Schedule 7 may be applied to walls which form part of any storey of a building other than a basement, basement storey walls needing a structural check by calculation in accordance with BSI CP 111:1970 should this be considered necessary. It is assumed for this purpose that point-loads are properly distributed and that walls are properly bonded and solidly put together. There is an overall height limit of 12 m for the use of these rules (above which CP 111 should be used) and also a limit of 3 kN/m² as an imposed floor load. This is well above the imposed loads likely in residential construction but which could well be exceeded in other types of building, in which case CP 111 and special calculation would be required.

The Table to Rule 7 sets out certain minimum thicknesses for external walls and separating walls, in each case assuming that walls will have at each end either a pier, buttress, buttressing wall or chimney unless the wall concerned forms part of a bay window and is less than 2.5 m in both height and length. This Table is set out below:

Height of Wall	Length of Wall	Minimum Thickness of Wall
Not exceeding 3.6 m	Any length	200 mm throughout its height
Exceeding 3.6 m and not exceeding 9 m	Not exceeding 9 m	200 mm throughout its height
Exceeding 3.6 m and not exceeding 9 m	Exceeding 9 m	300 mm for the height of one storey and 200 mm for the remainder
Exceeding 9 m and not exceeding 12 m	Not exceeding 9 m	300 mm for the height of one storey and 200 mm for the remainder
Exceeding 9 m and not exceeding 12 m	Exceeding 9 m	300 mm for the height of two storeys and 200 mm for the remainder

For cavity walls the thickness of the wall should be at least 250 mm or the thickness required for a solid wall under Rule 7, plus the width of the cavity, except in the case of the upper storey of a two-storey dwelling house where the inner skin may be 75 mm (giving an overall width of 225 mm) subject to certain special rules including a doubling of the normal number of wall ties, roof loads being carried partly by the outer skin, a strong mortar being used, and the wall being not more than 8 m long and 3 m high (5 m high to a gable).

For the purpose of Rule 7, the heights are measured from the base of the wall immediately above the foundation or footing and not from ground or finished floor levels.

Walls are regarded for this purpose as being divided into separate lengths by piers, buttresses, chimneys and buttressing walls. These separate lengths are measured centre-to-centre of the piers etc, provided that piers and buttressing walls themselves meet the necessary requirements and are fully bonded.

Fig. 4.2 shows part of an end-of-terrace Victorian cottage. Note that the brick cross-wall construction is separated from the flank wall on both levels by door openings so that little or no effective cross-wall bonding exists. The stud cross-wall is of no benefit to the stiffness of the flank-wall either. The flank-wall is 225 mm thick and divided into three lengths, these being 3 m, 5 m and 3 m respectively, this flank-wall being carried up to form a gable-end with an effective height exceeding 3.6 m.

If the chimney breasts are removed a single length of 11 m of wall exceeding 3.6 m high results which should be a minimum of 300 mm thick at ground floor level. Since this is not so, the removal of the chimney breasts is not recommended; they add essential stiffness to the flank-wall construction. If soft lime mortars are used, the removal of buttressing from the flank-wall may still be ill-advised, even if a check by reference to Rule 7 raises no technical objection, because the slenderness ratio by reference to CP 111 is excessive.

Slenderness ratios (SR) should be calculated in accordance with the formula laid down in CP 111. For two-storey residential buildings the Code recommends that the SR for walls built in cement mortars should not exceed 24, or 18 if built in the older type of lime mortars (12 if more than two storeys).

Figure 4.2 Ground and first floor plans of end-of-terrace Victorian cottage

The SR is determined by the length and height of the wall, the lateral restraint provided and the nature of the construction. A superficial examination of the overall construction will show if a building 'feels' right. Experience will tell whether a problem may arise having regard to the layout of the crosswall construction and age of the structure. Newer practitioners may find it necessary to check such details by approximate calculation until they have acquired the necessary experience.

Having assessed the condition of the main walls and the manner in which they are likely to cope with the forces imposed upon them, the surveyor should then consider the other factors determining whether those walls are likely to be satisfactory or not. These are: (a) their resistance to dampness rising up, penetrating through or percolating down the walls, (b) their thermal efficiency, and (c) in the case of separating walls (or party walls), their soundproofing properties. It is proposed to deal with each of these factors in turn.

Dampness

Concerning dampness, it is recommended that a certain minimum standard be applied, this being the standard of good modern building practice as required by Building Regulations. Anything less than this standard should be made clear to the client with the necessary advice. A good standard would be cavity-wall construction with clear, unobstructed cavities, having damp-proof courses at the base of walls at least 150 mm (two brick courses) above surrounding ground levels and with vertical and horizontal damp-proof courses at all points of contact between the outer and inner skin, and damp-proof cavity trays at all points of bridging. Additionally, there should be an impervious damp-proof membrane in solid floors contiguous with the damp-proof courses in all walls. By such means the passage of moisture into the interior from the exterior, or the site, is avoided.

The fact that a particular building is modern will not, of itself, ensure that a good standard is met since, in practice, poor detailing of cavity walls, obstructed cavities, punctured membranes and other faults abound. Nevertheless, a good yardstick to apply is that described. In so far as any construction under review fails to meet this standard, then this should be pointed out to the client, and many older buildings will not reach this standard.

Before about 1938, much residential construction was in solid brickwork or stonework and the main barrier against weather penetration in such construction is the condition and pointing of the external brick or stone face. In such circumstances this should be explained to the client and he should be advised to maintain the exterior surfaces in good order in future years and make a particular point of checking periodically for gutter and downpipe leaks. Leaking overflows will also cause considerable damage to internal plasterwork if neglected since the moisture can easily penetrate directly to the inside.

The clearance of 150 mm between exterior levels and damp-proof courses is recommended in order to prevent gutter-splash reaching the wall above damp-proof course and to allow some margin of clearance. Experience indicates that the ground levels around houses tend to rise by about 300 mm every 100 years, due to the addition of soil to gardens and the laying of new paving over old. It is essential to resist this trend.

When there is insufficient clearance to damp-proof courses it is recommended that ground levels be lowered. A general lowering of levels is best with the surplus soil or paving being carted away. Alternatively, a channel may be formed alongside the wall, at least 150 mm wide, suitably formed with cementwork sides and benching and having a fall-away from the main walls and adequate drainage to suitable storm gullies. A channel which fails to drain adequately is worse than useless since it will actually exacerbate any dampness. The brickwork then exposed at the base of the wall should be made good as necessary by pointing, cutting in new bricks or rendering to a suitable standard.

Vertical damp-proof courses of slates set into a rendered plinth are a traditional remedy. They are inserted between the high exterior levels and the walls where damp-proof course clearances are inadequate or the courses themselves are bridged. Such vertical courses often prove ineffective in the long run as the slates become porous and the bedding mortar between slates is rarely impervious to moisture. Any vertical slate damp-proof courses found between high exterior ground levels and the external walls of older buildings should be regarded with a critical eye and consideration given to a general lowering of levels or tanking applied to any at basement or semi-basement.

Damp-proof courses become porous with age and rising damp results. Specialist contractors now provide remedial services either by chemical injection of the walls or electro-osmosis to prevent capillary attraction in the walls, or by inserting new damp-proof courses in sections using a bricksaw to cut out chases in the walls, generally of about 1 m at a time. Electro-osmosis is now generally considered to be expensive compared with other methods and one large specialist firm has discontinued its use. Electro-osmotic damp-proof courses should be given special consideration if encountered during a survey.

Before allowing a client to employ such a specialist contractor it should be confirmed that the dampness found actually is due to rising damp. Many cases of diagnosed rising damp are not due to failure of the damp-proof courses at all but from penetration or bridging. It is significant that guarantees offered by specialist contractors will normally exclude liability for dampness due to causes other than moisture rising up the walls by capillary action. Before employing a specialist contractor it is recommended that obvious defects likely to cause dampness should first be eliminated and the structure subjected to a period of observation, if this is possible. It will often be found that dampness can be cured by such simple steps alone.

Having said this, occasions will undoubtedly arise when dampness may be diagnosed as rising damp due to failure of damp-proof courses. In such circumstances all main walls will need attention since the damp-proof courses will be of the same age and type unless parts of the structure date from different periods. The provision of new damp-proof courses in only a part of a building and leaving the original damp-proof courses in other parts may be unwise since further work in the other areas will be necessary in due course if the damp-proof courses are failing due to their type and age.

Specialist contractors are commercial men seeking work and there is nothing wrong with that. As a professional, however, the surveyor should be able to say whether or not the specialist's proposals are unnecessary or premature.

Bridging of damp-proof courses can arise from inside the building as well as from outside. Frequently there is a build-up of rubble and debris under suspended timber floors. Whenever such floors have to be exposed for building works or services it is recommended that the over-site areas be cleared out and swept and a check be made that all vents are free from blockage. Solid floors in older buildings may also bridge the damp-proof courses. The use of membranes in solid floors was not general practice in pre-1939 construction, and in halls, kitchens and sculleries quarry or ceramic tiles were often laid directly on the screed and thus provided a passage for moisture to rise up into the base of adjoining walls. It will often be found that plaster at the base of walls next to such floors has been affected by damp and a high moisture-meter reading obtained due to this damp transference.

In modern construction the failure to ensure that membranes are lapped over or under damp-proof courses and sealed at all joints can give rise to local bridging. Polythene can also tear or puncture, especially if laid under a concrete slab on gritty or stony blindings. Often, 500-grade polythene has been used as a cheaper substitute for the more durable 1200-grade which the writers would recommend for this purpose.

Thermoplastic tiles and woodblocks, commonly employed in houses of the nineteen-fifties, were laid in a bituminous backing which was itself the damp-proof membrane. Sometimes such tiles or blocks are removed by a do-it-yourself owner and replaced with other surfaces, the bituminous backing being disturbed or removed altogether. Modern vinyl asbestos tiles or welded sheet vinyl flooring cannot be laid with spot adhesive on a floor surface unless this surface rests over a suitable membrane. Failure to observe this will result in the floor screed sweating under flooring and causing it to lift and loosen. The bituminous backing to tiles and woodblocks should be contiguous with the damp-proof course in the walls but this may not always be so and can also be a source of bridging and moisture transference into the wall above damp-proof course level.

In older houses with damp solid floors or with timber floors in poor condition below recommended levels a useful remedy can be to have them replaced by new solid floors at a higher level. This can often be done usefully in kitchen and scullery areas where ceiling heights are sufficient. The ceiling height should not be reduced below 2.3 m (current Building Regulation minimum), preferably higher. The new floor can then incorporate a damp-proof membrane lapped at the sides and contiguous with the damp-proof courses in the walls. These should first be exposed by chasing the wall plaster and removing skirting boards as necessary. The client will then be able to lay vinyl asbestos tiles, sheet flooring or similar surfaces on the new screed in the knowledge that the floor will be dry and will not transfer moisture into the surrounding walls.

Apart from normal moisture-meter tests which should be made at selected points around the base of the main walls and at other points at risk, the wall surfaces should also be examined for signs of deterioration in the plaster, staining to wallpaper and mould growth, all signs of dampness (although not necessarily rising damp). Rust stains from skirting board nail heads are a good indicator of moisture behind the skirting board.

One final point regarding dampness in modern buildings is that in many post-1945 houses the pipework for plumbing and heating systems has been buried under solid floor screeds above the membranes and if an isolated point of dampness is found at the base of a wall, especially an internal wall, it is well worth while investigating the possibility of a leak in the system under the floor. If a serious leak is taking place from a heating system this can be confirmed by tying up the header tank ball valve, marking the side of the header tank at the existing level and then checking this level periodically to see if it drops. Any rapid loss of water from the header tank will indicate a leak to the central heating pipework in the floors which will have to be traced and remedied.

Thermal insulation

The thermal insulation requirements in current Building Regulations are reasonable standards to adopt and if the building under review is likely to be less satisfactory then the client should be warned. Generally, a cavity wall with insulation block inner skin and cavity fill is a minimum present-day requirement. Older solid wall construction will allow greater heat losses, as will all-brick cavity construction of the nineteen-thirties and nineteen-fifties, especially if the cavities are vented and open at the top as was common practice during those times. The standard of insulation of an all-brick cavity wall with well-ventilated cavity is, in practice, not much better than that of a half-brick wall.

Still considering thermal insulation, it should also be borne in mind that some buildings are inherently less efficient than others. Bungalows have twice the roof area for the same floor space as two-storey houses and a bungalow with a number of projecting wings and bays will be presenting a large external surface area, especially if it is detached. The ideal structural shape from this point of view is a square box which encloses the maximum volume for the least external wall area. In view of the importance of thermal insulation, this topic should be covered by the surveyor in his report and if any steps should be taken to improve insulation, then these should be incorporated in the report.

All brick cavity walls could be provided with sleeved vents through the cavities and the cavities sealed at the tops. Cavity-wall fillings may be employed. Solid walls can be improved by the provision of 3-mm polystyrene insulation under wallpaper on inside faces of exterior walls, and this will compensate to some extent for the lack of cavity construction. 'False' walls may be employed inside exterior walls with dry linings on battens and insulation.

Sound insulation

Current Building Regulations provide that party walls must be of 225-mm brickwork or dense blockwork, plastered both sides, to give the necessary sound-proofing. In practice, the older, denser party walls, often incorporating substantial chimney breasts, have been found to be more satisfactory in this respect than the more modern party walls. In a Building Research Establishment current paper, 'Field Measurement of the Sound Insulation of Plastered Solid Brick Walls' (BRE CP 37/78 March 1978), it was found that in houses built during the nineteen-seventies the test results indicated that walls constructed to meet the deemed-to-satisfy specification of the Building Regulations actually failed to meet that standard in practice in about 35% of cases.

The reasons for this include the fact that voids may arise in brickwork and blockwork if the workmanship is poor and frogs not fully filled. Chases for electrical and aerial conduits etc, often corresponding in location on both sides of a party wall, may allow local channels for sound to pass. In so far as it is possible to do so, the surveyor should comment upon the degree of sound insulation in separating walls, although in many cases this will not be possible.

Wall design

Fig. 4.3 shows a sketch section through an unrendered solid brick wall of a type commonly encountered in Victorian and Edwardian construction having a solid internal floor covered with quarry tiles and no effective damp-proof membrane. A risk of damp penetration through the wall and dampness rising by capillary action via bridging arises with this type of construction. Wet-rot or dry-rot to grounds and skirting boards in such a location is likely if dampness is present. Simple remedies such as dealing with defective rainwater equipment and lowering ground levels may suffice but it will not be possible to confirm whether the slate damp-proof courses are effective or not since they cannot function properly anyway until the obvious problems are dealt with. Floors may be re-surfaced with a new covering of two good coats of Synthaprufe or similar bituminous coating, taking care to cut back old tiles, to expose the damp-proof courses and to finish the bituminous backing against the slates to ensure a contiguous damp-proof course and membrane. Pointing and soft brickwork should also be attended to as required.

Figure 4.3 Bridging of slate damp-proof course in undrenched, solid brick wall

Figure 4.4 Lack of damp-proof cavity tray to cavity wall over opening for living-room extension

The standard of thermal insulation of such a wall will be poor and heat losses excessive by modern standards.

Fig. 4.4 shows a sketch section through a cavity wall where a living room has been extended and two small rolled-steel joists inserted. In such a location, especially in conditions of high exposure or normal exposure facing the prevailing weather (usually south west), a damp-proof cavity tray should be provided, lapped over the exterior roof flashing and a few open perpends or weepholes allowed for so that any water running down the inside face of the outer skin is picked up and taken to the outside over the roof line. Similar provision is required in a cavity wall where a subsidiary pitched roof joins the outer skin using a conventional flashing and where the cavity continues downwards to terminate at lintels over rooms below.

The provision of rolled steel joists and other lintel work in residential extensions of this type is often badly done but the detail can rarely be checked. Apart from the provision of proper damp-proof cavity trays and weeping perpend joints as necessary, it is essential that proper bearings for joists are provided and that for all but the very short spans, the rolled-steel sections should be bolted together with spacers to provide improved stiffness and resistance to torsion.

Occasionally, walls will be found which are rendered both sides and which will appear from measurement to be of brickwork. Care should be taken in making assumptions since such walls may be of either solid or cavity concrete construction, formed originally in sections using shuttering. There was a vogue for such construction for a time in certain localities in the inter-War period, and more recently the development of such construction using no-fines concrete has been popular. The nature of the construction of a rendered wall may often be confirmed by checking inside air vents and at the top of walls around the perimeter of the roof-space. Good building practice requires that wall cavities be closed at the top but in practice open cavities are often found, especially in older cavity walls. It is possible to look down such cavities from within the roofspace in some cases in order to check for blockages, bridged wall ties and other defects as well as to confirm the nature of the construction used for the outer and inner skins. Special equipment is now available to permit inspection within wall cavities using fibre-optics by drilling through the outer wall skin. Although such equipment is not normally employed as a routine test in the first instance it could be recommended as a specialist service in some cases.

As regards cavity-wall construction, whether of brickwork, stonework, blockwork or a combination of materials, the overall stiffness of the construction relies upon the two skins being held together by effective wall ties. Since some cavity walls of a considerable age may now be encountered, many being more than 50 years old, it is worth considering how effective the wall ties are now likely to be.

Current Building Regulations require wall ties specified or manufactured to British Standard BS 1243:1978, 'Metal Ties for Cavity-wall Construction' or an equivalent including non-ferrous or stainless-steel wall ties. Galvanised wall ties usually take the form of either vertical twist, double triangle or butterfly types, and the durability of the ties is dependent upon the zinc coating given during galvanising. The possibility of corrosion and the possible resulting instability of cavity walls is a known hazard but so far few reports of structural failure of cavity walls for this reason have been made, except in cases where black-ash mortar has been used. In a BRE information paper, 'The Performance of Cavity-wall Ties', (BRE Information Paper IP 4/81 April 1981), it was concluded that vertical-twist ties may lose their zinc coating within 23 to 46 years and wire ties in similar conditions within 13 to 26 years, assuming zinc coating to the current British Standards. The use of wire ties was considered unsatisfactory, and more durable ties were recommended although the majority of existing buildings were regarded as sufficiently robust for widespread problems to be unlikely.

Faced with cavity-wall construction and black-ash mortar (where an ash-fine aggregate has been used instead of sand) the surveyor should beware of corroded ties. Faced with any cavity-wall construction over 50 years old he should be on his guard against the possibility that wall ties may have corroded to the point where there is no effective connection between the two wall skins. Conventional low-rise cavity walls will normally remain quite stable, even in the absence of effective ties, due to stiffness afforded by bonded cross wall construction inside and abutments over, under and around openings, these abutments having only limited resistance to tension between skins but good resistance against compression. Corrosion of ties could be more significant in low-rise construction with little bracing and in high-rise buildings which have masonry infill panels with galvanised metal ties.

The possibility should be borne in mind that galvanising of connecting ties used for certain types of pre-fabricated construction may be poor. Surveyors will occasionally have to report on local authority houses (some now privately owned having been purchased by the tenants) constructed by using various forms of pre-cast concrete slabs and pre-fabricated panels. A number of different systems were used during the post-War municipal housing programmes. Variations in such construction will also be encountered in commercial and industrial structures including pre-cast concrete panels fixed using bolted connections and spacers with galvanising to bolts and fittings often of a poor standard. In addition to problems associated with rusting of galvanised fixings, some systems incorporated a framework of tubular supports which are prone to corrosion and the pre-cast concrete panels themselves may be subject to the rusting of the reinforcement bars inside, this causing disintegration of the panels.

The fact that many local authority pre-fabricated houses are now passing into private hands may pose a problem for surveyors in the future since instructions to report on such buildings are likely to be received in increasing numbers. It is felt that in addition to all the usual procedures involved in a survey of residential property, the surveyor may have to advise that special exposure work be undertaken to sample reinforcement and concretes used with a view to obtaining a laboratory report, and also that enquiries be made regarding the technical specifications for the particular system involved. Local authority personnel are generally most helpful in looking out files and technical specifications from their records, and if an older building surveyor can be located at the council offices he may prove to be a source of valuable information.

The overall performance of walls may normally be confirmed from a single inspection, unless the structure is very new, and assuming that the walls have not been covered recently by rendering or other applied surfaces. It will be possible to see whether or not movements have occurred in the past or surfaces damaged by dampness or for other reasons.

Monitoring walls

Occasionally walls will be either quite new or have surfaces recently covered in such a way that evidence of past damage will not be discernible. In these cases procedures will be available for monitoring the performance of the walls and sometimes, in an initial report, it may be necessary to recommend such procedures.

One of these recommended procedures is the accurate monitoring of crack damage in distressed buildings, this generally being undertaken using calibrated tell-tales, these being rigid indicators fixed over cracks walls and showing measured horizontal and vertical movements over a period of time. Tell-tales should be given reference numbers and all measurements of movement logged at regular intervals in a permanent log book. After a suitable period has elapsed, the information collected will be useful in showing the extent and direction of structural movement and whether or not it is seasonally variable.

Movements in walls due to thermal expansion and contraction can show a distinct pattern of measurement, with conditions in hot and cold weather differing. Movement in walls due to progressive settlement of parts of a structure relative to other parts will show a general progressive overall measurement. Structural settlements followed by heave due to shrinkage and swelling of clay soils will produce distinct seasonal patterns. Expansion due to chemical deterioration of concrete members may be found to be more noticeable during periods of wet weather. The variety of movements which may be caused by subsidences and landslips of the subsoil are considerable, and by accurate monitoring over a period of time it is possible to confirm overall downward movements of parts of a structure, progressive leaning and tilting of walls, rotational movements of projecting wings and other structural manifestations.

Figure 4.5 Crack width (a) is the shortest distance between edges, and crack size (b) is assessed in the direction of movement

Clearly not all clients will be in a position to benefit from the monitoring of crack damage since if the client is a prospective purchaser he may need to decide quickly whether or not to purchase a building. If he is proposing to take a repairing lease he may have no time to spare for lengthy structural monitoring. Similarly, prospective mortgagees will be unlikely themselves to be able to commission structural monitorings of walls prior to confirming any mortgage advance although they may be able to require the prospective mortgagor to undertake this and allow a suitable period for him so to do prior to confirming their offer. This situation is unlikely to be helpful to a prospective mortgagor who is himself an intending purchaser and under pressure to exchange binding contracts.

One feature of crack damage occasionally encountered in Victorian and Edwardian construction of a cheaper type is that some solid walls were built without cross-bonding and snapped headers used to the outer face, such walls having the appearance of 225-mm solid brickwork but, in fact, comprising two skins of 112-mm brick with a continuous lime mortar joint rising vertically in the centre. Curious crack patterns and leaning and bulging of such walls may be found showing different patterns to inner and outer faces. This construction was used to minimise cost by saving all facing bricks for outside and in practice may be found to develop instability with age, especially where tall gable-ends are concerned.

Retaining and freestanding walls

In addition to the main walls of buildings, surveyors often have to assess exterior walls such as retaining walls, free-standing walls or parapet walls (generally of brickwork or stonework) which form adjuncts to or extensions of the main structure.

Such walls are examined to see whether or not they are plumb and level. The overall construction should be considered in relation to the importance of the walls and the requirements of their construction. Clearly, retaining walls may be very important indeed to a structure on a sloping site and may be essential to the stability of that site and thus of the structure.

The first design consideration is whether or not the walls under review are allowed adequate provision for movement. Generally, movement joints in brick retaining and free-standing walls are desirable at about 10-m intervals to cope with normal thermal expansion and contraction and occasional movements which occur as a result of chemical conversion in concretes and mortars. Movement joints at greater frequency may be recommended for free-standing walls on sites where the subsoil may be unstable and where, for reasons of economy, a shallow foundation is necessary. On shrinkable clays, for example, garden walls and the like could be provided with movement joints at 3- to 5-m centres, obviating later cracking in the brickwork due to seasonal ground movements.

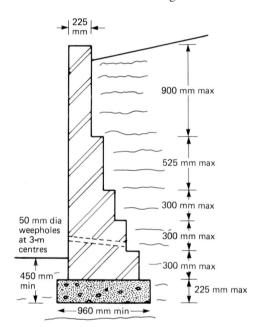

Figure 4.6 Typical design for all-brick retaining wall, using special-quality brickwork which does not require tanking or weathering. The wall is stepped back in half-brick increments. Backward-sloping drain-holes prevent staining down the face of the wall from very small quantities of groundwater discharging over a long period. Note that ordinary-quality brickwork requires special tanking, damp-proof courses and weathering, otherwise frost damage will result

The second design consideration is whether in the case of retaining walls the construction itself is adequate. Where a retaining wall is essential to the stability of a structure a consulting engineer's report should be obtained if the construction standard is doubtful. This will generally involve some site investigation behind the wall. In *Fig. 4.6* a cross-section of a brick retaining wall is shown. It will be noted that 225-mm brickwork should be used only for retained heights of up to 900 m, and that progressively thicker wall construction is required as the height of the wall increases. Regard should be given to the bearing pressure values of the retained ground, which may require special consideration. *Fig. 4.5* shows a typical free-standing wall. It should be noted that 225-m brickwork is a minimum thickness and that piers or buttresses or, alternatively, thicker overall construction is required for heights greater than 900 mm. A check on the slenderness ratio is recommended in doubtful cases, paying particular regard to the strength of the mortar, which is often poor, exterior brickwork and stonework, especially if this is old.

The third design consideration is whether the wall material will deteriorate should groundwater be able to enter the wall, and taking into account conditions of exposure. Special-quality brickwork or stonework resistant to frost damage and chemical attack from groundwater will be normally be suitable. Ordinary-quality brickwork or stonework which may not resist such deterioration should not be used in conditions of high exposure. In the case of normal exposure, ordinary-quality

Figure 4.7 Free-standing wall construction. Throated weathering projecting at least 45 mm, plus damp-proof courses at top and bottom, allow ordinary-quality brickwork to be used for normal exposure conditions, but special-quality bricks are necessary for footings below dpc

Figure 4.8 Mass concrete retaining wall with brick face

brickwork or stonework may be used provided that certain precautions are taken, these being the provision of tanking to retaining walls, and horizontal damp-proof courses at the tops and bottoms of walls, also the provision of adequate copings with throated over-hangs. In *Fig. 4.8* a sketch of a mass concrete retaining wall with a facing of ordinary-quality brickwork is shown. Below damp-proof course at the base a special-quality brick footing is necessary.

When large quantities of groundwater are likely to need draining through weepholes, it is a good idea to set the weephole drains with a backward slope. This then deals with the main discharge of water but any continuous trickle of groundwater is avoided, thus preventing an accumulation of moss or staining of wall faces and adjoining paved areas.

Chapter 5

Floors

When we first bought the house we thought the ramps in the floors at the door openings were there because the house was built for someone with a wheelchair. It was only later that we realised that the floors have all sunk by three or four inches, which is why a second set of skirting boards has been fixed lower down on the first set of skirting boards.
Extract from letter from potential client to surveyor

During the survey the nature of the floor construction in each part of the building should be confirmed as far as possible in the circumstances.

The ground floor may be of suspended timber construction, or suspended concrete slab construction, or solid slab construction on a hardcore base. Settlement problems in solid slab floors have been found by the National House-Building Council (NHBC) to be the most common source of complaint in new houses and they now require that any construction on sloping sites which needs deep fill under solid floors should be built using suspended floors instead, as detailed later in this Chapter.

Suspended timber floors

Suspended timber ground floors may be of the traditional type supported on intermediate sleeper walls or may be of the fully-spanned type. With either type it is clearly essential that the decking and the supporting timbers are of adequate type and size for the spans involved and a check by reference to the standards laid down in Building Regulations is recommended, using Schedule 6, Table 1 of the Regulations, and also by reference to 'The Structural Use of Timber', CP 112, Part 2:1971, the relevant British Standard Code of Practice. Part of Table 1 for dead loads of not more than $25 \, \text{kg/m}^2$ is reproduced below.

The Code provides a standard for stiffness and deflection in floors having particular regard to possible damage of surface materials. For floors, the Code provides that deflection for general purposes should not exceed 0.003 of the span when floors are fully loaded (CP 112, Part 2: 1971, para. 3.13.2). The use of brittle surface materials may call for a standard better than this and could require the use of solid floors or suspended concrete slabs rather than timber construction in order to obviate surface damage, for example, to tiles. The amount of permissible deflection allowed by the Code is considerable.

In older houses the surveyor may encounter uneven and sloping floors, some with considerable gradients when floor joists are over-spanned, either being so originally or having had intermediate support removed from below. An overall gradient in one direction will, of course, not be due to deflection but will indicate some more fundamental movement in the bearings to the floor joists. Faced with a

Schedule 6, Table 1, 1976 Building Regulations
Floor joists for dead loads of not more than 25 kg/m^2 excluding the mass of the joist.

Size of Size of joist (mm)	Maximum span to centres of bearings (m)		
	400 mm spacing	450 mm spacing	600 mm spacing
38 × 75	1.03	0.93	0.71
38 × 100	1.74	1.57	1.21
38 × 125	2.50	2.31	1.81
38 × 150	2.99	2.83	2.46
38 × 175	3.48	3.29	2.86
38 × 200	3.96	3.75	3.26
38 × 225	4.44	4.20	3.66
44 × 75	1.18	1.06	0.81
44 × 100	1.97	1.78	1.38
44 × 125	2.62	2.52	2.05
44 × 150	3.13	3.02	2.64
44 × 175	3.65	3.51	3.07
44 × 200	4.16	4.50	3.93
50 × 75	1.33	1.19	0.92
50 × 100	2.10	1.99	1.55
50 × 125	2.73	2.63	2.29
50 × 150	3.26	3.14	2.81
50 × 175	3.80	3.66	3.27
50 × 200	4.33	4.17	3.72
50 × 225	4.85	4.68	4.18
63 × 150	3.51	3.38	3.09
63 × 175	4.08	3.93	3.59
63 × 200	4.65	4.48	4.10
63 × 225	5.21	5.03	4.60
75 × 200	4.90	4.93	4.33
75 × 225	5.49	5.30	4.85

floor which slopes in one direction only, the surveyor should confirm whether or not this is due to failure of the joist bearings or to a downward settlement of the wall on which they bear. A wall plate, for example, which is eaten away by beetle attack or softened by rot may simply crush under the weight of the joist ends resting on it and a downward movement equal to the depth of the wall plate could occur. This is a particular danger in old structures with wall plates built into the damp wall construction.

Upper floors in traditional dwelling-house construction are normally suspended timber floors, fully spanned between ground floor walls and supporting certain point-loads such as airing cupboards and tanks, blockwork or stud partitions and the like. A check should be made on such floors similar to that recommended for ground floors, especially having regard to the possibility of over-spanned joists in older buildings.

For higher dead loads, reference should be made to the other parts of Table 1 or to structural calculation in accordance with CP 112 Part 2:1971.

For bearings greater than 100 mm a notional bearing of 100 mm may be used so that in most cases the maximum clear span will be 100 mm less than the span to bearing centres shown above.

The Tables to the Building Regulations assume new timbers in good condition, classified as Group 11 in CP 112, Part 2:1971, or graded in accordance with certain minimum standards for a particular species. It will be appreciated that timbers in existing buildings, and especially older buildings, may not meet the grades of Group 11 specification laid down and some allowance for this may need to be made in applying Table 1 as a rule of thumb to check the adequacy or otherwise of floor joists, particularly where the span is marginal.

In domestic construction the most commonly found joists will be 50 mm × 150 mm, 50 mm × 175 mm and 50 mm × 200 mm, generally at 400-mm centres, with maximum permissible clear spans of 3.16, 3.7 and 4.23 m respectively (i.e. the Table spans less the distance to bearing centres on notional 100-mm bearings).

In domestic construction which has suspended timber ground floors resting on intermediate sleeper walls, the joists will normally be found to be 100 mm × 50 mm and the Table to Schedule 6 of the Building Regulations would assume clear spans between sleeper walls of 2 m, assuming 400-mm spacing and dead loads not exceeding 25 kg/m². It follows that ground floor construction with spans between sleeper walls exceeding 2 m clear may be over-spanned and this is a useful avenue of investigation for the surveyor to explore if the floors appear to flex unduly underfoot. In some newer properties where joist sizes have been calculated to comply with the Building Regulations rather than use of Tables, such unacceptable flexing may often occur and can prove embarrassing, particularly, for example, in dining rooms where walking across the floor can make cutlery rattle.

Intermediate strutting to suspended timber floors is required where the span exceeds 2.5 m, using herringbone or other strutting to prevent undue warping or torsional distortion of the joists. The *Registered House-Builders' Handbook* recommends and requires one set of such strutting for spans of between 2.5 and 4.5 m and additional strutting for greater spans. It is important that the strutting be neatly done and tightly fixed otherwise it will not prove effective. In the event of strutting being absent in spans over 2.5 m, the surveyor may have to consider whether or not any undue warping or distortion of the joists has resulted, and recommendations to this effect are required. In practice, intermediate strutting is often found to have been omitted with no apparent ill effects.

It is important that bearings and floor joists be so constructed as to eliminate the possibility of moisture transference from adjoining masonry and from oversite into timbers. In older buildings, joists are often built into the outer walls where the construction is in solid brickwork and a likelihood of rot attack to joist ends then arises, especially if the wall concerned faces the prevailing weather or is in a porous condition.

In some older buildings the joists will rest on wall plates which are themselves built into the outer walls or fixed to the face of walls, and the possibility of decay and even complete disintegration of the wall plate arises, causing serious loss of bearing to the joists.

It may also be found that sleeper walls or other means of support lack effective damp-proof courses under sleeper plates and joists, thus giving rise to decay and insect attack to the timbers. Commonly the air-space under a suspended timber ground floor will be found to contain large quantities of debris left over from the original construction or later building works, and this can cause moisture transference into timbers from the oversite and also block ventilation.

The provision of adequate underfloor ventilation to a suspended timber floor which is above an oversite in contact with ground moisture is essential since lack of good ventilation can give rise to condensation on the timbers and resultant decay. A careful check must be made for any 'dead' areas of air-space under such floors which may not be adequately ventilated. Generally a good standard of underfloor ventilation to a suspended timber ground floor in domestic construction would be 225 mm × 75 mm terra cotta airbricks, sleeved through wall cavities, sited at 1.5-mm centres. Iron grilles are not recommended since eventually they rust and permit the access of vermin. A vent should be provided at or near each extremity of the floor void to prevent areas of 'dead' air.

Solid floors

Solid slab ground floors of concrete on hardcore are more durable in the long term than suspended timber ground floors. In older buildings where timber floors are in poor condition, replacement with a solid concrete floor is often to be recommended for a number of reasons, especially if the adjoining ground levels are high and it is difficult to provide the necessary clearances to air vents.

The main problems likely to arise with solid floors at ground-floor level will be due either to settlement of the floor slab or rising dampness. Settlement and dishing of post-War solid concrete floors due to inadequate consolidation of the hardcore filling beneath or the use of unsuitable fill material is a common problem, so common in fact that the NHBC list it as being the major source of complaint in houses covered by their scheme.

On reasonably level sites, the NHBC will still approve solid concrete ground floors on a hardcore base and, in theory at least, such construction should be quite suitable for most ground conditions provided that the standard of worksmanship is satisfactory. Most problems arise when workmanship is poor and site supervision lacking.

On sloping sites where a deep fill would be required under concrete ground floors, the NHBC now require suspended-floor construction to be used where fill would exceed 600 mm in depth. On a sloping site it may be that a mixture of solid concrete on fill and suspended timber (or concrete) floors would be necessary to comply with this requirement (NHBC Practice Note 6, 'Suspended-floor Construction for Dwellings on Deep-fill Sites').

Unless the laying of fill material is supervised constantly and thoroughly it is virtually impossible to ensure that consolidation is adequate and that all material used is suitable.

Occasionally problems may arise due to the use of fill material which is still chemically active, such as cases where industrial waste material or ash blinding is used. It is essential that all fill material be chemically inert, otherwise damage to floor slabs from expansion or contraction of the fill are possible and chemical attack to the concrete and surrounding masonry could occur.

It is also possible for a solid concrete ground floor slab to be built over ground affected by existing leaking drains or for such drain leaks to arise after construction. Occasionally old land drains may exist and continue to discharge groundwater into the subsoil under the slab, thus causing erosion.

When inspecting a building with a solid concrete ground floor the general floor levels and amount of deflection which may be present in relation to the age of the floor should be considered. Some initial consolidation is often inevitable. If the floor has been in place for some years and the extent of any deflection is acceptable (say up to 0.003 of the span), this may be regarded as a matter for mere comment. If the deflection is greater then it may be necessary to consider undertaking investigations under the slab to confirm the nature and quality of the fill material. A core sample or small sample inspection hole is the best means of achieving this result. The sample material should be examined and, if necessary, a laboratory report obtained. When taking samples care must be taken to check for excessive moisture under the floor. Under normal conditions both the fill material and any subsoil under a floor should be nearly dry. Excessive amounts of water in samples may indicate a plumbing or drain leak under the floor and this could be one cause of the problem.

Where solid concrete floor slabs have settled due to inadequate consolidation of the original fill, a remedy may be required to stiffen the fill. This can be carried out, without taking up the floor, by using pressure-grouting techniques. Floor surfaces can then be re-screeded level, taking care to ensure the integrity of damp-proof membranes and also checking that membranes remain contiguous with the damp-proof courses in the surrounding walls in order to prevent moisture transference.

An examination around the perimeter of a floor is always to be recommended since this could reveal any gaps which may have opened up below skirting boards. If the surveyor is satisfied that the skirting boards are at their original height, a measurement of the gaps will indicate the extent of any downward movement around that perimeter. If quarter-round beading or similar additional trim has been applied at the base of skirtings, this may indicate that gaps have appeared and subsequently been covered. This feature should place the surveyor on this guard over the possibility of settlement in that floor. New skirting boards may have been applied and this could be due to a number of causes, including the possibility of such settlement in the floor surface.

Floors should be checked for level using a spirit level where a visual inspection suggests a slope. Some surveyors even carry a marble and use this to see if solid floor surfaces are uneven. However, since most floors are uneven to a greater or lesser degree, the fact that a marble may roll on the floor will not of itself be a means of accurately gauging the extent of such unevenness. A long spirit level is much better. In a larger building it may be necessary to take levels using a dumpy level or similar apparatus in order to assess the degree of unevenness in the floors. A series of spot levels will often reveal considerable fluctuations in a wide-based structure which are not apparent visually.

In good construction, timber and suspended concrete ground floors will be separated physically from any contact with the site or structure below damp-proof course line, and floor surfaces should therefore be dry. Solid concrete ground floors are made dry by the provision of a suitable damp-proof membrane, and in the absence of an effective membrane the surfaces of such floors become damp due to moisture rising up from the site, especially if the surfaces are covered with carpets or sheet flooring.

Damp-proof membranes may be located below the floor slab, in which case polythene film of at least 500-gauge, and preferably 1000-gauge, should have been used, or alternatively, a bitumen sheet to British Standard 743. It is essential that all joints in such membranes be lapped and sealed and that the membranes are carried up around the perimeter and lapped under the damp-proof courses in the surrounding walls so as to provide a completely imperforate barrier against rising moisture. Lapping should be at least 300 mm. Such membranes should have been laid over a suitable blinding of inert ash or sand, free from any sharp protrusions which could puncture the membrane.

Damp-proof membranes in sandwich construction may be located within the slab and could comprise polythene film or bitumen sheet (as before described), hot-applied mastic asphalt, pitch or bitumen, 0.6 mm minimum thickness of cold-applied bituminous solutions, or composite polythene and bitumen self-adhesive. In such construction the concrete slab is first allowed to dry thoroughly and the membrane applied to the surface and lapped up to the damp-proof courses as necessary. A surface screed is then applied which, to avoid 'shelling' or lamination, should be a minimum of 50 mm depth.

Membranes also may be located on the floor surface in the form of hot applied mastic asphalt, pitch mastic or cold-applied pitch/epoxy resins. In older construction hot-applied mastic will generally be found as a base for woodblocks or thermoplastic tiles, the use of polythene and other modern materials not becoming general practice until post-1960.

In pre-1939 and older construction, solid floors were often not provided with any damp-proof membranes at all and the surveyor will often encounter flagstoned floors, quarry-tile surfaces or ceramic tile surfaces of various types and ages which may be performing adequately when fully exposed but which would immediately begin to 'sweat' if covered with tiles, sheet flooring or carpeting. In advising a client in such circumstances, and before modern surface materials may be applied, it is essential to explain the significance of the modern practice of providing membranes and the special attention required to older floors which lack such membranes.

For the first half of this century most housewives were content with a kitchen equipped solely with a sink and draining board, gas-point for an oven and a quarry-tile floor which could be periodically washed down with soap and water and polished on Sundays. Quarry tiles are not impervious to moisture but they present a reasonably adequate barrier and the need for a dry floor surface was not important in those days. Nowadays a wife would wish to see a modern kitchen installed in an older house in order to make it acceptable and the old quarry tiles replaced by vinyl asbestos tiles or sheet vinyl floorings. It is essential that any new floor surfaces be laid over a suitable membrane which is contiguous with the damp-proof courses in the surrounding walls. To achieve this it may be necessary to remove skirting boards together with wall and floor material at the skirtings in order to expose damp-proof courses in the walls and to seal the new membranes against these damp-proof courses to avoid moisture transference.

Flagstone floors may be lifted and re-laid over a suitable membrane if flagstones are required as a finish, again paying particular attention to the need to joint the membrane to the surrounding damp-proof course.

In commercial structures, solid floors may be laid as dry floors or without any membranes. Again, provided that the floor surfaces are exposed, it will often be found that concrete floors will remain reasonably dry on the surface even if no membrane is provided, but once the surfaces are covered they will sweat. The needs of the client may required consideration since certain types of storage and warehousing, for example, would require dry conditions and dry floor surfaces.

Concrete floors in commercial structures can be dusty and a suitable treatment of concrete paints or special sealants to reduce surface dusting may be recommended. For many types of manufacture a dust-free atmosphere is essential especially where precision work or electronics are concerned.

Where a garage is either an integral part of a house or is attached to it with a communicating doorway into the main accommodation, the garage floor will normally be a solid concrete slab. This slab should be on a lower level than the main ground floors inside the house with a step up at any doorway of at least 150 mm. The purpose of this is to prevent burning petrol in a garage from spreading under the door and into the main house. Garage floors should also have a slight slope down towards the main entrance to allow water to run away.

Particular attention should be given to providing adequate drainage to paved areas outside garages, especially where driveways slope down towards the building, in order to prevent driving rain or stormwater running in through the main door opening. Generally a driveway which slopes down towards a garage should always be provided with a suitable stormwater gully and a suitable drainage fall to this gully. This is often found, in practice, not to be the case with the result that ponding of stormwater in driveways and garages occurs. In such cases a channel and grating across the threshold of the door and drained into a gully should be provided.

A surveyor should confirm, if possible, the nature of the floor material under any fitted coverings. If fitted coverings are not to be lifted this should be made clear at the outset and a statement that the condition of floor surfaces cannot be confirmed included in the report. The nature of the floor surfaces should be suited to the purposes for which they are required and if this is not so then some advice on the point should be given.

Suspended concrete floors

Suspended concrete floor construction can take one of two possible forms, either pre-cast construction with or without a composite screed, or cast-*in-situ* construction. The latter is more commonly encountered in older buildings.

Cast-*in-situ* construction may be identified where the underside is exposed, mainly in commercial buildings, as the pattern left by shuttering is visible where it used to support the floor during curing.

When the floor construction is covered on all surfaces it will be impossible to confirm the nature of the construction without some special exposure or core samples being taken.

Pre-cast concrete floors appear in a wide variety of forms and slab sizes. It is more likely that defects due to conversion of concretes may arise in pre-cast construction, particularly if high-alumina cement (HAC) is present. HAC had an advantage in the production of pre-cast concrete members as it allowed a rapid drying time and quicker production. During the post-War period until 1974 a great deal of pre-cast floor slabwork and beams were made using HAC.

In February 1974 two roof beams in a school in Stepney collapsed and a major question arose as to the condition of beams and slabs in post-War buildings where HAC had been used. The Building Research Establishment undertook urgent investigations to establish the degree of risk likely to arise in buildings with pre-cast concrete beams made with HAC. The results of their investigations were published in April 1975 in Current Paper CP 34/75 'High-alumina Cement Concrete in Buildings'.

The outcome, according to the BRE, was that the risk of structural failure to floors of up to a 5-m span made with pre-stressed pre-cast beams using HAC is very small.

Spans of more than 5 m are unlikely to be encountered in residential construction, including blocks of flats, except in exceptional cases, bearing in mind that cross-wall construction is generally used and the spans will normally be the shorter of any two room dimensions. In most cases a surveyor will be able to see when the existence of spans greater than 5 m is unlikely in floor slabs, although it is rather more common in blocks of flats where beams are used. In commercial buildings spans exceeding 5 m will often be encountered in both floor slabs and beams. If the building was erected between 1925 (when the use of HAC in the United Kingdom began) and 1975 (when it ceased) the possibility of chemical conversion of the concrete resulting in a loss of bearing capacity may then arise.

In cases where there is a risk of the presence of HAC in spans exceeding 5 m, the surveyor should recommend that a consulting engineer be asked to carry out tests and advise independently on the position.

Chapter 6

Roofs and chimneys

I looked into the loft myself and thought it was rather light in there – I assumed there was a skylight. I now realise it was because so many of the slates were missing.
Note from client to surveyor when paying his account

There are two basic types of roof. Pitched roofs with an inclination of 10° or more and flat roofs with an inclination of less than 10°. The results of roof failures can be serious since leakage of water into a building may give rise not only to the need for repair of the defect but also consequential losses. Special attention should be paid to the requirements of clients interested in non-residential buildings such as factory and warehouse space. If materials are to be stored in circumstances where roof defects could cause damage, special attention should be given to this point.

Life of roof covering

Most roof coverings have a reasonable and well-defined effective life span beyond which re-covering may be necessary or trouble may be anticipated. In practice, there is considerable variation in the quality of materials from different sources, especially traditional materials, but the following is a list of the principal roof-covering materials likely to be encountered and a guide to their life span.

	Years
Hot-bonded, built-up mineral felt flat roofs to BS 747, well constructed	15–20
Hot-bonded, built-up felt roofs constructed to lesser standards	5–15
Good quality flat lead roofs, well detailed and laid with rolls	80–100
Good quality flat copper roofs, well detailed	30–75
Zinc roofs, well laid with rolls, in areas not subject to chemical pollution	20–40
Zinc roofs in situations of chemical pollution	15–20
Asphalt, well laid and detailed, in two coats to BS CP 144, Part 4:1970	20–40
Hand-made clay tiles with battens and sarking felt	60–70
Machine-cut clay tiles with battens and sarking felt	40–60
Plain concrete tiles, double lap with battens and sarking felt	50–90
Interlocking concrete tiles with battens and sarking felt	50–80
Interlocking Dutch or Belgian clay tiles	40–60

	Years
Asbestos-cement tiles or roofing sheets	20–25
Good quality Norfolk reed thatch	50–60
Straw thatch	20–25
Local stone slabs (depending upon porosity)	10–100
Good quality Welsh slates with battens and sarking felt	60–90
Poorer slates, subject to lamination with age	40–60
Shingles (depending upon quality and frequency of treatment)	5–30
Perspex, clear or obscure uPVC sheets etc. (depending upon brittleness etc.)	5–25

The surveyor should confirm during his survey the nature of the roof coverings in various parts and assess their likely age. He should then consider what advice may be given in each particular circumstance. Where roof coverings are likely to give problems in the foreseeable future the position should be explained to the client having regard to the possibility of either repair or renewal of these coverings. There will be many situations where re-covering might be recommended, but where the client could, if he so wished, extend the life of the roof more or less indefinitely by undertaking periodic overhauls and renewing individual defective slates or tiles as the necessity arises. Many clients are quite happy with an old roof covering which needs such periodic attention and will happily spend the money needed to renew it on something else. It seems quite reasonable in the circumstances for the surveyor merely to present the facts and leave it to the client to make the decision. Many examples of old slate and tile roofs will be encountered, still giving service well beyond the time scales indicated above.

Pitched roofs

Undersides of roof slopes will generally be lined with sarking felt in buildings erected post-1938 and in some cases earlier. Only a very limited view may be available of the underside of the roof covering if felt is loose or torn, and there will be no view of it at all if it is tightly and correctly laid. Unfelted roofs will normally allow an examination to be made of the underside of the covering, but where feather-edged boarding is used then very little access to the underside of the covering will exist. This is encountered mainly in 1920–1940 property.

It is helpful to examine debris which may have accumulated on ceilings in older roofs. Extensive deposits of clay-tile laminations and broken tile nibs will indicate that the tiles are laminating and becoming porous. Slate laminations, sections of cracked slates and rusted nail heads will all indicate that a slate roof is approaching the end of its recommended life span. Often a roof covering will have been replaced and the debris in the roof void will indicate the type of previous covering, a point which may be significant if a heavy covering has replaced a lighter one since roof timbers designed for the lighter covering could deflect under the weight of the heavier.

Pitched roofs without underfelt should be regarded nowadays as below the acceptable standard. Clients should be warned that the degree of weather-proofing, especially in driving rain and snow, will not be as good as with a modern felted roof and also that the roof void will become dusty and items stored there will therefore need some protection.

The scantling of the roof timbers should be checked. In older buildings, rafters may lack effective purlin support, or purlins may lack sufficient strutting. Sagging rafters or purlins should generally not be jacked back into line but recommendations to stiffen up the purlin or strut construction to a reasonable standard should be given. A cross-check by reference to Schedule 6 of the Building Regulations should be made, bearing in mind that the older timbers may not be of an equivalent standard, and it is better to over-size purlins, struts and the like in marginal cases.

Figure 6.1 A familiar sight. Hand-made, double-lap clay roof tiles showing signs of advanced deterioration and surface lamination (Middlesex 1982)

In older roofs a check for roof spread is advisable. The rafters should meet the ridge board tightly and if they have pulled away, this could indicate insufficient provision of collars, inadequate fixing of joists at the rafter feet, or insufficient binders to roof slopes which are at right angles to the main rafters.

In modern trussed-rafter and roof-truss systems certain important points are often overlooked. First, diagonal restraint is required to trussed roofs with gable-ends to prevent a parallelogrammatic, or 'racking', sideways movement of the trusses. Diagonal planking from the eaves at each corner to the ridge at the centre with two good galvanised nail fixings to each truss is essential, especially if the gable-ends themselves are of poor construction. Secondly, the end two or three trusses should be strapped with galvanised-steel strapping built into the gable-ends to prevent separation. Thirdly, no cutting or alteration of such truss construction should be undertaken, and if this is found to have been done, a warning should be given that the overall stability of the roof construction could have been seriously affected. Fourthly, only light storage on roof truss ties is advisable. The size and spacing of trussed rafters are not designed to accommodate heavy point loads.

Flat roofs

Most modern flat roof construction used in post-War dwellings is of hot-bonded, built-up mineral felt on timber decking, supported by timber joists and with a ceiling beneath. Built-up felt construction should normally comply with British Standard 747:1977 which sets out certain minimum standards for the materials to be used and the manner of laying. From a superficial inspection it is generally not possible to confirm whether or not the standards have been met. However, there are certain important matters which can be confirmed and borne in mind for future maintenance.

First, for roofs situated over habitable rooms the felting should be in three layers laid in hot bitumen with the surface covered in bitumen-bedded chippings for protection from the sun. If chippings are not used the surface felt will lift and crack after only a short time, particularly on roofs with a south aspect. Periodic inspections should be carried out to confirm that the protective layer of chippings is in place and has not been washed away.

Secondly, the void underneath the decking must be provided with some ventilation. The decking itself may be of tongued-and-grooved or butt-jointed boards; it may comprise Stramit board, made of compressed straw, which was popular in the nineteen-fifties and nineteen-sixties; it may be of chipboard or some other type of manufactured boarding, either pre-felted, with only two additional layers of felt rather than three, or unfelted. The purpose of ventilation is to prevent an accumulation of trapped vapour under the decking which can otherwise wise cause lifting or 'blowing' of the felt. This may then indicate trapped water vapour in the void due to lack of ventilation. Ventilation may be provided quite easily by allowing for spacers under the perimeter fascia boards of small roofs and by setting vents into the surface at intervals where larger areas of flat roof are involved. Adequate ventilation is essential to prevent interstitial condensation.

Thirdly, the roof void should be protected from the entry of warm, damp air rising from rooms beneath (especially bathrooms and kitchens) by the use of suitable vapour barriers or vapour checks. This means that the ceilings beneath should be virtually sealed and airtight. If narrow ceiling cracks, holes or joints exist, particularly where electric wiring passes through, then warm, damp air will enter the void and condense on the underside of the cold decking in the roof void, a feature encountered mainly in wintertime. Polythene sheets may be used as vapour barriers provided that they are carefully lapped and sealed at all joints and are placed on the warm side of any insulation — generally this will mean directly over the ceiling plasterboard. Electric wiring should be run not through the sheets but under them so as to maintain the integrity of the vapour check. Foil-backed plasterboard is often used but in this case joints should be sealed. Metal foil, however, makes the best vapour barrier.

Fourthly, the roof should be insulated. Experience indicates that flat roofs tend to suffer greater heat losses in winter and heat gains in summer. This may be reduced by the provision of ceiling insulation which should be laid over the vapour barrier or vapour check but with an adequate ventilation gap to permit free circulation of air directly under the decking.

Fifthly, special care is needed to maintain the flat roof detail in good order since most problems start with small leaks at flashings, upstands and parapets and at points where openings are formed for soilpipes, flues and the like. Warm boiler flues will present a special problem since the built-up felt around them will be softened by the heat and the weather-sealing will often be deficient.

Where the roof forms a dished tray with an internal rainwater pipe, frequent inspections would be advisable to clear leaves and debris, especially if trees are near, since if the internal rainwater pipe blocks, the tray will fill with water which could then penetrate the decking at any weak points around the perimeter.

Well-constructed built-up felt roofs have a useful life span of 15 to 20 years, after which renewal of the covering will generally become essential. Occasionally a felt roof may last longer, especially if sheltered from the sun, but poorly-constructed felt roofs often have a shorter life.

A problem arises in giving advice on the action to be taken where a flat felt roof is weathertight but is of an age when re-covering may be anticipated. To some extent local repairs in the form of patching defective areas and renewing flashings and upstands are often possible and may prolong the overall life of the roof. The main problem arises from the fact that small leaks, often undetected for some time, will cause rapid deterioration of the decking and timbers beneath and destroy the effectiveness of insulation and the vapour barrier. In these circumstances the condition of decking and timbers cannot be accurately assessed without full exposure.

Stramit board decking will absorb moisture and convey it over a wide area by capillary action. If ventilation is poor, this warm, damp atmosphere will encourage wet- or dry-rot fungus to grow. Chipboard deckings will also absorb moisture and deteriorate rapidly, often without any moisture reaching the ceilings beneath to give warning to the occupants that all is not well above. Conventional butt-jointed or tongued-and-grooved boarding have, in the writers' experience, proved more durable. Any decay occasioned by small leaks in the surface covering has tended to be more localised than would be the case with chipboard or Stramit, although boarding is often more prone to outbreaks of wet- or dry-rot if it is unseasoned and ventilation is poor.

The re-covering of a flat felt roof in new built-up felt to British Standard 747 will be a fairly straightforward building operation and, for a small area, can be completed rapidly. If a small domestic roof is involved it is generally possible to strip off the old covering, have one or two layers of felt laid and the joints sealed in one day, thus avoiding the need for weather protection in the form of temporary canopies and scaffolding. However, if the roof area is large, or the decking and joists need repairs, then the roof will be exposed for some time and the cost will have to be increased to cover not only the need for weather protection but also the repairs to the joists and decking. In such circumstances, defective flat roofs can cause considerable inconvenience to a property owner and result in substantial expenditure to put things right.

The purpose, therefore, of periodic inspections of the roof surfaces and ancillary items is to pre-empt any trouble in the form of small leaks which could result in major expenditure later on.

Thatch

Occasionally a surveyor may be asked to report on a thatched roof. There are some thatched properties in suburban areas and a considerable number in rural locations, probably more than one would expect. Thatch gives considerable advantages as a roof covering. It has good insulation properties against both heat loss and noise, and the noise of rain on the surface goes unnoticed. Generally a deep eaves overhang is provided, obviating the need for gutter or rainwater pipes and rainwater is allowed to run off the eaves overhang well out from the main walls of the building.

Vermin infestation in the thatch can be a problem. Birds cause considerable damage during the nesting season and squirrels and mice are very destructive to thatch once they have gained an entry. Many thatched roofs are covered with a fine galvanised steel wire mesh to prevent birds or vermin removing or burrowing into the straw or reeds but this can make access very difficult in the case of a thatch fire and a PVC mesh is now often used, melting when heat is applied.

Clients buying a house with a thatched roof should be warned that insurance premiums may be higher in respect of fire cover on both building and contents. A specific point should be made of notifying the insurers when a roof is thatched, this being a matter relevant to the risk. Certain obvious precautions should be taken by the property owner. He should not light garden fires near the building or use blow lamps for stripping paintwork near the roof and, in an urban location, some check should be made on Guy Fawkes' night and similar occasions and a hosepipe kept handy in case of ignition by fireworks or bonfire sparks.

Further, warning should be given concerning the estimated life span of the particular material. In the case of reed thatch about 60 years is typical but straw thatch has a much shorter life. During the life of the thatch the covering should be periodically inspected by a thatcher and may need an overhaul, generally taking the form of combing the surfaces, making good defective areas and renewing hips, ridges and details where these have deteriorated. A property owner should cultivate an association with a local firm of thatchers or, if no such firm is available, contact the nearest available rural locality where thatching skills are still practised.

When thatch reaches the end of its useful life it will need replacing in its entirety. Replacement may be undertaken with a different covering such as slates or tiles or with new thatch if thatchers are available. In many cases re-thatching will be realistic and not more expensive than tiling, bearing in mind that tiling will certainly involve new battens and sarking felt, possibly joists and the provision of gutters, rainwater pipes, fascias, soffits and different detailing around stacks. If the property is in a conservation area, or is a listed building needing special consent from the local planning authority, it may be that a change in the type of roof covering will not be permitted.

The fire risk associated with thatch will obviously be greater in older timber-framed buildings where the ceilings and walls may be of lath and plaster or similar construction which is itself a potential fire hazard in some circumstances. The need to maintain the electrical equipment in a property with a thatched roof in good order, and to test the wiring regularly, is self-evident. This is extremely important since when the thatch is renewed or repaired, the old thatch is often left lying in the roof void. This dry, brittle, dusty material is highly combustible, particularly in the case of straw thatch.

One final warning concerning thatched roofs is the prevalence of insect infestation - in particular furniture beetle and the death watch beetle where oak timbers are involved. There is hardly a thatched roof in the West Country which does not contain some form of insect infestation, usually *anobium punctatum*.

Roof coverings in general

Lead is a traditional covering for both flat and pitched roofs with the life dependent upon the lead thickness adopted. Heavy cast lead was used in period houses, churches and other buildings and may last hundreds of years. Modern leadwork is generally the thinner milled lead which is more likely to suffer from 'creep' on slopes, flashings and other details, and from splits in exposed locations or where subject to movement. Generally a life span of 80 to 100 years is typical for modern leadwork. Modern lead is clearly preferable to mineral felt for flat areas and detailing, and the authors prefer to specify leadwork where possible if the client's pocket is deep enough, especially in locations with a southerly aspect where mineral felt tends to rapid deterioration.

Large areas of leadwork without rolls or drips at suitable intervals may fail due to thermal movements which cause rippling and splitting. In its original state the lead is a bright silver colour but on contact with the atmosphere this changes to the familiar matt grey due to a coating of lead carbonate which forms on the surface. This surface carbonate protects the lead from further deterioration. The only chemical deterioration likely to occur is from strong acid attack and acid can occur in rainwater if this is discharging on to the lead from a roof area where there is moss growth, or material subject to moss such as ageing shingles A point discharge such as regular dripping from a mossy roof will cause pitting to the leadwork due to such an attack.

Zinc was often used as an alternative to lead for flat roofs and detailing, especially in chimney stack flashings and soakers and small flat bay roofs in traditional dwelling construction. In pollution-free localities the life of such zincwork is generally in the range of 20 to 40 years and sometimes even longer. Good detailing to zincwork is essential for durability, and the rolls and drips are necessary to accommodate thermal movements. When chemical pollutants are present in the atmosphere, the life of zinc is shorter and failure in the form of pitting and splits is possible after as little as 15 years. As with leadwork, a particular problem can arise with a constant drip of rainwater at a specific point over a period causing the acid in the rainwater to wear away the zinc and create a point for leakage. Zinc, like lead, also develops a carbonate on the surface which affords some measure of protection but this is thinner than the lead carbonate and does not provide an effective protection, especially where the atmosphere is polluted by sulphur dioxide.

Asphalt is often used for better quality flat roofs and is more durable than built-up felting provided that the surface decking is sound and free from excessive thermal movement. A life span of 20 to 40 years is generally found to be possible, depending upon the quality of the original job and the degree of exposure to sunlight. Deterioration is indicated by the appearance of surface splits and cracking and by surface bubbles which form from the expansion of vapour trapped in the decking. Minor surface crazing may not of itself indicate general deterioration since the surface asphalt is trowelled into place and the trowelling is often overworked, as it is on stucco renderings which craze for similar reasons. This overtrowelling brings to the surface a skin of bitumen which may tend to craze due to slight differences in rates of expansion and contraction on the surface compared with the deeper material.

A normal thickness of asphalt is about 20 mm and anything less than this may be regarded as sub-standard and of a potentially shorter life span. Asphalt is not a suitable material for point-loads and will indent and spread under the weight of water tanks and other imposed weights. Very often considerable damage can be done to an asphalt roof by indentations created by chair legs, flower tubs, duckboards and the like. Detailing of asphalt coverings is where most problems arise. If the material is laid at angles to slopes and vertical upstands without suitable tilting fillets, creep will occur, especially in a south-facing location.

Copper is a traditional roof covering used for small areas of flats roofs for detailing, and for pitched construction in domes and spires where the distinctive green patina is required for aesthetic reasons. Copper sheet used for this purpose is thin but surprisingly durable, although not quite so durable as lead. In time the metal ages from the effects of thermal movements and splits and ripples to the surface which will appear indicate that renewal is required. Rainwater with a high acid content attacks copper in the same way as with zinc and to a greater degree than in the case of lead. The thin metal - especially the rolls - is prone to damage from any foot traffic or ladders which may be used for maintenance.

As a general rule all flat roofs should have a natural drainage fall and should not hold water. The reason for this that ponding on the surface, especially with asphalt and built-up felt, will result in marked differences in temperature between the wet cold areas and the dry warm areas, especially in warm sunlight following overnight rain. This causes relative thermal movements between cold and warm parts which result in rapid deterioration of the surfaces. Generally, in new construction a fall of at least 1-in-40 is desirable to allow for possible bedding down of the construction in later life and to accommodate any minor deflection in timber joists. In existing flat roofs where any bedding down and deflection has ceased, a shallower fall may be acceptable but this should not be so shallow that the surface holds water.

Detailing

Experience tends to indicate that most problems with roof construction arise at the detailing rather than the main areas of covering. Rain penetration of flashings and soakers of stacks and fire walls or to upstands and flashings at the perimeter of flat roofs is common. On close examination many roofs will exhibit a history of repairs to such details, the repairs often being of a highly unsatisfactory nature. Unfortunately the average building owner or lessee will rarely carry out any close inspections himself and in the event of a leak will rely upon the judgment of a roofing contractor. The eventual bill will be paid without knowing whether or not the work done was necessary, suitable or reasonably priced. Often it is only when the building is subjected to the scrutiny of a surveyor that the nature of the past repairs comes to light.

Chimney stacks and copings

Particular problems may arise with downward damp penetration through soft brickwork and mortar in chimney stacks and parapets. The design of stacks and parapets is often poor and for the correct construction of parapet wall copings two conflicting requirements have to be met. First, copings should be suitably mounted on impervious damp-proof courses and should be adequately weathered with overhangs and throating. Secondly, copings should be firmly bonded in place with mortar joints which will not deteriorate and be built of materials which are sufficiently durable and resistant to frost damage. Since the damp-proof course beneath the coping is a point where adhesion is poor, the design of copings must be a compromise between these two requirements. All brickwork to copings and

Figure 6.2 A close examination of chimney stacks on older buildings invariably reveals loose pointing, cracked and loose brickwork, cracked and soft flaunching, and loose pots – all matters about which clients should be informed (Middlesex 1982)

stacks above damp-proof courses where exposure is continuous should be in special rather than ordinary quality brickwork since the latter will suffer frost damage in time. Similarly, tiles, coping stones and other finishes to copings must be of a suitably durable type for the conditions of exposure involved.

When chimney stacks are redundant and clients are quite sure that they will not be required again, an opportunity arises to remove the stack above the roof line and to tile or slate over. This is often the most suitable solution as an alternative to rebuilding where a stack is in poor condition. When stacks are disused but in adequate condition they may be retained provided that suitable ventilation is applied at the top and bottom of the flues. If an unventilated cap is used or no ventilation is provided at the base of a flue, weather penetration downwards coupled with the effects of condensation within will often result in deterioration to the parging and brickwork and brown damp stains appearing on chimney breasts inside.

Gutters

Generally, all good roof design should incorporate the provision of adequate guttering and rainwater pipes to carry all roof water away to a storm drainage system. It is important that stormwater be taken away from the perimeter of the building to prevent damp penetration through walls and to avoid subsoil erosion from continual discharge of roof water into soil adjoining the main walls.

Certain traditional roofs encounterd in period construction will not have gutters or downpipes, particularly in the cases of thatch and traditional stone slab construction where a deep eaves overhang is provided instead. It is vital with this type of construction that the area around the building should be paved, with a suitable drainage fall away from the main walls and with a good clearance between exterior and interior levels. A rendered plinth treated periodically with a bituminous water-proofing paint would also be advised. An examination of a number of thatched cottages over the years will reveal that dampness at the base of the main walls, especially on the weather-sides, will invariably be a problem unless the run-off of water from the roof slopes is adequately catered for. A combination of thatched roof, solid rendered walls of stone and lime mortar, and high exterior ground levels is often encountered; not surprisingly in such circumstances, invariably there will be a damp problem at the base of walls internally with a history of plaster repairs, or false walls applied over damp plaster.

A client proposing to buy a cottage with a thatched roof may have seen it through rose-coloured spectacles, especially if he first viewed in summertime. Such a client may have thought it quaint that visitors step down into the building instead of up, and will view uncritically the moss-covered and loosening rendering around the base of the building. The vendor's panelling to dado height around the ground floor rooms could be considered part of the charm. It may not be until the following winter that the client begins to detect the effects of damp penetration at the base of the walls internally and that the carpet underlay is becoming mouldy around the skirtings. Perhaps then the significance of the high exterior levels and the nature of the construction will be appreciated and the client may feel inclined to look out the surveyor's report to see what was said on these subjects.

Often, small projections devoid of gutters or rainwater pipes are built and this will be commonly encountered in small bay roofs and porches of all ages. No matter how small the projection, guttering and downpipes are always advisable unless the roof overhang is very deep. Where these are omitted it will often be found that exposed sills and woodwork beneath have deteriorated from the effects of dripping rainwater. Staining down walls is also commonly found where guttering is omitted and this can cause considerable discolouration on north sides where moss growth is then encouraged.

Rainwater will occasionally be found taken to water butts instead of to stormwater gullies and this may be unsatisfactory, especially if the roof area is large, since overflowing from the butt will be undesirable. If water butts are needed it is suggested that gullies also be provided to take surplus water from the butts.

Modern uPVC rainwater systems have been found durable and maintenance-free if correctly installed with adequate brackets and sponge seals. Older rainwater systems will be encountered which may be less durable or suffer other drawbacks. Cast iron can be long-lasting if properly maintained but maintenance is often expensive and consequently poor and the hidden surfaces such as gutter interiors are often left unpainted. Asbestos-cement rainwater systems appear to have a useful life span of about 30 years and then become porous. Pre-cast concrete rainwater gutters, commonly used in the nineteen-fifties, need periodic internal bituminising to avoid downward penetration of water into the walls beneath, especially at joints. Where an existing rainwater system needs repair and repainting it is often advisable to consider complete renewal in uPVC since the cost is often comparable and the final result should require no further maintenance in the foreseeable future.

Chapter 7

Joinery and carpentry

The woodworm is some of the worst I have seen. The only thing that is holding the roof together now is the fact that the grubs are holding hands in the holes
Surveyor to worried client

The survey of accessible joinery and woodwork is intended to reveal possible timber defects and to make recommendations accordingly. The surveyor should be conversant with the main species of wood-boring insects and wood-rotting fungi although he will undoubtedly encounter unfamiliar wood-borers from time to time and may often have difficulty in identifying the fungus responsible for timber decay in the early stages when no fruiting growths have yet appeared.

Wood-boring insects

The common furniture beetle (*anobium punctatum*) is probably present in about 80% of pre-War houses in the London area and no doubt in a higher proportion of pre-1914 buildings. It is now becoming evident even in timbers in the earlier post-War houses dating from the nineteen-fifties.

Evidence of activity will be small circular flight holes, smooth inside and accompanied by deposits of bore dust – generally to be found in softwood roof timbers, floor timbers and staircases and especially prevalent in plywood panelling under stairs and to joists and sleeper plates in suspended timber ground floors of inter-War origin.

The furniture beetle normally attacks only sound wood, although it is encouraged by timber which has been affected by damp. The flight holes are generally about 1.5 mm in diameter and the bore dust contains small faecal pellets which give it its characteristic gritty feel.

The death watch beetle (*xestobium rufovillosum*) is often present in old hardwood beams and other hardwood timbers in period structures. On occasion, fungal attack may be required for this insect to become active so that damp conditions and poor ventilation would normally be an initiate for attack. Mostly oak is affected and many oak beams used in period buildings were formerly used elsewhere, either in other buildings or as ships' timbers, so that they were already second-hand, perhaps carrying with them death watch beetle grubs when first used.

Figure 7.1 Common furniture beetle

Figure 7.2 Undersides of Victorian floor boards showing flight holes of the common furniture beetle. Interestingly, no flight holes were apparent in the top surface of this board (North London 1982)

Death watch beetle flight holes are larger than those of the common furniture beetle, being 2 to 3 mm in diameter. The bore dust contains characteristic ovoid pellets.

Wood-boring weevils (*pentarthrum huttoni* and *euophryum confine*) infest damp and decayed wood where fungal attack is also present. The flight holes are smaller than those of the common furniture beetle, being less than 1 mm in diameter. Weevil attack will commonly be found in the ends of joists and sleeper plates under suspended timber floors, and in other situations where there is contact between the

Figure 7.3 Death watch beetle

Figure 7.4 Death watch beetle damage

timbers and damp masonry. Weevil attack often causes the complete distintegra-
tion of a damp sleeper plate or joist end resulting in the partial, if not total, removal
of support from a floor.

Bark borer (*ernobius mollis*) attacks the bark and sapwood of softwood timbers
and is often found in roof rafters and joists. The flight holes and bore dust are
similar to those of the common furniture beetle but if bark borer is confirmed, the

Figure 7.5 Wood-boring weevil

Figure 7.6 Powder post beetle

surveyor will be able to reassure his client that no specific remedial action is required since this insect is not structurally destructive and will eventually depart of its own accord from the areas of infestation.

The powder post beetle (*lyctus* family) attacks hardwoods, mainly oak, ash and elm, and especially elm. The insects are active only in the sapwood with the grubs reducing it to a fine powder. The activity of the powder post beetle may be distinguished from that of the common furniture beetle by the very fine, as compared with gritty, bore dust and the fact that activity is confined to the sapwood edges of roof timbers, boarding and other members. The elimination of powder post beetle requires the careful selection of timbers to exclude those with excessive sapwood before use.

The house longhorn beetle (*hylotrupes bajulus*) attacks softwood timbers in the timber yard and in buildings. Because it causes rapid deterioration in the affected wood this pest is notifiable in certain areas. The flight holes are oval-shaped, 3 to 9 mm in diameter. A feature of the damage caused is that the timbers are eaten away internally, often with little external evidence to show the severity of the attack. At present this insect is generally found to be confined to buildings in the Home Counties but there are reports of it appearing further afield.

Figure 7.7 House longhorn beetle

For information regarding damage caused, distribution within the UK, and the area within which preservative treatment of softwood roofing timbers is mandatory for house longhorn beetle, see 'House Longhorn Beetle Survey', BRE Information Paper IP 12/82, July 1982.

The larvae of the digger wasp has been known to attack teak timbers, normally thought to be immune from such infestation, resulting in almost complete disintegration.

Various other wood-boring insects will leave flight holes in new wood, especially imported wood, and may be found in new buildings where such wood is used.

Pinhole borers may be occasionally found to have been active. However, some flight holes in new wood are permitted by current Codes of Practice since it would be unrealistic to discard useful timber merely because of a small number of old flight holes. In such circumstances it is sufficient to confirm that the timbers have in fact been suitably pre-treated before use and that all insect activity has ceased. CP 112, Part 2:1971, Appendix A.12 states that 'Scattered pinholes and small occasional wormholes are permissible in all grades. All pieces, however, showing active infestation should be rejected or subjected to preservative treatment in accordance with CP98, 'Preservative Treatment for Constructional Timber', (superseded by BS 5268, Part 5:1977).

Wood-rotting fungi

Wet-rot is normally associated with the fungus *coniophora puteana* but there are several other fungi capable of causing the symptoms of wet-rot and identification of the actual fungus responsible will be difficult until an attack is at a severe and late stage.

Figure 7.8 True dry-rot fungus (*serpula lacrymans*)

Figure 7.9 Wet-rot (*trametes serialis*). Brown fungus with cuboidal cracking

The main factor distinguishing a wet-rot attack from the true dry-rot (*serpula lacrymans*) is that wet-rot requires damp timber in order to become active and spread and will confine itself to the affected and immediately adjacent timber. Dry-rot requires a humid atmosphere to become established, and damp timbers in situations lacking ventilation are ideal targets for attack. Once established, however, dry-rot fungus will extend readily into adjoining sound timbers and will travel through masonry and plasterwork in order to reach other sound timber which then in turn becomes infected.

Wet-rot is most often found in external joinery, especially lower window frames and sills, door posts and wood thresholds in contact with the ground. Garage door posts and fascias subject to driving rain penetration can also be affected. It is also found in roof timbers around stacks where weather has penetrated and in cellars and sub-floor areas subject to dampness. In an advanced stage the fungus will produce dark brown or black strands similar to old cobwebs and these will often be found forming patterns on the wall plaster in damp cellars.

Wet-rot is very common in the painted softwood window units used in the nineteen-fifties and nineteen-sixties due to the lack of adequate treatment of such timber before use. Often complete replacement of such window joinery will be found now to be necessary due to this problem. In coastal areas and areas of high exposure this defect is quite general. In certain districts reference may be made to 'south coast rot' which is essentially due to difficulties arising from exterior woodwork of poor quality used in post-War speculative developments. One avenue of investigation open to the surveyor during his inspection is to probe carefully the exterior woodwork, paying particular attention to the obvious areas at risk and including especially any porches, conservatories or similar timber-framed structures, particularly those facing the prevailing weather.

Figure 7.10 Constant saturation by water from defective roof overflow has caused serious wet-rot in this painted softwood bay window. The south-west facing location is also subject to the prevailing weather (Middlesex 1982)

Remedial measures in the event of a wet-rot attack in exterior woodwork should be made by cutting out affected wood well back from the point of decay and splicing in new pre-treated timber, preferably also using pre-treated wooden dowels and connecting with suitable tenons. Considerable care is required to achieve a proper repair and if wet-rot is extensive, this is often not justified. When rot is widespread, complete replacement with new units will generally be preferred. Filling repairs to exterior woodwork affected by rot will often be encountered in practice and such repairs must always be regarded as unsuitable as the decay will invariably return. Filling repairs, painted over, could be used by a vendor to disguise the nature of the rot and with a view to helping the sale of the property.

When the property under review is suffering from attack by the true dry-rot fungus, the necessary remedial action will include not only the replacement of all affected wood with new pre-treated timber but also a suitable programme of treatment for adjoining timbers, brickwork, plasterwork and sub-floor areas well away from the actual point of decay. Considerable care is required in devising a suitable specification for such works to ensure that the fungus is eradicated.

Generally a dry-rot fungus will be more likely to attack sub-floor timbers, spread unnoticed behind panelling and inside flat roof voids, all being points where a warm damp atmosphere may arise due to poor construction and lack of ventilation. Such conditions will mostly be found in older buildings where the amount of timber built into the structure may be considerable. Timbers such as those in stud partitions, lintels and wall plates may provide a passage through the structure which the fungal mycelium can travel, sometimes for considerable distances. The dry-rot fungus is able to spread in this way and attack dry timber because of its ability to produce water-carrying strands, or rhizomorphs, which are modified hyphae and are vein-like structures which can be as large as 10 mm in diameter. These rhizomorphs convey water from damp wood into dryer wood elsewhere, passing over masonry and through mortar joints in walls. They also 'store' food so that even if the rotted wood is removed the rhizomorph is still able to grow and infect new wood.

The mycelium of the dry-rot fungus is a snowy white colour (as compared with the brown or black strands of the wet-rot) and grows rapidly in damp humid conditions. Where the edge of the mycelium is in contact with light it turns bright yellow. Timber decayed by the mycelium exhibits deep fissures and the wood breaks up into cubes with the cuboidal cracking becoming apparent on the surface. Eventually when an attack is well established the sporophore or fruiting bodies will appear, these being thin and pancake-like, white around the edges, giving off rust-coloured spores and a strong mushroomy odour.

The sporophore or fruiting bodies of the wet-rot fungus are rarely encountered indoors but may occasionally be found in decayed external fascias and sills. They are smaller than those of the dry-rot fungus, generally brown in colour and in the form of thin plates attached to the face of affected wood.

In modern structures, one particular area where timber decay from either wet-rot or dry-rot is possible is within the void to a flat roof, especially if this is of sub-standard construction. Built-up felt roofs will often be found without any void ventilation and lacking any effective vapour checks. The climate within such roofs is ideal for the rapid growth of these fungi. The decking material may be Stramit board or chipboard which conveys water from a small surface leak by absorption through the roof area without any staining becoming apparent to the ceilings beneath. In such circumstances the dampness in the roof void, coupled with the warmth from the sun on the roof surface, will produce very rapid deterioration so that eventually when the roof covering has to be stripped for renewal, renewal of the decking and joists may also be found to be required.

An inspection of timber members used within the structure of a building can rarely be complete even if the building is empty of all contents and floor coverings and exposure of floor joists in all areas is possible. The reason for this is that some timber surfaces may be permanently hidden and lie within the structure in such a way that precludes a full inspection of all surfaces without taking the structure apart.

Timber frame constructions

A surveyor may be asked to prepare a report on a timber-framed building, that is a building in which the outer walls are constructed in load-bearing timber-work instead of traditional brickwork, blockwork or stone. Construction time can be much shorter on site since the panels will generally be delivered in a partially assembled form. Also the standard of thermal insulation can be higher and the cost of the main structure lower than would be the case with traditional construction.

The concept of timber-framed buildings is, however, not new. Some surveyors may be familiar with the older type of timber-framed construction still encountered in rural areas. This construction was regarded, rightly, as being inferior to more permanent materials and a tradition of looking at any timber-frame structure in the same light has grown up. The timber-framed housing industry is now anxious to change this view through the information disseminated by the Timber Research and Development Association through their guide *Timber-frame Housing Design Guide*, Section 9, 'Structural Recommendations'.

The modern type of timber-framed building is constructed of panels of studwork which may be clad in a brick or block veneer. In many cases the internal walls and separating walls will also be of timber-framed construction. At present it would appear reasonable to assume a life expectancy for a modern design timber-framed house of about 60 years. This is well below the potential life expectancy for more traditional forms of construction. It may be that timber frames will be found to last longer but only experience will tell. Difficulty may arise in the future if large estates of freehold timber-framed houses begin to fall into disrepair and the economics of redevelopment with new housing are not viable. Buildings in brick and stone may be careful maintenance and periodic upgrading be made to last almost indefinitely.

The survey of an existing timber-framed building presents certain difficulties as all important structural elements are hidden. There are seven main considerations in good timber-frame design which are:

(1) The design of the main structural members and fixings to resist all forces to which the building will be subject;
(2) The adequate pre-treatment of timbers against rot and beetle attack;
(3) The provision of damp-proof courses and membranes;
(4) The provision of vapour checks in the wall panels to prevent interstitial condensation;
(5) The provision of barriers against weather penetration;
(6) The provision of adequate external claddings;
(7) The provision of adequate thermal insulation within the panels.

None of these matters can be checked from an examination of the internal and external wall surfaces except perhaps item (6).

Concerning the design of the main structural members and fixings for resistance to all forces to which a timber-framed building will be subject, a surveyor in inspecting such a building may well have to undertake a structural check on the design from details available from the manufacturer. Timber-framed housing manufacturers normally sell standard house types and these will have been design usually by consulting engineers to comply with the Building Regulations. A local authority responsible for checking compliance with Building Regulations will normally insist that full structural calculations are submitted with the deposited plans before approval is granted.

Suspected variations in the actual building as compared with approved plans should be checked, especially in the sizes and locations of openings in main walls or variations in the layout of the timber panels. This is most important as the structural principles involved in timber-framed construction are quite different from those of traditional in brick, block or masonry building. Panels in timber-framed work require lining and diagonal bracing to give lateral restraint, unlike traditional work which obtains lateral restraint from the cross-bonding and intersection of walls. If lateral restraint in timber-framed construction is inadequate then the structure may be distorted parallelogrammatically by a process known as 'racking'. The danger of racking damage to a timber-framed building is at its greatest where openings are formed in the walls near to corners or if openings larger than specified are formed, thus reducing the overall stiffness of the framework.

The surveyor could ask to see structural design details and calculations for any newer timber-framed building which he is asked to survey. Clearly it would be advisable for the owners of such buildings to keep a copy of the details and calculations to be passed on to subsequent owners since questions are bound to arise from time to time when such properties change hands. In cases of doubt it is recommended that the details and calculations be referred to a consulting engineer for checking, and in any event a careful comparison should be made between the design and the actual building with a view to detecting any changes which may be structurally significant.

Structural alterations or conversions made to an existing timber-framed building should be undertaken only with the benefit of expert professional advice and if such a structure is found to have been modified subsequently, the nature of any modifications should be carefully checked.

The external brick or block skin used as a cladding to modern timber-frame designs is not of itself structurally important. It often comes as a surprise to clients to learn that a building which appears superficially to be built of brickwork is in fact of timber construction. In some designs the base of the brickwork is used to hold down the base of the adjoining panels using angle clips but brickwork or blockwork claddings are otherwise not normally structurally important to the design.

Preservation

It will be appreciated from the previous descriptions of the main wood-boring insects and wood-rotting fungi that good timber preservation in the form of pre-treatment is necessary to ensure durability in new work. A surveyor's knowledge of preservation techniques is important to assess the defects which will be found in older buildings and the remedies which may be proposed.

Different species of wood show great variation in their resistance to decay and beetle attack. Generally softwoods are most vulnerable; for example, ash and beech decay rapidly if conditions are suitable. Hardwoods are more durable in most cases and may be resistant to fungal attack even in conditions where fungal activity would be likely. Oaks and teaks, for example, are remarkably durable in damp conditions. In all timbers the heartwood is most resistant to decay and the sapwood least resistant. However, the sapwood will more easily absorb preservatives so that preserved sapwood of a non-durable species can be more durable than unpreserved heartwood.

Preservation is partly a question of good design to ensure that all timber members are kept dry and are not in contact with damp oversites or masonry. The climate around timber members should be cool, well ventilated and free from excessive water vapour. Areas most at risk will be suspended timber ground floors and enclosed roof voids, especially under flat roofs. In timber-framed construction the wall panels also require careful design, especially to give protection against weather penetration and provide vapour checks.

Preservation also covers the treatments and surface coatings which may be applied to timber. Any water-proofing surface applied to timber will assist in preventing fungal decay since this will present a barrier to the absorption of moisture. Exterior woodwork is normally then painted in an oil-based paint, generally with two coats plus primer. Well-painted exterior surfaces are protected from moisture absorption by the paint and this degree of protection will be good if joints and putties are carefully sealed and painted over in such a way that no small passages for moisture remain. Painted surfaces reflect sunlight but surfaces with a hard clear finish such as varnish absorb the sunlight to some extent and this generally causes the surface to crack and peel quickly, especially on south-facing elevations. Hardwood sills and thresholds which are varnished generally deteriorate quite quickly if south-facing.

An alternative to painting or varnishing is to give the exterior woodwork a periodic preservative stain finish so that instead of covering the wood with a surface weather-resistant shell, the treatment consists of regular brushing or spraying with absorbent preservative which soaks into the wood. It is possible that exterior woodwork treated periodically with an absorbent preservative stain will become more common in the future as the cost of traditional painting continues to rise.

To prevent fungicidal activity a wood preservative must so permeate the wood that fungal hyphae are unable to feed on it. To prevent insect activity within the timbers a wood preservative requires insecticidal defence properties against that specific species for which protection is required. Different wood-boring insects have different susceptibilities. Different treatments may be required for timbers where insects are known to be active and timbers where pre-treatment against future activity is required. In the former case eggs, grubs, pupae and adult insects may all be present in the wood and require eradication; in the latter case the protection required is protection against the ingress of egg-laying adults.

Chemical treatments should take a permanent or semi-permanent form to protect the timbers from fungal and insect attack for a suitably long period. Generally 30 years' protection would be a good standard at which to aim. This is possible because the chemicals are absorbed by and retained within the wood to a considerable depth and for long periods, unaffected by sunlight or other causes of deterioration.

Timber preservation may be undertaken in any one of five ways using chemical preservatives, these being: (a) Pressure-impregnation, (b) dipping, (c) steeping, (d) spraying, (e) brushing.

Pressure-impregnation involves the use of sealed tanks of preservative into which timbers are placed, the wood preservative then being forced into the timber under pressure. This is suitable only for pre-treatment.

Dipping involves immersing timbers in an open tank of preservative for short periods, perhaps a few minutes, and then allowing the excess preservative to drip from the wood.

Steeping involves treatment similar to dipping but extended over period of hours, days or even weeks, depending upon the nature of the timber involved and the degree of penetration required. Dipping and steeping are suitable only as pre-treatment before timbers are used.

Spraying may be used as treatment for *in situ* timbers. Generally a coarse spray nozzle is used so that droplet size is large and rapid saturation of the wood surface is obtained without producing a fine airborne spray which could prove unpleasant or hazardous to operatives.

Brush treatments are often less effective than spray treatments since areas which are inaccessible to a brush may be reached using a spray nozzle, especially in suspended floors, behind panelling and in the extremities of roof voids.

Chemical wood preservatives are classified according to three main groups (and by reference to British Standard 1282:1959 (revised 1975)) as being tar-oil types, organic solvent types and water-borne types, and these are further sub-divided in accordance with the main chemical base of the preservative.

Treatment

Faced with an existing building which suffers from the effects of dry-rot, wet-rot or attack by wood-boring insects, a surveyor will have to make some recommendations as to a suitable course of treatment in addition to commenting upon mere facts and describing their significance.

It is suggested that the existence of wood-boring insects in timbers where the timber strength is not affected and where the activity is indicated by scattered flight holes only is best treated by spraying timbers until rejection, with an insecticidal preservative of a type appropriate for the species of wood-borer involved. The question of how far such treatment should extend into areas of adjoining timber construction is difficult, but in residential property, for example, it is preferable that all accessible timbers in a building be treated. If the common furniture beetle is apparent in a staircase it would be sensible to treat all floor, staircase and roof timbers on the assumption that flight holes indicate that insects have emerged to lay eggs elsewhere in the building, the results of which may take three years or more to appear. If timbers have been structurally weakened by wood borers it will, in addition, be necessary to recommend replacement or strengthening of weakened timbers, paying particular regard to the ends of floor joists and the stiffness of principal members in roofs.

A suitable specification for wet-rot attack may be prepared on the assumption that if the cause of damp can be removed and the timber allowed to dry out, no further attack will develop in timbers not already attacked. The specification should then include the renewal of all affected wood well back from the point of decay, the protection of surrounding timbers (necessary to prevent decay arising in the future) and the eradication of the source of dampness where this has been traced and found to have caused the attack. All new wood should be spliced and jointed into place to provide a lasting repair, free from weak points externally or inadequate weather protection. All replacement wood should be adequately pre-treated.

Specifications for dry-rot control require rather more details if these are to prove suitable, having regard to the particular nature of this fungus as already discussed. Depending upon the circumstances, a suitable specification should generally include the following specific provisions:

(1) Cut out, carefully remove from site by the shortest practicable route and burn all the following: timbers showing cuboidal cracking, brown colouration, white mycelium or soft areas when probed; all sound timbers within 1 m from any of

the foregoing defective timbers; all debris within roof voids, sub-floor voids or other areas adjoining, particularly timber off-cuts and similar debris.

(2) Remove wall plaster, rendering, skirtings, wall panels, ceilings and other coverings as necessary to trace full extent of fungal activity in adjacent construction. Carefully clean out all exposed areas and clean down all surfaces within a distance of 2 m from actual fungal activity. Sweep out all sub-floor voids, roof voids and similar areas. Remove all dust and debris from site by the shortest practicable route and burn.

(3) Blow-lamp all masonry surfaces within an area of 2 m from area of fungal activity until surfaces are too hot to touch. When cooled, liberally apply fungicidal solution to all such surfaces.

(4) Apply fungicidal solution to all remaining woodwork within 2 m from point of fungal activity in two liberal coats.

(5) Make good to all timberwork in pre-treated wood which has been first given two good coats of fungicidal solution on all surfaces.

(6) Make good disturbed wall and ceiling surfaces using 5 mm of floating coat of zinc oxychloride plaster over the rendering coat in the area of fungal attack and for a distance of 300 mm surrounding such area. Apply zinc oxychloride paint to painted surfaces where plaster is not to be applied and over a similar area and distance from previous attack.

(7) Make good all design defects responsible for original dry-rot attack, including additional airbricks and improved ventilation, renewing defective damp-proof courses, preventing moisture penetration, eliminating condensation, clearing the bridging of damp-proof courses, repairing roof and plumbing leaks and timbers in contact with damp oversites or masonry as necessary and in accordance with good building practice.

With all timber treatments recommended for existing buildings it is essential that advice be given regarding the requirements of protection and ventilation having regard to the specific nature of the chemicals used and the manufacturers' recommendations. Chemical spraying of ceiling joists will often result in stains appearing on surfaces beneath. Redecoration should be postponed until the effects of staining are unlikely to become apparent and often a delay of six months or more is required. Staining can cause a special problem with fibreboard ceilings. Carpets should not be laid over recently treated floorboarding unless over polythene sheet or similar protection, otherwise carpets can be damaged from absorption of treatment fluids from the floor beneath. Enhanced ventilation may be necessary to remove residual odours and it may take some time for all odour to disperse.

Chapter 8

Finishes and surfaces

All of a sudden, there was a noise like an express train running through the house. The wife opened the door to the hall and found that the whole of the landing ceiling had come down. The mess was unbelievable. The last time we saw anything like it was during the Blitz.
Tenant's letter to landlord

Plaster finishes

In most parts of the UK, dwellings built after 1938 will have ceilings of gypsum plasterboard. Exceptions to this will be found occasionally where timber laths and plaster or steel-mesh lathing and plaster have been used, but plasterboard will be the more normal. Prior to 1938, timber laths and plaster were generally used.

The life of the older lath-and-plaster ceilings will depend upon the quality of the original work and the degree of exposure to dampness from roof and plumbing leaks. Lath-and-plaster affected by serious leakage from any source will invariably have been weakened and will require renewal. During the course of the survey the condition of any lath-and-plaster ceilings should be checked by probing from below and, where possible, examination of the plaster key from above. If loose, soft or 'off-key' areas of ceiling plaster are found, general renewal in plasterboard should be recommended. Most lath-and-plaster ceilings will now have a limited remaining useful life and in most cases clients should be encouraged to budget for renewal in plasterboard.

Occasionally, fibreboard ceilings will be encountered, particularly in older buildings which may have been war-damaged during the Second World War, and also in some nineteen-thirties houses. This is inferior to plasterboard. It is not fire-resistant and is soft and easily damaged. Any chemical spraying of roof timbers, for example, furniture beetle disinfestation undertaken over fibreboard ceilings, will result in stains appearing beneath due to high absorbancy, a point which should be borne in mind with this material.

Suspended ceilings of various types are commonly employed in commercial buildings and will occasionally be encountered in dwellinghouses. In most cases there is no problem about lifting a panel or two to examine the void behind and this can be quite instructive as that void will probably be in its original undecorated condition with a past history of defects on view and services exposed.

Wall plasters in modern buildings should be checked for loose or shelling areas by tapping and probing as necessary. Problems of shelling wall plaster can often arise in speculative construction if walls are plastered when they contain a high water content and if the plaster used is almost impervious when set. Occasionally major or complete replastering of new houses becomes necessary from this cause. The shelling and bulging of plaster finishing coats on clinker or breeze block walls and partitions generally arises about six to nine months after completion. Replastering of the defective finishing coat can be difficult because of the high suction of the undercoat. The Building Research Establishment published a note on this topic in 1971, 'Shelling of Plaster Finishing Coats', BRE Information Sheet TIL 14 1971.

Wall plasters which are well set after the first year or so in the life of the building should prove durable, but plasterwork in older buildings will become defective in the presence of dampness. Soft, damp and defective wall plaster in older buildings should be reported upon with the necessary advice. Where replastering is required, any special requirements should be mentioned, including the need for special plasters to be used where past dampness could give rise to efflorescence and surface staining of the new plaster.

Other wall and ceiling finishes

Walls and ceilings can have a wide variety of finishes other than plaster skim. Ceilings may be of plasterboard with scrimmed joints and may have a textured coat of Artex or similar finish. This will absorb the slight movements which concentrate in plasterboard ceilings and would otherwise cause a pattern of hairline cracks to the joint lines; it will not absorb more severe shrinkage cracks, however, and anything greater than hairline will probably appear eventually through the textured coating. Various patterns of swirls, combing and other effects are possible with textured coatings, depending upon the skill of the plasterer.

Walls can also be given a textured coating over existing plaster skim. In older construction, a stippled wall plaster may occasionally be encountered as an original feature. Whereas the modern textured coatings are slightly flexible, the older type of stippled plaster finishes do not have any flexibility and tend to be rather brittle. As a consequence, these stippled plasters to walls and ceilings may suffer cracking and the cracks may be difficult to eradicate or disguise since a stippled finish cannot be papered over with lining. If a smooth backing is required for wallpaper, the stippled surfaces have to be removed and the walls or ceilings re-skimmed in a new surface coat which could prove a major exercise in a house where all walls and ceilings are so treated.

Generally, plasterboard ceilings which are given scrimmed joints and a thin board-plaster finish will tend to suffer from a pattern of minor shrinkage cracks following the joint lines in the plasterboard panels. This arises more in ceilings to top floor rooms under timber joists due to the tendency for lightweight ceiling joists in roofs to be used for occasional maintenance access and storage which causes some flexing. If lightweight ceiling joists are used for an amateur loft conversion as a playroom or similar then the amount of flexing in the ceilings may be considerable and cracking to joint lines extensive.

A skim finish is not really sufficient for a plasterboard ceiling, and if crack lines are to be minimised then lining with a stout lining paper such as Anaglypta or woodchip is recommended before painting.

All internal surface coatings which are applied in successive layers, such as textured coatings over existing plaster, are only as durable as the material beneath and the correctness of the application. A temptation arises to use surface coatings as a means of covering soft and loose plaster with the result that the surfaces eventually laminate or shell away from the bases. During the course of any survey it is recommended that wall and ceiling plaster be checked for loose and hollow areas and particular attention be given to areas recently covered over with new coatings or decorations in circumstances where soft or loose plaster beneath may be suspected.

Condensation

Problems of decorative finish to internal surfaces will be exacerbated by the presence of excessive condensation. Condensation is a major source of complaint in post-War buildings, especially buildings with a poor level of thermal insulation to external walls and poor overall design. Condensation problems at their worst can make a building uninhabitable due to the mould growth which forms on wall and ceiling surfaces and inside cold cupboards. This problem was virtually unknown in pre-War construction and has resulted from a combination of factors including changes in living patterns and construction methods.

Causes

In order to achieve a satisfactory surface finish, the effects of dampness and condensation must be dealt with at source. It is not sufficient to cover over problem areas which will subsequently reappear. Dampness to wall and ceiling surfaces may arise either from one or any combination of five possible causes, which are:

(1) Direct weather penetration from the outside;
(2) Leaking rainwater equipment and overflows causing a point of penetration;
(3) Plumbing leaks within walls, behind ceilings or in adjoining areas;
(4) Rising dampness originating in the site;
(5) Condensation.

It is necessary to distinguish dampness created by (1) to (4) and involving specific remedies from condensation problems which are more complex and difficult to eradicate. Condensation occurs when damp air comes into contact with cold surfaces. Put at its simplest, the remedy lies in raising the temperatures of the wall and ceiling surfaces to above dew point. Alternatively, the amount of water vapour in the air may be reduced. Steps could be taken both to raise the surface temperatures and also reduce the amount of water vapour in the air. By such means condensation would be eliminated.

Remedies

Before dealing with the means by which surface temperatures can be raised it is necessary to discuss the more obvious causes of high water vapour content in the air. Certain simple precautions may be taken by the occupier of a building to reduce condensation levels by adjustments to living habits. Paraffin or flueless gas heaters discharging the waste products of combustion directly into the air within a building are a major source of condensation, and a change in the method of heating could be all that is required to eliminate the problem. Since the burning of hydrocarbons in oxygen produces large quantities of water vapour, paraffin heaters and flueless gas heaters of various types are really unsuitable in many situations and decorations are often affected, even on well insulated and warm wall and ceiling surfaces. Frequently windows will be found to be running with condensation where a paraffin heater or flueless gas heater has been in use for some time. One litre of paraffin produces about one litre of water in combustion. Experience tends to indicate that this type of heating is used intermittently, often in older buildings and frequently by occupiers in lower income groups for economy. Intermittent heating is itself a cause of probelms since the air within the structure is warmed but the structure itself remains cold, an ideal condensation-forming situation.

Kitchens and bathrooms are obvious sources of water vapour, and when these rooms are in use their doors should be closed and good ventilation provided. The amount of steam in a bathroom can be reduced by the simple precaution of putting a little cold water in the bath first before running the hot water tap rather than *vice versa*. Appliances such as tumble dryers should always be provided with ducting to the outside air and damp washing should not be dried indoors in front of fires or over radiators. By means of small changes in heating methods and living habits, the amount of water vapour generated within a building may be substantially reduced and in a survey report, a client could be advised accordingly.

Having dealt with the question of high water content in the air and the means by which it can be reduced, a condensation problem may still remain and this invariably arises from the bad design of the building, a matter about which a client will need to be informed. Poor design can arise from the use of unsuitable materials, from an illogical accommodation layout or from lack of attention to thermal insulation and ventilation.

The thermal insulation standard to apply as a suitable measure giving the performance of walls and ceilings should be that prescribed by current Building Regulations, and if that standard in a particular building falls short then it is recommended that this be explained to the client. Thermal insulation standards have risen appreciably in recent years so that many older buildings will fall well short of modern requirements. However, it should not be assumed that this fact will be accepted unquestioningly by clients. A client moving from a modern house with cavity walls and an insulation block inner skin, perhaps with a cavity filling and 100 mm of fibreglass quilt over first-floor ceilings, will need to be warned about the much lower standards which may apply in a house built inter-War with solid 225-mm brick walls and negligible ceiling insulation. In particular, the walls in bathrooms and kitchens in such a house may be prone to surface condensation, especially if the client keeps all the windows shut, takes frequent hot baths and showers and uses mobile gas heaters for heating. Such a client will not take kindly to the resulting peeling wallpaper and mould growth in the back of fitted wardrobes fixed to the external walls.

A note should be taken of the accommodation layout. For maximum efficiency, the greatest volume is enclosed by the least area of outside wall in a two-storey building in the shape of a cube (discounting curved walls). It follows that heat losses in single-storey buildings are higher and heat losses are also higher from projecting bays and wings. If a kitchen or bathroom forms a projecting wing to a building, perhaps on one floor only, then it may have three external walls plus a roof and a consequentially high level of heat loss. It will often be found that large old houses converted into flats will have small wings added to provide bathrooms or kitchens, or these may have been converted out of existing sculleries and outhouses with the original solid walls retained. In such circumstances these rooms may be cold, damp and ideal condensation traps.

The level of insulation above ceilings which are under flat roofs or balconies can rarely be checked without special exposure. In general, the heat losses associated with flat roofs and balconies are higher than would be the case where conventional pitched roofs are used. The interior of pitched roofs can normally be inspected and additional insulation may be provided without too much difficulty. The provision of additional insulation inside a flat roof is more difficult, necessitating either the lifting of the top surfaces or the removal of sections of ceiling. As a result, a number of methods have been devised for improving the thermal insulation performance of flat roofs, by the provision of either additional material above the decking or false ceilings beneath it, these then incorporating insulation.

In considering the design and thermal efficiency of a structure, small projections and areas of heat loss should not be overlooked. For example, small roofs to bays in older buildings often have no insulation at all. The floors of rooms located over integral garages, verandas and open porches should generally be separately insulated to reduce heat losses through those floors into the areas beneath. This is frequently overlooked.

Condensation is the likely cause if high moisture readings are obtained in wall plaster located on a cold external wall and readings are higher in the main and upper areas of the wall but lower at skirting level. Mould growth on wallpaper and within cupboards at high level is typical of condensation damage. Dampness from penetration is less general and related to specific exposed walls or points of penetration. Dampness from rising moisture will be concentrated at skirting level and will reduce in severity with wall height, rarely extending to higher levels above, say 1 m from damp-proof course level.

When mould growth on wall surfaces and inside cupboards is found this can be treated using fungicidal paints or fungicidal wallpaper adhesives. The use of fungicides to limit the development of moulds must, however, be regarded as a palliative rather than a cure and to be unsatisfactory in the long run. It is clearly preferable that the basic underlying causes of mould growths be dealt with by seeking out the sources of excessive water vapour or defective design leading to cold internal surfaces.

One useful means of raising surface insulation standards is to line the internal face of exterior walls with 3 mm polystyrene under wallpaper. This is particularly suitable in older residential property with solid walls and will help to compensate for the lack of a cavity. The disadvantage with this type of surface application is that the wallpaper and lining is prone to damage from denting. The overall thermal efficiency of the exterior walls is, however, much improved and condensation problems on walls are generally reduced or eliminated. When re-papering becomes necessary, the insulating lining usually has to be renewed at the same time.

Condensation on windows can be reduced appreciably by double glazing. Metal-framed windows are more prone to condensation difficulties than timber-framed, particularly the older type of single-glazed galvanised-steel casements much used in pre-War and nineteen-fifties construction. Often the condensation from windows will cause staining to the reveals inside and this may be incorrectly diagnosed as weather penetration around the frame. The polystyrene lining already mentioned is effective in preventing such staining to window reveals but again, it must be regarded as an expedient rather than as a permanent cure.

Tiled surfaces

Tiled surfaces are usually found in bathrooms, shower rooms, cloakrooms and kitchens. Good quality wall tiling should be plumb, level with all joints evenly proportioned and neatly grouted. It is a good idea carefully to examine wall tiling not only to inspect the standard of workmanship but also because the pattern of the tiles at wall junctions will give an indication of the evenness or otherwise of the wall surfaces and the extent to which walls may be out of plumb. Wall tiling, being inflexible, will show clearly the extent of any structural movement as accurately as any glass tell-tale so that gaps or cracks which have appeared in the tiling can indicate the extent of past structural deformation. Similarly, tile sills, internally or externally, may show signs of past separation at window openings.

The tiles should be tapped lightly all over to detect loose or hollow areas. The modern practice of tiling using spot adhesive is not always as durable as the traditional tiling applied to rendering encountered in older buildings. Older tiling will often be found to be very firmly fixed indeed and removal of tiles presents a problem. During renovation work it is often easier to re-tile over the original tiles rather than persevere with attempts to hack them off, and tiling over tiles can be satisfactory provided that the older surface glazing is cleaned and abraded first to provide an adequate key.

Tiling of various types is commonly used on floors. Over timber floors, the tiling should be capable of accepting flexing inherent in timber construction, while brittle tiles such as ceramic types, which require a firm solid base, are unsuitable for suspended timber floors. Vinyl asbestos tiles or vinyl sheet flooring can be laid over timber floors provided that an intervening layer of hardboard or plywood is provided and the degree of movement in the floor construction is minimal.

Exterior finishes

Exterior surfaces are often rendered and finished in pebbledash, spardash, smooth stucco, roughcast or stippled surfaces of various types. Such surface treatments must be suitable for the conditions of exposure in order to resist frost damage. They must also be designed to accommodate any movement in the construction beneath and to allow for the evaporation of trapped vapour.

In all cases the life expectancy of a rendered surface will only be as good as the adhesion to the surface beneath. Frequently, renderings are applied to walls which are in poor condition as a means of disguising the defects beneath and the key will be inadequate. In due course, the rendering will shell away from the base and the first signs of this, to be detectable by the surveyor, will be surface cracking and raised areas which are hollow underneath.

Various types of surface coatings are produced for painting roughcast and stucco renderings. Sprayed surface coatings are heavily promoted nowadays with various claims about the life of the treatment. As with the renderings themselves, the surface coatings will only be as durable as the base to which they are applied and the key is vital. Sprayed coatings are often used as a means of binding together loose or soft rendered surfaces and will not prove durable in such situations. Sprayed coatings are also employed as a means of limiting damp penetration through solid walls by providing an impervious coating and can actually be counter-productive in such a situation as, by preventing the escape of trapped moisture in the wall, they may increase a tendency for moisture evaporation from the internal surfaces where the barrier to penetration is incomplete or there is rising damp in the wall.

Some housing is given a new external facing of artificial stone on existing wall surfaces to alter the appearance of the building and (according to the manufacturers) improve weather-resistance and insulation. If such stone re-facing is encountered, certain basic questions need to be considered regarding the strength of adhesion to the base, the suitability of the base and any need to accommodate movement. Generally well-keyed brickwork or stone work in sound condition will provide a suitable base for re-facing, especially if shot-fired ties are used at suitable intervals. It is questionable, however, whether or not the re-facing of brickwork or stone in such conditions is worthwhile, discounting any aesthetic considerations. If brickwork or stonework is in poor condition and if re-facing is used for this reason, then this must call into question the long-term degree of adhesion between the new face and the base.

The application of traditional wall renderings requires degrees of skill, especially in the case of stucco which needs a careful selection of mix so as to be neither too lean nor too rich in cement. In such work, careful application is needed with a minimum of working of the surface. If stucco is overworked, the resultant surface will contain more finer particles than the backing and slight differences in the rates of expansion and contraction between surface and base will result in the familiar patterns of hairline cracking so often encountered in such a finish which has not been decorated recently.

Rendered exterior walls which are subject to constant water saturation from driving rain, leaking gutters, overflows and other causes, will be at risk from frost damage. South-west walls usually face the prevailing weather and will be most at risk. In parts of Wales, Scotland and the West of England where the degree of exposure is higher, it may be that all walls will suffer saturation from driving rain at some time. The crystallising into ice of the water between the rendering and the base will cause that rendering to fall away, sometimes large areas at a time.

Asbestos

In connection with finishes and surfaces in buildings special mention should be made of asbestos. Health risks associated with asbestos fibres are now well understood and during the course of any inspection surveyors should be careful to check whether asbestos has been used for cladding, pipe-lagging or other purposes; if necessary, and especially if the presence of blue asbestos is suspected, clients should be advised to obtain independent advice and analysis of any asbestos or asbestos-based materials.

Generally asbestos as used with cement to form roofing sheets, water tanks and the like is stable and unlikely to release fibres into the atmosphere in dangerous quantities; such stable materials can however become more friable with age so that any asbestos-cement found to be in a friable condition could be hazardous.

Blue asbestos is highly dangerous and should not be disturbed if found. It should be removed by specialist contractors using approved handling methods to avoid any release of fibres into the air. The material is unlikely to be found in private residences but will be encountered in some post-war and late pre-war industrial and institutional buildings, generally in the form of pipe and boiler lagging.

Chapter 9

Services

There are a number of things we are not happy about. For one thing the lavatories are flushing hot water.
New house purchaser

In all types of property, services will be a matter of major interest to any prospective purchaser. He will wish to know whether or not the services are functioning satisfactorily and if they are likely, in the future to give trouble needing expensive repair. Some clients will be remarkably knowledgeable about services and others will be entirely ignorant and require considerable guidance, especially regarding the effectiveness of heating systems.

During the course of the survey, the inspection should include an examination of services at all points where they are visible. Great care should be exercised not to assume that services which appear modern have been renewed in their entirety. Amateur workmanship is rife in the areas of electric wiring, plumbing and heating; nothing should be taken on trust.

Electricity

The surveyor would be advised to foster a continuing relationship with an electrician who can prepare test reports and make recommendations on electrical systems, in both residential and other types of building. It may well be, however, that the surveyor himself can tell a client a great deal about an electrical installation in the first instance and the suggested normal practice would be to inspect the wiring and switchgear first and then recommend a specialist report and test if this seems necessary.

As a general rule, if the electrical installation is old and the wiring clearly in need of renewal, no electrical test should be necessary since the surveyor can then advise the client himself. A periodic test report throughout the life of a building makes good sense, and modern wiring which appears sound should normally be tested as a routine safety precaution when a building changes ownership. Where amateur or sub-standard work is suspected, an electrician's test should be regarded as essential for confirmation purposes.

It is recommended that a test by a qualified electrician should, at least, cover the following points:

1. A visual examination of the system including cable in accessible voids.
2. A Meggar test on the cable insulation.
3. Polarity tests at the outlets.
4. A test for earth continuity, including continuity of plumbing and gas services.

The modern use of plastics in plumbing can give rise to sections of systems which are unconnected by conducting pipework. In these circumstances, several earth connections to the plumbing are then necessary. The standard to apply is the current Institution of Electrical Engineers' 'Regulations for Domestic Equipment'. Anything short of this standard should be reported to the client with the necessary advice.

Modern uPVC sheathed cable, used generally since about 1958, has proved durable and so far we have not encountered failures in uPVC sheathed systems except where grossly overloaded. Tough rubber, vulcanised India-rubber (VIR), and lead-sheathed cable, used prior to about 1958, must all now be regarded as due for renewal. Rubber-sheathed cable has a safe life-span of between 20 and 25 years, tending to become brittle after this time, especially on power circuits used regularly for high-wattage appliances, and is liable to attack by gnawing mice in the case of older properties. Lead-sheathed cable can be mistaken for grey uPVC cable, especially in say a dark roof void, but if a scrape with a finger nail leaves a bright shining line this will confirm the presence of lead sheathing.

The surveyor himself should be able to discover and comment upon certain obvious defects in electrical systems, and the following points should be checked:

1. At the service head, the overall condition of the switchgear and cable; generally a modern consumer unit with all circuits neatly labelled is to be hoped for, but invariably in older buildings a multiplicity of iron-clad or wooden boxes will be found and replacement of these by a modern consumer unit can be recommended. If rubber- or lead-sheathed cables are found, an assumption may be made that re-wiring will be required and the client should be advised to budget for this pending receipt of an electrician's report. It will be appreciated that ring mains used since the Second World War may themselves need re-wiring if rubber cable were used (mostly this applies to installations prior to 1958). Clients often believe that a ring main installation indicates that the system is modern and will therefore not need attention, but this is not always so.
2. The visible power sockets, light switches, pendants and fixed electrical appliances should be examined. For safety reasons cord switches are required in bathrooms and shower rooms where water is present and within certain distances of the switch. Immersion heaters should generally be on a separate 15-amp circuit with double-pole switch and have an indicator light. Such heaters on plugs and sockets, or spurred off a ring main, may not be satisfactory. A check should be made for frayed cables to immersion heaters and other appliances. Nowadays lighting pendants are earthed but this has not always been so. If the pendants are not earthed this may not, of itself, justify action but a client's attention should be drawn to the point. Unswitched power sockets are permitted by regulations but switched sockets are preferable. If unswitched sockets are found, clients may be told that these could be replaced with double or single switched sockets if required. Fixed electric wall heaters should be on

15-amp circuits with fused isolating switches and in bathrooms or shower rooms should be cord-operated and mounted high enough that they cannot be touched accidentally.
3. The visible cable on walls and in voids should be examined. Cable clipped to walls below a height of 1.5 m should be in conduit so as to be protected from damage. Unprotected surface-clipped cable run along skirtings is not satisfactory. In roof-spaces the lighting cables should be taken to junction boxes, and although neat clipping is not essential it is desirable, particularly if the area is likely to be used for storage or occasional access. Wiring joined with insulation tape is unacceptable.

If the system is modern but obvious breaches of the Institution of Electrical Engineers' Regulations are found, or the installation has not been made in accordance with good practice, then the surveyor should be on his guard over the possibility of sub-standard or amateur work and advise a test before the system is used.

If the client wishes to cook with electricity, a separate circuit with 30-amp, 45-amp or 60-amp fuse should be recommended with a suitable grade of cable, depending upon the nature of the appliance to be used. A combined cooker panel and power socket is normally provided on the kitchen wall. It is essential that cookers are not run off ring mains, since this will result in overloading.

Any external circuits have to meet with special requirements and be suitably encased in watertight conduits, whether below ground or above. Exterior wiring is often amateur and, if so, may be dangerous. A particular point should be made of having any such wiring checked for safety.

Gas

A surveyor should recommend that the gas service, together with any fixed gas appliances included in the sale, be inspected and tested for safety as a normal routine precaution when the property changes hands and before any gas is used. While some surveyors will undertake to do this themselves, it is generally better for the matter to be referred to the local gas board or a gas board approved contractor. Having given this advice the surveyor may also make any other comments which result from his own inspection.

The writers make a point of examining the gas service head and meter, and if any gas smell is detected (a not uncommon occurrence) then this should be brought to the client's attention. If the building is old there may be a considerable amount of gas pipework running under the floorboards. It is not unusual to find original pipework for gas fires and gas lighting still in place and although this may be capped off where appliances were removed, it may still be connected to the service and at mains gas pressures. Older installations were designed for town gas which was not only supplied at lower pressures than modern natural gas but also contained more moisture, and this assisted in maintaining seals on threaded pipe joints. The dryer natural gas at higher pressures will often find weaknesses in such old pipework and leaks often result.

Occasionally, gas pipework will be found to be heavily rusted and for this reason it may be on the point of failing. Underground gas service pipework often leaks and requires renewal if old, especially if the ground in which it is laid is subject to vehicular traffic. The surveyor may mention this possibility and point out that any such underground pipework will not have been inspected as part of his survey.

A gas leak under the front garden of a house usually seems to occur just after some expensive re-paving and re-turfing of the front garden has been carried out – with adverse effects on the client's blood pressure!

Ventilation to conventional flued gas appliances is a matter of the utmost importance and should always be checked. Generally, for safe running a conventional flue boiler or warm air heat exchanger unit must have ventilation of the equivalent of a 225 mm × 150 mm airbrick to the outside air at all times. The increasing tendency towards improved insulation and draught-proofing of houses means that the structure becomes virtually airtight and if no ventilation for a conventional flue is provided, this could result in the suffocation of the occupants by removal of oxygen from the atmosphere.

A careful check of ventilation provision must be made and a warning given to the client not to alter or block ventilation in any way.

Balanced flue appliances do not take oxygen from the room in which they are located and no requirement for special ventilation provision arises in this case.

Certain small flueless gas room heaters have been available in the past and are still sold. This type of heater, like paraffin heaters, generates considerable vapour during combustion, and good ventilation for their safe use is essential. With this type of heating deterioration of decorations invariably results, even where there is good ventilation. If ventilation is poor and the fabric of the building cold, serious condensation problems occur and to mould growth on walls and in cupboards.

Water

The plumbing for the hot and cold water supply must be examined where this is accessible. The location of both the company stopcock and the internal stopcock should be confirmed and if there is no sign of these the client must be advised to have them traced and checked.

Lead plumbing is still often found in older buidings and even if internal plumbing is modern, an original lead incoming and rising main supply pipe may have been retained. For health reasons lead pipes are no longer recommended. In the past it was believed that the lead could not enter the water in the system due to the protection inside the pipes provided by the coating which forms when the surface of the lead oxidises. This is no longer considered sufficient protection since the health risk which arises does so from a total long-term build-up of lead in the body from a variety of sources of which lead plumbing may be only one. Accordingly, while it would be foolish for the surveyor to be alarmist on this topic, it is suggested that a mention should be made when old lead pipes and mains are encountered and the client may then decide what action, if any, he would wish to take.

During the course of the survey, the accessible plumbing and all sanitary ware, taps, cisterns and waste pipes are visually inspected and tested by normal operation. The surveyor should note any weeping or corroded joints, dripping taps needing new washers and noisy plumbing due to water-hammer or other causes as well as running overflows and the consequent possibility, if header-tank ball taps are found to operate correctly, of a leaking coil in an indirect cylinder.

Occasionally in an older building, the plumbing may have been turned off at the stopcock and the overall age and condition of the system may be such that re-charging the system with water would be ill-advised. In such circumstances it would be better not to charge up the system for tests but to advise the client generally that having regard to the obvious defects in the system, it should not be used until inspected by a plumber or perhaps renewed. Old stopcocks may be difficult to turn and can even seize or break off after they have been opened. Considerable damage could be caused then to a property if defective plumbing is charged up in circumstances where it may be difficult to turn off and drain it down again quickly.

It is a good idea to check the fixings to wash basins as these are often found to be loose. The caulking to bath edges is important and it is difficult to maintain a good seal with acrylic baths due to their flexibility. Caulking around showers and baths with shower attachments is essential and a watch should be kept for any points where a regular spillage of shower water may have taken place with possible adverse effects on timbers or ceilings beneath. Water-closet waste-pipe and flush-pipe seals are often found to be weeping at the back of the pan and any long-standing leak in this area may have resulted in deterioration to the floor or ceiling beneath. This often arises if the pan is not mounted exactly square to the cistern, or if modern press-fit joints have been wrongly used, or if the pan is mounted on an insufficiently rigid timber joist and boarded floor.

Certain combinations of metals in plumbing systems can give rise to galvanic corrosion. Galvanised-steel cisterns and hot tanks, for example, will rust through rapidly in the presence of a lead and copper piping. A sacrificial anode consisting of an aluminium block earthed to the steel tank may extend its life although all galvanised-steel cisterns and hot tanks will rust through in time, whether protected or not, and replacement with a modern plastic or glass-fibre type is usually necessary once rusting has set in.

Central heating

Fig. 9.1 illustrates diagrammatically the layout of a typical water- and central-heating system likely to be installed in a small residential or commercial property dating from the nineteen-sixties or nineteen-seventies. Such a system is simple with only a single pump on the heating circulation and very little to go wrong. Provided that the system is correctly installed and the radiators and pipework are protected from chemical corrosion by an inhibitor, such a system should prove reliable and serviceable for 20 to 30 years before major renewals or repairs are needed. Occasional servicing and attention to the boiler and pump may be expected and a minimum of annual maintenance is recommended before each heating season.

Certain elementary principles apply in such a system. Overflows should be taken separately to the eaves and the header overflow should not be run into the main cistern. All expansion pipes should be of greater diameter than corresponding feed pipes and an overflow pipe diameter should be greater than that of the corresponding supply pipe. Cylinders must be indirect otherwise a mixing of circulation water and hot service water will occur. It is essential that this should not occur as the addition of fresh water into the circulation will add oxygen and cause rapid corrosion to steel radiators and fittings. This may happen where the coil in an indirect cylinder has a split or pinhole and can be confirmed, as previously explained, by a continuous running of the system's overflow.

Figure 9.1 Diagrammatic layout of a simple domestic water and heating system using copper piping in 15, 22 and 28-mm diameters. Indirect gravity primary circulation is provided to the cylinder. A pumped heating system is provided in small-bore, two-pipe layout to pressed-steel panel radiators

Occasionally it is puzzling to find an indirect system which does not have a separate header tank. This invariably will be a system with a self-priming cylinder, commonly used in the nineteen-fifties and nineteen-sixties, and can be confirmed if the cylinder has a 'Primatic' label. Self-priming cylinders employ a one-way valve to permit the addition of water from hot into indirect service. In self-priming systems, defects can easily arise involving a mixing of the water and the lack of an expansion header tank means that inhibitors and corrosion proofing chemicals cannot be added to the system. A separate header tank and indirect cylinder are much to be preferred as seals have a habit of breaking down which can introduce rusty radiator water into the hot water service.

Some central heating systems are found to be laid out as a one-pipe rather than a two-pipe layout. In one-pipe systems, all circulating water enters and leaves every radiator via a single pipe, usually of wider diameter than normal small-bore or micro-bore. One-pipe systems can be gravity fed or pumped. In either case they suffer the disadvantage that the circulating hot water cools progressively as it runs through the radiators so that the radiators nearer the end of the circulation in a pipe run are colder than the earlier ones. Traditionally the progressively cooler running can be compensated by employing progressively larger radiators towards the end of long pipe runs but this is of limited use when radiators are turned off. One-pipe systems are also generally difficult to balance.

Gravity heating circulation uses wide-bore pipework of either copper or iron and is used in many older buildings including houses, blocks of flats and commercial structures of one kind or another. Gravity circulation is more sluggish than pumped circulation and older gravity systems inevitably contain a considerable sludge build-up with furring in pipework which further restricts the flow. A specialist heating engineer's report on older systems is inevitably necessary in order to confirm whether or not they are still functioning with reasonable efficiency.

All tanks and plumbing in lofts, under floors and at other points where frost damage is possible should be well lagged and tanks should always be covered. Various unsavoury items may be found in uncovered tanks including dead birds and, apart from the health hazard posed, there is a real danger of blockages occurring in the pipes and overflow outlet.

System control

In current domestic central-heating systems a system of control and layout may be adopted which is more sophisticated than the simple system illustrated in *Fig. 9.1.*

A fully-pumped system could be employed using either two pumps, one for heating and one for hot water, or a single pump and two motorised valves, or a single pump and motorised valve giving heating or hot-water priority. The advantage of fully-pumped systems is that the programmes for hot water and central heating may be quite separate, giving greater flexibility of control, and cylinder and radiator temperatures may be separately set using a strap-on thermostat to the hot water cylinder.

A secondary advantage of the fully-pumped system is that the boiler does not need to lie close to and below the level of the cylinder as is necessary for gravity circulation. The cylinder warm-up is then more rapid than with a gravity feed.

In addition to the use of a normal wall thermostat for setting room temperatures, systems of zone thermostats can be employed sited either floor-by-floor in a building or as thermostats controlling individual radiator valves. Generally speaking, the more sophisticated the system becomes, the more there is to go wrong and a point is reached beyond which the advantages of sophistication are outweighed by the disadvantages of complexity, including the cost and inconvenience of additional maintenance and repair.

Small-bore systems have, in some cases, given way to micro-bore, especially where central heating is installed in an older building previously not so heated. Micro-bore (or mini-bore) is easier to install since pipework is flexible and more easily concealed. Most micro-bore systems will incorporate some small-bore pipework around the boiler with the main pipe runs in micro-bore taken from central manifolds and either run under the floors or boxed in. Such systems require careful design to ensure that the small pipework is adequate for the velocity of circulation required to achieve the desired room temperatures.

Heat emissions from a boiler casing are equal to those from a small radiator so that if a boiler is located in a small room, say a kitchen or utility room, the benefit of heat emissions may be valuable in winter-time, making the overall performance more efficient. Often boilers are found to be located in exterior boiler houses, in which case the benefits of heat emissions from the boiler casing are lost on the outside air. In domestic installations the use of external boiler housing appears to be a practice dating from a time when fuel costs were low before energy costs began their present steep rise and the overall efficiency of the system and prevention of heat loss were not regarded as being so important.

The controls for most systems incorporate timed switching. A programmer is preferred with a selection of timed programmes so that heating systems may be left to run automatically as required. In a residential property, a fully-pumped small-bore system with two motorised valves is ideal with a strap-on thermostat regulating cylinder temperature and a wall thermostat in the main living room regulating radiator temperature. Such a system may be either gas- or oil-fired, the former being considerably cheaper than the latter in present circumstances. Solid fuel systems may be used but they lack the flexibility of control and automatic operation of gas- and oil-fired systems.

In addition to conventional water-filled central-heating systems a wide variety of other methods of heating may be encountered which could form part of the structure under review, or alternatively are chattels, including various types of free-standing gas and electric fires, electric storage heaters, mobile gas and paraffin heaters and solid fuel appliances including wood-burning stoves. As such items are chattels included with the property it is recommended that clients be advised to satisfy themselves on the condition of appliances and their performance, including their running costs. Heating requirements are generally somewhat personal and a means of heating which will be satisfactory for one client may be unacceptable to another.

Flues

In the case of heating systems which use flues it is recommended that clients should be advised that flues must be swept and checked as a normal routine when a building changes hands. A build-up of soot in a flue can cause a chimney fire and this can be a hazard in an old building where a flue lining may be poor or non-existent. A risk can arise of timbers having been built into chimney walls, especially at roof level, this giving a combustible access for a chimney fire to spread into a roof space. Many cases have occurred in old buildings of beams or purlins having actually been built into a flue and smouldering for perhaps months before bursting into flame with disastrous results.

A cautionary note should be sounded over flues from wood-burning stoves which are often installed in existing fireplaces. Manufacturers of these appliances will often recommend that they should be opened every 24 hours and used at maximum heat to burn off the tar deposits which accumulate in the flue. The temperature of the flue linings can reach 850°C, and if tar ignites it could reach 1500°C, and serious fires have occurred as a result. Moreover, chemicals are sold to the owners of wood-burning stoves to assist in dissipating flue deposits. Chemicals using phosphorous cause intense heat and those including chlorine can result in chloride attack to linings, especially old parging and brickwork.

If roof and floor timbers are in contact with the walls of flues or even built into these walls (a not uncommon fault in older buildings), they are likely to be subject to intense heat to the point of combustion by this practice of flue tar burning. Only flue linings of a very high standard will resist such aggressive conditions and when a wood-burning stove is encountered, it is suggested that the suitability or otherwise of the flue arrangements should be reviewed critically.

Drains

Stormwater drains generally consist of gutters and rainwater pipes which discharge into either open or sealed gullies and with surfacewater gullies provided to paved areas. The stormwater may run to soakaways or to a separate stormwater sewer or into a combined foulwater and stormwater sewer. It is recommended that the surveyor should familiarise himself with the accepted practices in the locality concerned as local water authority regulations may provide, for example, that stormwater should not be run into the foul sewer, especially in inland locations where large quantities of stormwater would overload the foul system. Soakaways are suitable in porous, well-drained soils but unsuitable for heavy clay or non-porous soils which drain reluctantly, unless there is no alternative.

Frequently the surveyor will find the storm drainage system to be a mystery. There will often be no manholes nor any indication of the drain runs. Soakaways tend to block eventually and the pipework becomes choked, especially if leaves fall in the gutters and no cages are provided over rainwater pipes. Soakaway systems often need to be relaid after a period of time as they cannot easily be rodded through.

The importance of avoiding point discharges of stormwater into the soil around foundations has already been stressed in Chapter 3. In many cases the surveyor should consider whether or not the storm system ought to be exposed and checked. Perhaps the best guide to this is to suggest that a client checks the system during a period of really heavy rain to see if the storm gullies allow a free flow. If they are blocked it is likely that stormwater is draining into the soil around the building from overflowing collars and gullies, and this is undesirable. A good modern practice is to lay storm drains watertight for a distance of at least 3 m from the main walls and thereafter in land drains to a soakaway if required. Some intermediate rodding access is recommended in the form of small rodding chambers over any bends. If the storm drains run into the foulwater sewer or to a separate storm sewer, a watertight system of a standard similar to the fourwater system is required with suitable rodding access.

Foulwater drains should always be provided with adequate means of access for rodding and attending to blockages, and provision for rodding at each change in direction and each branch drain connection is necessary. If this is lacking, it is suggested that this be mentioned in the report together with suitable advice. Lack of good rodding access on a branch drain from a gully may not be critical but lack of access to a branch drain from a WC or soilpipe serving a WC is unacceptable if a good standard of design is to be maintained.

Sewers

Foulwater drains will normally take the form of either a public sewer or a private sewer or a private drain. These distinctions are important since they affect the client's potential liability for drain repairs both within and outside his own curtilage.

A public sewer is maintainable by the local water authority or its agents and will normally be laid under a public highway or grass verge but can also run under private land. Generally, defects in a public sewer will not be the liability of the adjoining property owners connected to it once it has been adopted and it is not normal practice during the course of a building survey to attempt any examination or testing of public sewers serving the property under review. In some localities the public sewers, both for stormwater and foulwater, may become overloaded from time to time, and if the surveyor is aware of any such problem it would, of course, be open to him to discuss it in his report. The ability of sewers to cope with storm- and foulwater discharges may be relevant when changes of use or more intensive use are proposed. Changes of use normally require local authority permission and it is possible for consent to be refused if the existing public sewers are inadequate. Such cases are, if anything, on the increase, particularly in rural areas.

A private sewer is a shared drainage system serving a number of properties. The Public Health Acts provide that such drains are the joint responsibility of all property owners connected. In order to be able to confirm the extent of a client's potential liability for a private sewer, it would be necessary to inspect and possibly test the whole system. Clearly this is often impracticable; frequently 20 or more houses will be connected to a private sewer and a surveyor could find himself testing half the drains in a street in order to cover that potential liability. Where the subject property is connected to a private sewer, it is suggested that the significance of this be explained to the client and that he be given the opportunity to decide how far he wishes to pursue the matter.

In addition to the Public Health Acts which impose a liability for the maintenance of private sewers which can be enforced by the local authority, the question of responsibility for shared drains may also be covered in title covenants for freehold property, or lease covenants for leasehold property, or their Scottish equivalents. If the title or lease specifically identifies drains for which a client may be liable, these may require special attention from the surveyor, possibly needing access to other parts of a building or adjoining properties.

It is rare for a local authority to serve notices under the Public Health Acts requiring repairs to a private sewer but this situation does occasionally occur. It is clearly a matter of concern to a client buying a property to find that he may have to pay a contribution for some drain repair, perhaps some distance from his own property and about which he may be unaware until he is served with a formal notice. It is debatable whether or not all property owners connected to a private sewer must contribute or only those 'upstream' from the defect, as local authority practice in serving notices under the Public Health Acts appears to vary.

A private drain is a system which is exclusive to a particular property and runs through its curtilage and into a public sewer. Up to the point of connection to the public sewer the private drain is entirely the responsibility of the property owner (or lessee) concerned. Testing procedures for private drains are clearly much simpler than for private sewers.

Testing and maintenance

Two main forms of drains test are normally used by a surveyor, these being water-pressure tests (particularly suitable for traditional pipework between open manholes) and smoke tests (particularly suitable for above-ground soil stack systems). Drain testing procedures and the various types of drainage systems are well documented in the building text books and are not discussed in detail in this volume. However, certain comments on the interpretation of test results would seem worth stating.

The first point to bear in mind is that the standard of test result required for new drainwork will rarely be achieved in existing drains. Old drains may well be watertight in normal use when running perhaps one-third full and, as such, may be perfectly serviceable. A water-pressure test to any height will impose abnormal pressures on the pipework and manhole benching and will often indicate leakages. Such leakages may not of themselves justify the relaying or pressure-grouting of the pipework, and the degree of leakage, the invert depths and the general condition of the system should be taken into consideration when deciding whether or not major repairs are justified.

It is an undoubted fact that a majority of pre-War drainage systems will leak under test if the head of water used is high enough, but many will flow freely and be otherwise quite serviceable under normal conditions.

It is perhaps worth considering that a client might expect from his drainage system:

(1) That the drains will flow freely in normal use without blockage.
(2) That in the event of blockage occurring it can readily be cleared.
(3) That the system be airtight at ground level and within the building so that no drain smells or health hazards arise.

Most common blockages are caused by stepped fractures in pipework, tree-root intrusion or rough workmanship to joints and manhole benching. These matters will often be detected on a visual examination within manholes and through pipework using a mirror. Shallow drains running under or close to trees should always be checked for tree-root intrusion, even if the test result is reasonable, since the fine root tails can enter the drains through narrow fissures and even effectively seal them off in some cases.

If the drain gradient is too shallow this may cause blockages and rough checks on the invert depths will generally indicate whether or not the gradient is too shallow. If a level is not available, a check can often be made on drains around a building by taking invert depths in relation to the main damp-proof course line of adjoining walls (assuming damp-proof courses are not hidden).

Manhole covers will, more often than not, need cleaning, greasing and re-setting to provide an airtight fit and cracked manhole covers should always be renewed to keep them airtight. Loose frames should be re-set in new cement haunching for the same reason.

In some districts fresh-air inlets in conjunction with interceptor traps were used on private drains in the past but may no longer be regarded as necessary where a vent pipe is provided at the head of the drain. When this is so, we generally suggest that fresh-air inlets be sealed airtight in cases where other ventilation is provided to a suitable modern standard. The exception is where an interceptor trap is fitted in the last manhole before the sewer and a fresh-air inlet with mica flap valve ventilates the drain in conjunction with a vent pipe at the head. Mica flap valves in a fresh-air inlet are often found to be broken or missing.

Some modern uPVC underground drain systems, such as the Marley rodding point system, dispense with traditional manhole construction for most purposes and instead provide angled rodding eyes at ground level for each change of direction. Testing using drain plugs or inflatable bags is still possible but a visual examination is not possible through the pipework without recourse to video equipment and this is not usually suitable for the narrowest pipe diameters.

In rural areas, private drainage systems encountered vary from the modern, efficient and self-cleansing to the ancient and insanitary. The writers have encountered drains with no access whatsoever and no indication of where they terminate, also drains discharging directly into ditches and watercourses or into bore-holes. For example, in the Mendip Hills, house drainage systems used to discharge into pot-holes known locally as 'swalletts' which eventually directed the effluent into the cave system beneath. Clearly such primitive systems are often highly unsuitable and advice may be given that a modern system with ample access for cleansing be provided instead. This solution has recently been recommended to the owners of a 63-room country mansion built at the turn of the century and where the foul drainage discharges untreated into a stream, the main sewer being a quarter of a mile distant.

Cesspits

Cesspits are watertight sealed tanks which are periodically emptied by the local authority, their agents or specialist contractors and subject to emptying charges. If possible, the capacity of the tank and the amount currently charged for emptying should be checked. Clients may then consider if the tank capacity is adequate and the arrangements for emptying suitable. It is common practice for local authorities to insist on watertight cesspits and for these to be built in 225 mm brickwork, rendered both sides. However, empty milk bottles would be built furtively into the brickwork and rendered over so that when the cesspit had passed final inspection, the ends of the bottles would be broken out thus permitting the tank to drain into the surrounding subsoil and reducing the frequency and cost of emptying. Rustic cunning of this type might be expected if the cesspit is required to be emptied only at infrequent intervals. The local authority or their agents will generally keep a record of emptying dates for all cesspits in their area and a telephone call can often elicit details of the number of emptyings over the last few years together with the amounts emptied. To confirm this confusion which sometimes arises, one examination candidate wrote: 'The client may not realise he has a cesspit, thinking he has a septic tank. In Cornwall this has been known to happen'.

It is essential that cesspits be located within range of the suction pipe from an emptying vehicle and that a parking area for the tanker is provided with suitable access from the highway. If there is any doubt about the correct location of the cesspit, this point should be checked with the local authority.

Septic tanks

Septic tank systems are well described and documented in the textbooks and we will omit any technical details of these. If a report is required on such a system, the following points should be borne in mind:

1. Septic tanks, like cesspits, also need emptying periodically. The frequency of emptying is, however, much less with a septic tank, perhaps annually or even every two years, depending very much on the design, capacity and the amount of solid material with which it has to cope and consequently, the amount of humus which accumulates in the bottom of the tank. Accordingly highway access for a tanker with a parking area within suction range is again necessary.

2. It will often be found that filters and soakaways become choked after a time and land drains sometimes need to be relaid if the system is old. Any evidence of a tendency for the system to block or flood may indicate choked soakaways. This depends to some extent on the length of the soakaway pipes, the lie of the land and the draining capacity of the soil. Gravel or chalk soils drain very well whereas heavy clays drain badly and are not suitable for taking soakaway systems unless considerably extended.

3. If there is any doubt about the design of the system or its suitability for the client's needs, a specialist drainage engineer's report could be suggested and the client given the opportunity to commission such a report before he buys the property. Always lift the covers to the tank itself and look for the 'crust' on the surface which indicates that the septic tank is working correctly.

To sum up, private drainage systems are inevitably less satisfactory from a client's point of view than connection to a public sewer. If a public sewer is available and the cost of connection is not prohibitive, then the option of connection should be considered and, if necessary, recommended in the report.

Chapter 10

The report

The defendant failed to exercise the reasonable care and skill of the prudent surveyor which he had impliedly promised to exercise when he received instructions to survey the house. He committed a breach of contract with the plaintiff and provided him ultimately with a report which was so misleading as to be valueless.
Judge Kenneth Jones – Morgan v Perry (1973)

The surveyor's report should always be made in writing and be prepared with great care so that nothing intended to be included is omitted by mistake. It should be typed neatly on good quality paper and bound with a reasonably durable cover.

Paragraphs in the report should be numbered as well as the pages, or alternatively, sub-titles used so that in the event of discussion between the surveyor and his client either by telephone or otherwise, each party may readily refer the other to the section concerned.

The report should have regard not only to the particular circumstances and condition of the property under review but also the circumstances of the client. The preparation of a surveyor's report is a personal service between two parties and the service needs to be tailored to meet the needs of the consumer.

All surplus comment, padding and attempts at humour must be avoided. Few clients would feel happy about paying a fee for anything other than facts and information on the basis of which they will be taking an important personal and financial decision — possibly the biggest personal financial decision in their whole lives.

At the conclusion of the report it should be signed by the surveyor giving his name and qualifications.

Standard headings and clauses

In order to assist in drafting and in order to make the report intelligible to the reader, it should be divided by a series of main headings and sub-headings, the following list of headings and sub-headings being ideal for most situations although practice will naturally vary from one firm to another and in differing circumstances. From time to time a surveyor will be faced with the drafting of a report in circumstances where an entirely different layout from that normally used will be necessary, for example, in the structural report for a church quinquennial survey.

A suggested framework for the report could be as follows:

Part 1
Generally
Situation
Description
Accommodation   *Ground floor   First floor   Second floor   Outbuildings*

Part 2
Construction

Part 3
Condition   *Main walls and structure*
                 Roofs and chimneys
                                    Joinery and woodwork
                                    Finishes and general matters

Part 4
Services   *Electricity   Gas   Water   Central heating   Drainage*

Summary
Valuation   (if required)
Discussion   (if necessary)
Conclusion

A report should contain four separate elements. The first part is intended to set the scene by describing the situation, description and accommodation of the property. At this stage, the surveyor should have regard to the fact that many reports will be read by persons who have never seen the property and therefore some description is necessary for their benefit. The preamble to the report should also contain details of instructions, specific saving clauses limiting the scope of the report, and should advise the client of any matters, such as investigation of title, local searches and the like, which would more properly be dealt with by his solicitor or other adviser.

The second element is the 'construction' section of the report. The intention of separating construction and condition in this particular format is that it assists drafting as the surveyor may explain how the building is put together and take the opportunity to comment upon the standard of insulation, the quality of the overall design and criticise some of the features if necessary

The third element of the report is the 'condition' part which should set out the inspections and tests which have been made, the results obtained and the advice which follows. This section should also indicate the inspections or tests which have *not* been made, the implications and the recommendations.

It is clear from reported cases of professional negligence arising out of this type of work that a surveyor is not expected to expose and inspect all parts of a building and that the degree of exposure and inspection will depend upon circumstances. The important point to bear in mind is that in the event of areas of the structure being inaccessible, a competent surveyor may feel intuitively that problems may arise in such areas. This fact should then be brought to the attention of the client who would be given the opportunity to decide whether or not he wishes to pursue the matter any further on the basis of weighing the balance between the costs of special exposure and investigations and the risks involved in not undertaking such additional work. (See Chapter 19).

An example is the difficulty which can arise in respect of foundations. In inspecting a building for a potential purchaser in the first instance a surveyor should not feel obliged to expose and inspect any of the foundations, undertake trial bores or conduct other detailed investigations of the site. If site features encountered during the survey lead the surveyor to think that foundation exposure or site testing would be advisable then he should explain his reasons and thus give the client the opportunity to decide what to do.

Another example arises in the case of hidden floor construction. A suspended timber kitchen floor may be encountered having a covering of vinyl tiles on hardboard. A washing machine may have been leaking over this floor for some time and an inspection of the floor boards, joists and sleeper plates beneath could entail considerable disturbance and damage to the surface tiling. The surveyor is not expected to undertake such exposure during his initial survey but he should point out the circumstances to the client. This then gives the client the opportunity to have the necessary exposure carried out, subject to a builder's attendance and the vendor's agreement.

The last element of the report, apart from the ultimate conclusions and summaries, is that section dealing with services which again, to assist in drafting, may be separated from the parts dealing with fabric and structure.

The most effective way to assemble a report is to have a folder available containing all the standard report headings, sub-headings and clauses normally used by the surveyor's practice. This folder should contain a list of all the items which are to be covered in the report so that nothing may be overlooked. The information may also be stored on disk if a word processor is used.

In Chapter 18 specimen reports are included which could, if desired, be adapted and enlarged by the practitioner to form the basis of a personal folder of standard headings and clauses. Such clauses may also be fed into a word processor and used in this way to reduce repetitive typing work.

Standard clauses will not cover more than perhaps half the total report at the most, and whenever they are used care must be taken to ensure that they are fully appropriate in the circumstances. Unless appropriate to the situation in all respects they should be discarded and alternative wording used.

It is essential that a folder of standard headings and clauses be kept up-to-date and that it be continuously reviewed and re-written to keep abreast of current trends. In a partnership practice, periodic meetings of the partners are essential to discuss their own reports and possible improvement in their format so that standards are maintained.

Presentation of the report

The following, extracted from *The Chartered Surveyor* (April 1981), indicates one view taken by the Royal Insutitution of Chartered Surveyors' Professional Practice Committee:

The Professional Practice Committee recently considered a structural survey report provided by a member and was much concerned by the careless way in which the report had been prepared with regard to spelling, grammar and technical understanding.

The Committee agreed that the report, as presented, prejudiced the professional status of the member and the reputation of the RICS.

Further, the Committee directed that the attention of members generally should be drawn to the need to be satisfied, when contemplating accepting instructions, that their professional experience was such as to enable them to carry out the instructions competently; and that the time available was sufficient to enable them to carry out the instructions satisfactorily, particularly in instances where the work involved was not within their normal sphere.

The Committee also wished it to be emphasised that in all cases, reports should be carefully checked by a responsible person before despatch.

It must be a matter of concern to all Chartered Surveyors that their Professional Practice Committee felt it necessary to issue such a statement at all. Members of the RICS and other surveyors will appreciate the emphasis thus placed on the maintenance of the highest possible standards of presentation and technical understanding at this point of contact between the profession and the general public.

The Practice Note 'Structural Surveys of Residential Property' makes certain specific recommendations regarding surveyors' reports on residential property. Reports, say the RICS, should:

(1) Be clearly typed with headings and sub-headings to aid digestion and facilitate future reference, with each page indicating the address and reference of the property.
(We would add to this that pages and paragraphs should be numbered clearly to facilitate reference and avoid the possibility of pages losing their sequence or being mislaid should the report be taken apart for copying. It would clearly be a very serious matter for an incomplete report, or copy, to be relied upon by a client or a third party).
(2) Be prepared in simple, direct, grammatical English free from specialist technical expressions unless they are explained. Be presented in a logical sequence which can be readily followed by the reader, and allow a variation of emphasis to be applied to matters of varying significance.
(3) Be factual and unambiguous wherever possible, distinguishing between fact, the surveyor's firm opinion and any speculative comments included for guidance or discussion.
(4) Should provide a record of the building, its construction and materials. Compare these with modern standards and other properties of a similar type, giving a balanced view of the property which describes the separate elements sufficiently to identify their position, construction and condition.
(5) Should advise on necessary repairs or modifications needed to remedy defects, further investigations which may be required and the future development of defects which could be significant.

Some surveyors' reports include a list of approximate buildiing costs likely to be involved in undertaking specific recommended works. They may, in conclusion, provide a summary of items of disrepair with a list of costs. This approach could sometimes be misleading and place the surveyor in a difficult position if the actual costs which arise differ significantly from his estimates. As a general rule, attempts to cost building works at this initial stage are unwise. There are two reasons for this.

First, in order to price many items with reasonable accuracy the surveyor will need to measure the work involved and prepare approximate quantities which will involve time and will increase the fee. It may be that on receiving the report the client may decide not to proceed with the purchase, in which event the need for such estimates will not arise. It is preferable, in the first instance, to present the facts to the client and to prepare approximate quantities in the form of a supplementary report at a later stage if requested.

Secondly, there are many items of building work which can be undertaken in a variety of ways depending upon the client's requirements, and in the absence of full knowledge of the client's needs it may be impossible in practice to assess the costs accurately. If estimates are provided, the Practice Note recommends that the surveyor should be careful to state at some length the reservations and limitations of such advice.

In some cases, however, a surveyor may be commissioned by his client to specify and supervise any subsequent remedial works which may be found necessary as a result of his survey. In such circumstances, when the surveyor would have control of the works, an estimate of costs at survey stage would be admissible.

In the drafting of a report for a private client, the need for simple, direct, grammatical English, free from specialist technical expressions and capable of being readily followed by the reader is paramount. There will, of course, be occasions when a surveyor will need to prepare a report for a fellow professional in circumstances where technical expressions may rightly be used, but such situations will be unusual for most practices although perhaps more common where pending litigation is involved.

Tenses

Difficulties sometimes arise with the correct use of tenses when drafting reports. Often a mixture of tenses has to be used and there is some difference of opinion as to the best way in which this may be arranged. For example, it is reasonable to say, 'The main roof is of flat construction surfaced in asphalt', or, 'The asphalt surfaces were satisfactory at the time of our inspection', drawing a distinction between the facts ascertained during the survey which apply at the time of despatch of the report and those facts which must be described in the past tense in order to make clear that between the time of the survey and the publishing of the report, events could occur which would invalidate the comments made.

To say 'the asphalt surfaces are satisfactory' may be unwise since this indicates their condition as at the date of the report, correct in most cases but which could be incorrect in unusual circumstances.

To say 'The main roof was of flat construction surfaced in asphalt' is a form used in many surveyors' reports where a practice is made of presenting all facts and description in the past tense, but this can engender a note of uncertainty in the mind of the client who may feel that this suggests that the roof, in some way, has changed. Similarly, 'The main walls were of cavity construction' suggests that perhaps they are no longer so.

Matters of description and descriptions of the construction of a building are best presented in the present tense. Those sections detailing the investigations made and the conclusions drawn should be presented in the past tense as applicable only to circumstances as at the time of the survey, especially in matters which may change significantly in a short space of time such as the state of roof coverings in storms or damp levels in walls following wet weather.

Generally, sentences and paragraphs should be kept short with adequate punctuation to facilitate the reader's understanding. It is no disrespect to the average client to say that he, or she, may well be unfamiliar with the reading of any type of document and that a surveyor's report may seem initially to be a formidable item to digest.

Nomenclature

It is often difficult for a surveyor to appreciate that expressions and terms appearing to him self-explanatory may cause confusion to a client and may require clarification. Some mention may be made by the surveyor in his report of the fact that the client should not feel inhibited from discussing any points needing clarification and that any time spent explaining such matters to clients be regarded as an essential part of the service. Most clients will understand what is meant by brickwork but may not know what 'pointing' is, nor may they understand expressions such as 'plumb' although they will understand what is meant by 'level'. To some extent the degree of technical expression used in the report may be tailored to suit the client if the client's business or profession is known. In one instance, some time was spent explaining to a client in simple terms a minor point of structural design in a building. The client sat patiently through the description only at the end revealing, in passing, that he was a chartered engineer specialising in structures. The structure did not collapse but the surveyor almost did!

The skill needed to draft a well-presented, rounded report is fundamental to the practice of a surveyor who inspects and reports upon buildings. One who has great technical ability and who may undertake inspections and investigations thoroughly may still be unable to present the information needed by his client unless he can produce in the final report a clear, concise and readable document which provides all the information needed.

It is a matter for argument that the preparation of the report is more difficult than the surveying of the building. Both involve degrees of concentration over an extended period if the end result is to be satisfactory. The former is undertaken in the relative comfort of the office whereas the latter is sometimes carried out under inhospitable conditions and may be physically tiring. However, making the inspection may become a matter of procedure and habit whereas the drafting of the report is specific to a particular property and client and that process requires a high level of concentration in circumstances where distractions may arise. The result will be more satisfactory if a report is drafted in a calm, quiet atmosphere free from distraction of any kind – such situations are rarely achieved in a busy surveyor's office.

Drafting the report

Given that the inspection and other investigations have been completed, the surveyor will then have to sit down and commence the drafting process. How should this be carried out?

The surveyor should have before him his notes, the file and all the relevant information. He should have available and close at hand his office library of technical papers, textbooks and trade information. He should have a full note of the client's instructions and a folder or binder containing all the standard report headings, sub-headings and clauses used by his practice in the preparation of their reports. He will have a word processor, a pad of lined paper or an empty spool or cassette of tape in a dictation machine. Some draft their reports on paper but dictation is equally suitable, as is direct drafting from a display screen.

If it were possible to recall the single most lasting impression left by some years of surveying buildings and preparing reports, that chosen by the writers and colleagues with whom this was discussed is that of the empty sheets of paper waiting to be filled with facts and information. What a hard taskmaster that empty sheet of paper can be and how often, when faced with it, the surveyor suddenly finds that his mind is a complete blank, especially in the early years of his professional life when the routine for such matters has not yet evolved and become set.

On such occasions, standard headings, sub-headings and clauses are referred to. Hopefully these will have been carefully updated and improved over the years to provide a useful check-list of matters which need to be covered. The order of presentation is then established together with standard caveats and exclusion clauses. Soon the thoughts will begin to flow and a report draft begin to emerge from the gloom of a mental block. The first rule of drafting might, therefore, be described as having a clear framework within which to work.

In the section of the report dealing with the condition of the building, there should be an order of presentation consisting of:

(1) the investigations made,
(2) the facts ascertained from those investigations, and
(3) the advice which follows from the facts.

For example, 'We carried out a careful examination of the wall surfaces inside and out' conveys to the reader the exact nature of the part of the building investigated. The reader will appreciate immediately that material beneath the wall surfaces will not have been inspected and that the advice given will relate to the information obtained from an inspection of the wall surfaces only.

Then, 'A pattern of small fracture lines was found to the left side elevation, generally following the mortar joints in the brickwork but with two fractured bricks to the main central crack line. Cracks were between hairline and 2 mm wide in three main lines of separation indicating a total extent of separation in the brickwork of about 5 mm at the eaves, tapering down to nil at the damp-proof course line'. Thus the reader will follow the broad gist of the factual information obtained. 'No evidence of cracking to the other elevations is apparent nor is there any such evidence inside the house'. 'An examination of the left side elevation with a level and plumb line did not indicate any evidence of undue separation or distortion of the structure'.

Finally, 'Having regard to the fact that the building is new, it is not possible for us to confirm whether the tensions in the left side elevation are due to initial consolidation or thermal movement in the new work, or whether they indicate some defect below ground. At present the degree of separation in the wall is not severe and if it were found in an older structure which had been on the site for many years it would not of itself be significant. Having regard to the fact that the structure is new, we would recommend that we should excavate a small inspection pit at the side of the left elevation to confirm that subsoil conditions and foundation design are as described in the plans and calculations provided for our use. We also recommend that the left side elevation be subjected to a period of observation to confirm whether or not movements in the brickwork have ceased. The extent and cost of such further investigations are beyond that of this present report and we must await your instructions in this respect'.

In the foregoing examples the recommended order has been followed so that the manner of arriving at the advice may be appreciated by the client involving the maximum economy of words. A client receiving the advice may be disappointed that the result is not clearcut but at the same time he should be under no illusions as to what is being recommended. If he fails to take the advice, the surveyor will not be responsible if, at a later stage, some fundamental defect becomes apparent under the left elevation.

The second rule of drafting might therefore be to describe the investigations, indicate the facts obtained and give advice related to those facts (including advice to undertake further investigations if appropriate).

A statement such as, 'The main roof is in fair condition at the present time for its age' is much less satisfactory than, 'We inspected within the accessible roof void using an inspection lamp and we examined the roof slopes externally from an extension ladder. The roof covering was weathertight at the time of our inspection and the tiles were in satisfactory condition for their age. We would not anticipate that any general re-covering of the roof will become necessary in the foreseeable future but the occasional renewal of tiles may be needed and a periodic check of the roof slopes would be recommended using a ladder, say each autumn when the gutters are cleared out'. This gives a client the correct impression of thoroughness and soundly-based advice.

An alternative method of carrying out a structural survey and preparing a report is to dictate the report direct on to a portable tape recorder while carrying out the survey. This method is to be recommended for use only by the most experienced surveyor and where the property is unoccupied at the time of the survey. When carrying out a survey using this technique it is best to start with a checklist on the following lines:

The site
Gates, fences, boundary walls, paths, drives, car-parking areas, paved areas, site drainage, aspect.

Outbuilding
Garages, stables, greenhouses, toolsheds, remote stores.

Drains
Ventilation, gulleys, manholes, drains, interceptors, septic tanks, cesspools, soilpipes, waste-pipes, grease traps, petrol interceptors.

Building (exterior)
Chimneys, flashings, roof, gutters, rainwater pipes, bargeboards or gables, main walls, external woodwork, external ironwork, glazing, damp courses, sub-floor ventilation, foundations.

Building (interior)
Roof void including timbers, felting, insulation, water tanks, visual aspect of electric wiring;

First floor including all sanitary fittings and describing ceilings, friezes, walls, floors, windows, doors, carpentry and joinery, and electric lighting, power and heating;

Other floors all as above and basements with special reference to waterproofing.

Electrical

Wiring, lighting points, power points, lighting fixtures, meters, switches, main switches, fuses, any earth leaker trips.

Plumbing

Cold water supplies, hot water supplies, means of heating water, hot and cold water storage.

Space heating

Means of space heating including type of fires, whether solid fuel, oil-fired, gas-fired or any other means, central-heating boilers, separate water heaters, any other type of space heater.

Although there is no necessity to follow a checklist such as that given above, the survey must be carried out in a methodical manner so that every single part of the fabric is properly examined in a logical sequence. As explained previously, every surveyor should provide his own checklist as each will have his own peculiar sequence and routine.

In this case, the sequence of the survey differs from that of the more commonly used methods in that, for example, the interior of the property is inspected room by room starting from the roof void and working downwards. In each area which is surveyed, the structure, finishes, condition and recommendations are set out room by room.

This is by far the quickest and, as a result, the most profitable method to use and has the advantage of not having to take written notes in physically impossible situations. It has the additional advantage that items can be described as one is actually looking at them and there is consequently little likelihood of any defect being overlooked or forgotten.

The best equipment to employ in these circumstances is either the Philips or Grundig 'notebooks' with small cassettes of about 20 minutes dictation time each. The survey is subsequently typed straight off through a transcriber and stethoscopes either as a draft or, after more experience, as a finished document. The latter, however, is only advised in the case of simple straightforward domestic-scale properties.

At the back of the surveyor's mind is always the fear that he may have missed something of importance – that something could have been omitted from his report which would have serious future consequences either for the building, its occupants or for his own professionl indemnity policy! As well as cutting down the element of risk by using one of the survey methods described, a good memory is a distinct asset, as was pointed out by the late Mr Gerald Eve. He advised that when inspecting a property, if anything unusual is noted – no matter what it is – it should be written down. For example, in the case of a surveyor carrying out an inspection of a property he says, 'To your surprise, you discover in a third floor attic at the end of a passage a green parrot in a cage. *Write it down*: that parrot may come in useful'. For example, if something goes wrong and evidence is required in Court –

Question (in cross-examination): Did you go all over the house Mr Sparrow?
Answer: Yes.
Question: All over it?
Answer: All over it.
Question: Including the third floor, Mr Sparrow?
Answer: Yes, including the attic at the end of a passage which is the home of a green parrot.

Keen observation and a photographic memory are indeed useful!
Unnecessary words should be avoided and the message should be kept as plain and simple as possible.
As an example, there is the quoted instance of a ten-year-old child who was invited to write an essay on a bird and a beast:

The bird that I am going to write about is the owl. The owl cannot see at all by day and at night is as blind as a bat.
I do not know much about the owl, so I will go on to the beast which I am going to choose. It is the cow. The cow is a mammal. It has six sides — right, left, front, back and upper and below. At the back it has a tail on which hangs a brush. With this it sends the flies away so they do not fall into the milk. The head is for the purpose of growing horns and so that the mouth can be somewhere. The horns are to butt with, and the mouth is to moo with. Under the cow hangs the milk. It is arranged for milking. When people milk, the milk comes and there is never an end to the supply. How the cow does it I have not yet realised but it makes more and more. The cow has a fine sense of smell; one can smell it far away. This is the reason for the fresh air in the country.
The man cow is called an ox. It is not a mammal. The cow does not eat much, but what it eats it eats twice, so that it gets enough. When it is hungry it moos, and when it says nothing it is because its inside is all full up with grass.

The simplicity of the child of ten years makes his description clear, concise and even somewhat stylish. Contrast this with, for example:

The attitude of each, that he was not required to inform himself of, and his lack of interest in, the measures taken by the other to carry out the responsibility assigned to such other under the provision of plans then in effect demonstrated on the part of each, lack of appreciation of the responsibilities vested in them, and inherent in their positions.

This, of course, means that neither took any interest in the other's plans, or even found out what they were. This shows that they did not appreciate the responsibilities of their position.
At all costs avoid the vague, imprecise verbosity affected by some government departments, politicians and trade union speakers as this is usually a sign of an unwillingness to accept responsibility for one's expressed views.
Keep clear, clean-cut and concise.
To sum up, probably the most important part of the structural survey is the report which, if not written out correctly or accurately, can cost the surveyor dear in terms of his professional indemnity!

A scrupulous report writer in every sentence that he writes will ask himself, 'What am I trying to say? What words will express it?'. He will probably ask himself, 'Could I put it more briefly?' You are not obliged, however, to go to all this trouble. You can shirk it by simply throwing open your mind and letting the ready-made phrases come crowding in. They will construct your sentences for you, even think your thoughts for you to a certain extent and, if required, will perform the important service of confirming your meaning to yourself.

A written report should always be made although it is often necessary to make a verbal report to the client immediately after the survey, particularly if the client is under pressure to purchase. However, if such a verbal report is made, the client must be informed that the written report will take precedence over whatever you happen to have said to him over the telephone or in person.

As previously intimated, the report must be written in a precise manner without relying on obscure technical terms and must be couched in language which is understandable to the layman. A client's particular circumstances must also be taken into account when writing such a report. In other words, for the ordinary lay client, a non-technical report must be used as far as possible, whereas if writing a report for an organisation where fellow professionals are involved, many more technical terms may be employed in order to elucidate a situation.

When the description, age and design of the property are given these could be related to the cost of the annual maintenance to such properties.

The construction of the property, together with any defects which exist or are likely to arise, must be fully described and elaboration must be made of any defects so that the probable cause and the necessary remedies are immediately apparent to the client.

The points on which the surveyor is not able to advise must be set out clearly, and positive recommendations made for further inspection and reporting by specialists if this is considered necessary.

Approximate estimates of costs of necessary urgent repairs can be made but only in the event of specific instructions being given by the client for such information.

The surveyor's insurance company will undoubtedly require that any structural survey should include a clause required for professional indemnity insurance. Such an example is as follows:

In accordance with your instructions I have attended at the above property and carried out a structural survey and have to report as follows.

I have not inspected woodwork or other parts of the structure which are covered, unexposed or inaccessible and I am, therefore, unable to report that any such parts of the property are free from defect.

The report on services will not include electrical wiring test or a test of the water and drainage pipes unless especially required. My opinion and observations will be based on visual inspection of the services where these are accessible.

Central-heating, space-heating and hot-water boilers have been visually examined but no definite opinion can be given that the equipment is entirely free from defect or, if not operating at the time of inspection, that they are in good working order. A separate test and report can be arranged if so required.

This report is based on the condition of the property on the date of inspection and no liability can be accepted for any deterioration in the condition of the property after this date.

The report must conclude with a summary of the principal defects and the general advice of the surveyor must be given together with an opinion on the overall condition of the property. The age and construction of the building will have a definite bearing on its condition and the defects which exist must be coloured by these two factors. In other words, one would not imagine an old and inexpensively constructed building to have the same characteristics as a more modern building constructed to the latest principles and where cost is of little object.

It is not necessary to prepare a detailed schedule of the accommodation but it is usually advisable to do so in an older property in order to ensure that every single detail of construction and finishes is covered. In this connection, it is advisable to point out the good features of a property as well as the defects since this will have a considerable effect on the decision whether or not to purchase. The report should not, however, be written out as a schedule of condition.

Finally, it must be stressed that a structural survey must not be written as if it were a valuation or in the same way as a building society inspection report. A valuation of the property should only be included at the express instruction of the client, and if it is requested then such a valuation would be subject to a separate fee computed in accordance with the Royal Institution of Chartered Surveyors' conditions of engagement.

Chapter 11

Pro-forma reports

In view of the great variety of building types, designs and construction methods, no simple pro-forma report can convey effective, balanced and complete advice.
RICS Practice Note, 'Structural Surveys of Residential Property'

Can you be sure that the house you are buying is free from major structural defect or that it represents a sound financial investment? The simple answer is that you *can't* be sure. The RICS' 'House Buyer's Report and Valuation' is designed to remove these doubts
Buying a House?, RICS, 1981.

During the course of his work the surveyor may be required to complete a wide variety of pro-forma reports. Initially, such reports were used only by the building societies for their own confidential use. More recently, such reports have been introduced by banks, insurance companies and other lenders. In 1981 the provision of pro-forma reports became a service specifically sponsored by the Royal Institution of Chartered Surveyors with the introduction of their 'House Buyer's Report and Valuation'.

In that same year the major building societies also adopted a new practice of sending a copy of their own surveyor's report to the mortgagor for his, or her, own information, subject to various caveats and warnings concerning the limitations of the mortgagee's surveyor's inspection.

These changes came about as a result of pressure from house buyers for simple straightforward advice on the property in which they were interested. It was found that only about 20% of house purchasers took independent professional advice before buying their houses. Most took no advice at all but relied upon the building society to tell them if anything major was amiss; alternatively, they simply relied upon their own judgment.

Building society, insurance company and bank reports are, in most cases, intended to be used for all types of residential and small commercial properties. The space allowed for answers is often insufficient so that in completing the report, the surveyor will often find it necessary to insert 'See separate sheet' and then provide an addendum to the pro-forma report to include a specific comment or describe a defect. This appears to be universal practice among surveyors with a regular flow of building society and other pro-forma report work.

A similar situation arises with the RICS' 'House Buyer's Report and Valuation' which may be completed easily in those cases where the house is sound and in good order but which requires careful use where some significant defect is found or suspected. In such circumstances, an addendum in the form of an attached sheet would be necessary to answer adequately the point raised.

The RICS scheme is for an inspection of the property broadly the same as the basic inspection undertaken for a full structural survey report. It is unlikely that this inspection of itself will take less time than a normal full inspection. The RICS scheme is intended for houses and bungalows up to $200\,m^2$ in area and not more than three storeys high. The scheme is not intended for flats or period properties. The RICS scheme includes a set of pre-printed working report forms on which the surveyor writes his notes during the actual inspection, together with triplicated, four-page report forms and folders for the clients.

There are certain specific limitations on the inspection included in the RICS' 'House Buyer's Report and Valuation' scheme. The inspection will not include underfloor areas or a close examination of roofs more than $3\,m$ above ground level. No tests of services are included. The provision of the service is subject to certain specific conditions of engagement set out in an explanatory booklet, *Buying a House?* published by Surveyors' Technical Services.

On the following pages will be found a fairly typical example of a pro-forma report form which a surveyor might have to use when reporting for a prospective mortgagee. Since there is an almost infinite variety of report forms used in practice, it will be found that the questions asked vary considerably from case to case. However, there are certain questions which are common and which will therefore be generally encountered. These are:

(a) Description of the building and its locality, including age,
(b) detailing the accommodation and services provided,
(c) requesting information on the construction and condition,
(d) requiring dimensions or a plan for identification,
(e) requiring a valuation for mortgage purposes, and
(f) requiring a valuation for insurance purposes.

As regards questions aimed at obtaining a description of the building and locality, the reader will not normally have seen, or have intended to see, the property concerned and any comments, favourable or adverse, likely to assist the reader in forming a mental picture of the property would be helpful. The general age and character of the surrounding neighbourhood is crucial to the value of most types of property and is significant in considering whether or not the future trends in values will be satisfactory. If a house is modern but surrounded by much older and more run-down houses, this could be important. Such considerations will affect not only the valuation for mortgage purposes but also the percentage advance likely to be made and the term over which that advance may be recommended.

Measurement of the accommodation is often required, although generally given approximately on estate agents' particulars. The surveyor will then have to measure the rooms, a task which is not always as simple as it sounds since special treatment is needed for bays, alcoves, projecting fitted wardrobes and the like in order to convey accurately the room size and provide a fair comparison of room sizes between different properties where records are kept for valuation or statistical purposes. For such measurements in all types of property the Royal Institution of Chartered Surveyors and the Incorporated Society of Valuers & Auctioneers have jointly published a 'Code of Measuring Practice' and it is recommended that this Code be observed where possible.

The writers would normally measure rooms to include any fitted wardrobes and also chimney breasts but exclude bay windows and other small projections. Such dimensions have an advantage of being more likely to reflect the floor spans above as well as the room dimensions should a cross-check on floor spans be needed.

Concerning information on construction and condition, most of the questions and answers will be self-evident but a distinction needs to be drawn between minor defects which are commented upon, defects which might be subject to some condition on the advance, defects which are sufficiently serious to warrant a retention from the advance pending their remedy, and defects requiring further investigation before an advance can be confirmed.

The purpose of requiring a plan or the main plot dimensions is to confirm that the title plan corresponds with the property inspected. On occasion in the past attempts have been made, by fraud, to obtain a mortgage advance on the security of a property title and to encourage a surveyor to inspect quite a different property, perhaps by changing over house numbers or names. Occasionally it will be found that a house with a large garden or paddock will be inspected and that some, or most, of the grounds will be excluded from the title, being separately owned and rented under a tenancy or licence from an adjoining property owner. Obviously, if the property is mistakenly valued on the assumption that the garden or grounds are substantially larger than they really are, then this could be a very serious matter indeed.

A valuation for mortgage purposes should have regard to all matters ascertained by the surveyor during his inspection, including the condition of the property, and may be expressed as a 'forced sale' valuation, a 'current open-market value' figure or in some other way, depending upon the lending practice of the prospective mortgagee. Such a valuation may, or may not, be accompanied by an opinion from the surveyor on the recommended term over which a mortgage may be granted and the percentage level of advance appropriate, having regard to all the circumstances.

A valuation for insurance purposes will normally be required on a reinstatement basis, assuming a total loss and rebuilding of a comparable structure of similar type and appearance complying with the current Building Regulations. This figure will not have any direct relation to a valuation for mortgage purposes. It may be lower than the mortgage valuation if the building is modern and in any area of high land values. Frequently it will be higher, sometimes substantially higher, than the market value because reinstatement would require expenditure on a substantial scale in order to reproduce a building with high headrooms and other features no longer considered economic. Compliance with current Building Regulations or London Building Acts will have to be assumed and planning requirements taken into consideration. The whole question of valuations for insurance purposes could take chapters to discuss adequately and is beyond the scope of this volume but these are generally assessed on a rate of £/m^2 varying with type, age, use and situation of the property.

One further point regarding pro-forma reports for prospective mortgagees is that such reports may occasionally have to be issued in a provisional form leaving certain questions unanswered pending the results of further enquiries or investigations. Occasions when this may arise might be:

(a) If a structural fault is found or suspected, this requiring investigation and specialist reporting. In such a situation, a mortgage advance may be recommended subject to the mortgagor obtaining the necessary further advice or paying for the commissioning of a report from a building surveyor, consulting engineer or obtaining a laboratory test report. If the surveyor is not satisfied with the results of his own inspection and if he is required to return his report promptly, there would appear to be no reason at all why a provisional report conditional upon such further investigations or tests may not be immediately issued.

(b) If the mortgage security is affected by some other potential defect such as a possible planning scheme, road widening or other constraints which could affect the value, a provisional report might be issued subject to further investigations by solicitors being completed.

On the following pages we reproduce a typical example of a pro-forma 'Inspection and Valuation Report for Mortgage Purposes' and published by agreement with National Westminster Home Loans Limited. This particular form was introduced by the bank in 1982 for residential valuations.

In keeping with the generally accepted practice of major United Kingdom banks and building societies, the form is issued in triplicate with one copy for the bank as mortgagee, one copy for the borrower as mortgagor and one copy for the surveyor for retention on his file.

It will be noted that there are seven important notes for applicants (the borrowers) on the front page of the form, these being important exclusion clauses intended to limit the liability of the surveyor to the borrower. These clauses are very clear and unamibiguous; there should be no doubt in the mind of the borrower as to the nature of the inspection or the nature of the report. Nevertheless, these clauses would be subject to a test of reasonableness under the Unfair Contract Terms Act and the judgment of Mr Justice Park in *Yianni* v *Edwin Evans & Sons* (see Chapter 19).

It will be seen that the valuer must state that he has inspected the property both internally and externally on a particular date and that he has no interest directly or indirectly in the property being offered as security. Although the point is not specifically covered, the writers would feel that an inspection internally should include any accessible roof voids, especially having regard to the need to be able to say in answer to Question 5 (vi) whether or not there is any evidence of damp penetration or beetle infestation.

An 'interest in the property' is held to include:

(a) A relationship or friendship with the vendor,
(b) a surveyor or his firm being instructed to sell the property, and
(c) a relationship or friendship with the purchaser.

Clearly it is essential that a surveyor undertaking this work should have no connection whatsoever with the vendor or the purchaser so that advice given may be seen by all parties to be dispassionate. In the event of a surveyor's advice being called into question and a relationship found to have existed, this could seriously undermine the ability to defend his position, both in connection with a mortgage valuation or any other type of report.

In the past, pro-forma reports were prepared almost exclusively for mortgagees on a completely confidential basis with no liability assumed towards third parties. This situation has now changed for these three reasons:

Copy for Applicant(s)

Inspection and Valuation Report
For Mortgage Purposes To

National Westminster Home Loans Limited
PO Box No156, 12th Floor, National Westminster House, 10 Newhall Street, Birmingham B3 3EX

Full Address of Property _____

_____

Applicants Name(s) _____ **Ref No** _____

I personally inspected the property, both internally and externally, on _____
and hereby certify that I have no direct or indirect interest in the property.

Signature of Valuer _____   Qualifications: _____

Name of Firm _____

Address _____

_____

_____   Date _____

Notes for Applicants

1 This document is not a purchase valuation. A structural survey has not been carried out and the valuation figure given does not necessarily represent the value of the property to you.

2 The valuation has been obtained from a qualified valuer or firm of valuers for the sole purpose of enabling National Westminster Home Loans Limited (the Company) to consider making a mortgage advance. You cannot assume that, if no defects are mentioned in the report, any parts of the property are free from defect, or that other defects do not exist in addition to any specific defects mentioned.

3 This report is to the Company by its valuer(s) and neither the Company nor the valuer(s) gives any warranty, representation or assurance to you that the statements conclusions and opinions expressed or implied in this document are accurate or valid. Where the property is being purchased no warranty is given that the purchase price is reasonable.

4 The valuer(s) has/have made this report without any acceptance of responsibility on his/their part to you.

5 The contents of this report shall not be disclosed by you to any other third party but in the event of such disclosure no responsibility is accepted either by the Company or the valuer(s) to that third party.

6 If any repairs are indicated in the report you should satisfy yourself as to the cost of the work involved by means of contractors estimates. Any retention (shown in the report or any Offer of Advance) is made for mortgage purposes only and is not necessarily the actual cost of completing the work.

7 This report is not a substitute for an independent professional opinion and you may wish to obtain separate advice for your own purposes.

Freehold

1   Tenure   Leasehold _____ Years Unexpired   Ground Rent £ _____ per annum
Any tenancies or apparent tenancies should be reported.

2   **Description**

 (i) Age _____ If built at different times give age of   (a) main structure _____ (b) additions _____

 (ii) House/Bungalow/Flat (Converted or purpose built) in a _____ storied building

 (iii) Detached/Semi-detached/Terraced

 (iv) Number of (a) Bedrooms _____ (b) Reception Rooms _____

 (v) Is there a garage **Yes/No**   If not is there space available for a garage **Yes/No**

 (vi) Outbuildings — give description, construction and use: _____

 (vii) Area: (a)Main Buildings (& extensions) _____ (b) of plot _____

 (viii) If the property is used for any form of commercial activity please comment

  _____

 (ix) Special Features (if any)

  _____

3   **Construction**

 (i) External walls _____
  (give thickness, materials and whether cavity or solid where possible)

 (ii) Roof _____

 (iii) Dividing floors in the case of flats/maisonettes _____

 (iv) State if any way (a) non-traditional _____

     (b) prefabricated _____

 (v) As far as you were able to ascertain was High Alumina cement used in construction.

  _____

4   **Services (The Valuer is not required to carry out any tests)**

State system of:

 (i) drainage _____

 (ii) cold water supply _____

 (iii) hot water _____

 (iv) lighting _____

 (v) heating _____

5   Condition (The Valuer is not required to carry out a structural survey nor to inspect woodwork and other parts of the structure which are covered or inaccessible but should state if there are any factors which in his view make a closer inspection of these areas necessary)

(i) Main structure _____

(ii) Exterior decorations _____

(iii) Interior decorations _____

(iv) Boundary walls or fences _____

(v) Condition of electrical, plumbing and drainage installations (The Valuer should state if tests are considered to be necessary)
_____
_____

(vi) Is there any evidence of damp penetration or beetle infestation _____ _____
_____
_____

(vii) Essential repairs and estimated cost _____
_____
_____

6   Risks

Is the property likely to be affected by:

(i) Mining_____ (ii) Settlement _____

(iii) Subsidence_____ (iv) Ground Heave_____

(v) Landslip_____ (vi) Flooding_____

(vii) Other Perils_____

If there is evidence of the property having been affected in the past by any of the perils (i) to (vii) in this question please comment and state if further investigation is necessary
_____
_____

7   Roads

(i) Are the roads onto which the property fronts adopted_____

if not:

(ii) Conditions (made up to adoption standard/partly made/unmade)_____

(iii) Estimated liability for making up £_____

(iv) Has a bond or deposit been given to the Local Authority _____

8   Situation and Amenities

(i) Situation and locality_____
_____

(ii) Suitability of property to district _____
_____

(iii) Are there any adverse features which might limit marketability _____
_____
_____

9   Property in course of Construction

(i) Is construction under the National House Builders' Registration Scheme _____

(ii) Open Market Value of Property for mortgage purposes

(a) When completed according to plans and specifications £ _____

(b) When completed as (a) and roads made £ _____

(c) At present stage of construction £ _____

10   Existing Property – Open Market Value for mortgage purposes with Vacant Possession

(i) In present condition £ _____

(ii) When repairs in question 5 (vii) completed £ _____

11   Buildings Insurance Recommended
(Estimated present day reinstatement costs to include the cost of demolition and fees)

Main buildings £ _____ Outbuildings £ _____

Please refer to any unusual insurance hazards which are additional to any you have indicated in question 6

_____

_____

12   General

(i) Do you recommend the property as a suitable security for a mortgage advance

_____

(ii) Should the estimated cost of any essential repairs mentioned in 5(vii) be the subject of a retention from the amount of the advance or a condition of the advance

_____

(iii) Should any special conditions be imposed _____

_____

(iv) Is a further inspection necessary _____

13   Indicate whether there are any easements or Rights of Way in favour of other parties which affect the property _____

_____

14   The Valuer should supply a Block Plan for identification purposes in the Company's usual form for use by the Company's Solicitor in checking title.

The Valuer should send this copy of the Report, and the Block Plan to:

National Westminster Home Loans Limited
PO Box 156
12th Floor
National Westminster House
10 Newhall Street
Birmingham
B3 3EX

(a) The introduction of a service of providing pro-forma reports for prospective purchasers,
(b) the policy of the major lending institutions of releasing a copy of their reports to the borrowers, and
(c) the legal developments in recent case law which have called into question the extent to which a surveyor to a prospective mortgagee may limit his liability towards the prospective mortgagor. (See Chapter 19).

Whatever the future may hold in the form of new legal precedents or legislation, it is clear that the traditional confidential surveyor's report prepared without responsibility towards any third party is no longer viable. There are reasons to regret this, but the reasons why this situation has come about are entirely logical. Not the least is the fact that most lending institutions were in the practice of collecting a survey fee from the borrower with the application for the loan and borrowers felt aggrieved that they were not permitted to see the reports for which they themselves had paid.

Certain basic questions raised by these changes in climate are:

(a) Who should be regarded as qualified to prepare pro-forma reports?
(b) What minimum standard of inspection should be considered necessary?
(c) How much detail should be included in the completed report?

In the case of the RICS' 'House Buyer's Report and Valuation' this may only be prepared by a chartered surveyor, and the qualifications and experience of such a surveyor should be the same as those which are required for structural survey reports of the traditional type. Other professional bodies in this field also promote a service for their members along similar lines.

The standard of inspection for the RICS' scheme will generally be the same as for a normal structural survey but subject to certain specific limitations laid down in the conditions of engagement. The detail to be included in the completed report will be sufficient:

(a) To provide an answer to all the clauses, and
(b) to inform the client of all matters relevant to the value and purchase of the property which have been discovered.

In the case of reports for prospective mortgagees, it is suggested that the qualifications required must include:

(a) Adequate knowledge of building construction and building defects in the locality concerned, and
(b) adequate knowledge of property values of the type involved in the locality.

It would be inappropriate now, as in the past, to assume that unsupervised building society and other institutional inspections may be undertaken by the less experienced or younger staff in a surveying practice who would not be considered competent to prepare structural reports. The highest standards of professional competence are required for all reports, whether pro-forma reports or otherwise, and great care has to be exercised in all surveying practices to ensure that the routine pro-forma report work reaches a suitable standard.

Although the fees for a pro-forma report may be lower than for other work, this will not absolve a surveying practice from liability. If there is any question that such work be uneconomic then it is suggested that, in view of the current legal position it is better to decline instructions rather than to attempt an over-hasty inspection. It is to be hoped, however, that most practitioners will not decline instructions on these grounds since the hallmark of any learned profession is a willingness to provide a service to clients and to regard monetary gain as of secondary importance to the maintenance of that service.

The question as to the amount of detail which should be included in a pro-forma report is difficult to answer since the intention of using a pro-forma report system is to achieve economy for a client, bank manager or building society manager who will not wish to plough through many pages of descriptive text but wishes to have his attention drawn to the salient matters.

The authors recall the time when a student was accompanying an experienced surveyor accustomed to undertaking a large number of building society inspections and who was a master of the brief but salient comment. On one occasion, the main survey having been completed, this surveyor proceeded into the garden of the house to find a boundary wall about a metre high and ten metres long leaning severely towards the adjoining curtilage. The wall was built in 112-mm half-brick thickness with insufficient piers, using a black ash mortar and was clearly on the point of collapse. The surveyor carefully placed his foot against the wall to see if he could induce any movement in it and pressed slightly. The whole wall then proceeded to collapse on to the flower beds in the adjoining garden.

The surveyor was not ruffled by the course of events. He carefully looked about him to see whether or not the incident had been observed (which fortunately it had not) and wrote 'Rebuild west side garden wall' on his pad, before beating a rapid retreat to his car.

On another occasion the inspection was being made of an old and dilapidated cottage in an isolated country location. The report was for a bank who were going to lend on the basis of the borrower's proposals for restoration and renovation of the property. In his report the surveyor began, 'I can, perhaps, convey the flavour of the property best by saying that it was not necessary for me to borrow a key in order to inspect it because there are, at present, no doors'.

Chapter 12

Reports on non-residential buildings

We're taking a full repairing and insuring lease, but I'm sure that's all right. They are in rather a hurry so I have agreed to sign the contract this afternoon. I thought that you could just give it the once-over and 'phone me back before lunch. Incidentally, he says that the flat roof has been leaking but it's all right now.
Potential client's telephone instruction

The basic principles described for surveying and reporting upon dwelling-houses also apply to other types of building, the main distinctions being those of size and usage, although a larger industrial building may, if modern with open headroom and clear spans, be easier to inspect than a small house.

The larger older buildings will often require a lengthy inspection, perhaps lasting several days and the surveyor will need to ensure before undertaking such work that he can reserve sufficient time in his diary to complete the inspection to the necessary standard.

A special consideration arising in the case of the larger commercial buildings is the importance of concealed structural elements. Before a client can be advised on the construction of such a building and before any structural alterations can be contemplated, it is essential to determine the structural strength of the building, including the manner in which the loads are carried and transferred to the subsoil.

Where concealed structural elements are involved, the surveyor will have to undertake an initial inspection and then he may have to proceed with a process of research and detection in order to discover the facts. Such research will normally include searching for any existing architects' or engineers' drawings (in one case a most useful set of such drawings were found in a wall cavity), visiting the local authority offices or district surveyor to see if any drawings are available for inspection, and even perhaps opening up the building in question to confirm the position.

If the building has an engraved plaque or stone with the name of the original architect indicated, then the first step would be to see if he or his firm can be traced. The present occupiers or owners of the building may have been there since completion in which event they should know the identity of the original designer and perhaps even own a set of plans. Even if not the original owners, it is possible that plans, or information on the location of plans, may have been passed on to them by their predecessors.

If the present owners are a large company, contact with a long-serving member of the staff may help since such an individual may provide useful information if he can recall the building during construction. For example, the names of builders, architects, manufacturers of fittings, sub-contractors and other vital information.

Working drawings for steelwork may be obtained if the identity of the original steelwork sub-contractor can be discovered, since such contractors often keep records going back for many years. A large number of steel-framed buildings were erected between 1925 and 1949 where such a sub-contractor, if located, may be the only likely source of information.

Having exhausted these sources of original drawings, the surveyor could then go on to see if information is available from the local authority. Local authorities are now much more reluctant than in the past to permit an examination of their records. Such information as is available is often microfilmed and during that process, many older plans and documents may have been destroyed.

From the local authority point of view, there are two problems affecting a general inspection of their files and records.

First, it is considered that in order to avoid a breach of copyright no copying of deposited plans of any kind should be permitted without the original owner's or architect's consent. In order to take sketches from a deposited plan one has, on occasion, been required first to obtain a signed authority from the original author of the drawing. In many cases obtaining any such authority is impossible, particularly in the case of older buildings.

Secondly, local authorities are becoming increasingly subject to litigation over building defects and will often fear that attempts to examine closely approved plans may result in legal actions should any errors or omissions be found. A general reluctance to permit any inspections at all has, as a consequence, arisen with local authorities in some areas.

A surveyor who is a member of the local authority staff will therefore be in an advantageous position in this respect when investigating and reporting for his authority upon buildings in his area.

Having thus obtained all available information in the way of plans and working drawings and having carried out an initial survey of the building concerned, the surveyor will then have to consider the extent to which the building ought to be opened up in order to complete his report.

By this stage, it will have been possible for the surveyor to have formed a view of the superficial condition of the building and services, also the extent to which it complies with current standards for means of escape in case of fire, fire precautions, the Factories Acts, the Offices, Shops and Railway Premises Act and other legislation so that it may be that a preliminary report could be prepared for the client on this basis. If so, it is essential that the client be warned that no opening up of the structure has been undertaken and that the condition of the main structural elements has not been confirmed.

Post-War office blocks and other structures constructed in reinforced concrete present a particular problem and considerable care needs to be exercised if the structure has to be disturbed. Reinforced columns and beams cannot be opened up easily or exposed to see how reinforcement is arranged and such reinforcement is essential to the strength of the structure. If pre-stressed beams are suspected, it is most necessary that these should not be cut into or otherwise disturbed. In such circumstances, a surveyor should measure the overall sizes and spacings of the columns, the dimensions and spans of the beams and then undertake a surface inspection for evidence of chemical deterioration and like problems. Beyond this he would be bound to refer his client to a specialist consulting engineer so that any core samples may be taken or special tests made to detect the presence of high-alumina cement, chlorides, sulphate attack or other such faults having regard to the known facts.

Steel-framed office buildings and other structures dating from the inter-War and post-War years may be opened up more easily than reinforced concrete structures, and the quality of the original construction and the condition of the steelwork may then be judged. It is arguable as to how far one should take such investigations but if the surveyor can confirm sizes, spacings and spans of principle members, together with the loads imposed, it should be possible for him to obtain a check by calculation from a structural engineer and thus reassure his client that the steel-framing is technically adequate and, where seen, in satisfactory condition and protected against corrosion.

It is clearly essential for the client to be advised whether or not a commercial or industrial building will satisfy the Fire Precautions Act 1971 and the Fire Precautions Act 1971 (Modifications) Regulations 1976, together with any subsequent or additional legislation having regard not only to the results of the building inspection but also to the specific needs of the particular client and the use he proposes to make of that building. The provision and maintenance of fire precautions and means of escape form an increasingly important part in the day-to-day management of commercial and industrial buildings. If a need for certification under the Act arises, whether from a proposed change of use, structural alteration or other reason, the client will need to know in advance whether or not difficulties in obtaining certification could arise and exceptional costs occur in adapting the building to meet certification standards.

It is necessary to consider whether or not exceptional energy costs are involved in lighting and heating the structure under review, and the surveyor should then inspect the existing space heating appliances. Generally, a specialist report from a heating engineer should be recommended and some investigation then carried out into past energy costs. In most cases, the vendor or existing lessee of the building will be able to provide details of accounts for oil, gas, electricity and other energy inputs into the building and these may be used as guidance to current cost levels as the building is presently used. Care should be exercised when assuming that current energy cost levels will apply to that building in the future, and if the client's needs change then a change in energy costs may also arise.

At this point the surveyor may have to advise his client on the overall condition of energy-intensive services and whether or not they are efficient, or if the type of energy in use might be changed for a more economic type (for example, gas space heating instead of oil, assuming this can be made available). One should not assume that current relative differentials in energy costs will always be maintained. Energy which is proportionately cheap now need not always remain so and the capital cost of a change-over may not be economic if the differential in cost becomes less advantageous in the future.

As far as energy costs are concerned, the overall thermal efficiency of a building is most significant and should be considered by the surveyor. An industrial structure with a high eaves level, ideal for loading bays and overhead gantries, will be very wasteful of heat as compared with a similar floor space with low headroom. If there is no need for a high ceiling, then the provision of a suspended ceiling could be recommended to reduce space heating costs. This particularly applicable to a single-storey structure or the top floor of a multi-storey structure when, in addition, insulation over the suspended ceiling may be suggested.

When considering the services, thought should be given to the client's proposed use of the building and the numbers and sexes of staff likely to be employed therein. Recommendations may then need to be made over the suitable provision of lavatory and washing facilities. The Offices, Shops and Railway Premises Act 1963 demands sufficient and suitable lighting, a reasonable temperature in every room (15°C), sufficient washing facilities, a supply of hot and cold water, and adequate ventilation. It also covers a variety of other environmental needs. In so far as the premises inspected may fall short of the standards required, the necessary comments and recommendations should then be made.

Older commercial and industrial buildings are generally found to have been constructed in a great variety of ways. There is often a mixture of cast-iron, wrought-iron or steel columns and beams forming the basic structure, and load-bearing brick or stone walls to the exterior and around stairwells and shafts, with timber or solid floors of various types spanning between the main elements. The solid floors may be constructed using obsolete methods, often in the form of *in situ* poured concrete construction or part pre-cast and part *in situ* construction. Research into the various forms of construction which are found is a most interesting area of professional activity, particularly in view of the great variety of construction methods likely to be found.

Floors in older commercial and industrial buildings are often of filler-joist construction with a layout of steel or iron beams and an infilling of *in situ* concrete, the beams being either of solid or open-webbed types. In those structures erected before the advent of modern Portland cement concretes, it is likely that a lime mortar could have been used to bind together a clinker, brick or stone aggregate. Some caution is required in assessing the strength of these older types of lime mortar solid slabs since they will be most unlikely to have a strength comparable to the modern Portland cement concrete slabs. This may be significant if an older structure is to be used for different or heavier machinery.

Opening up older structures may be necessary to determine the sizes of the beams and columns, the thicknesses and strengths of load-bearing walls and the nature of the floor construction, including the effective spans of the flexural members and their manner of bearing. Finally, having traced the main forces and loads through the structure down to ground level, a final confirmation of the size, type and adequacy of foundations used may be needed having regard to both present loadings and any different future loadings which may apply. Samples would then be taken of concrete, bricks, mortar, steel, wrought iron, cast iron and timber to confirm the condition of such elements, and these can be sent to specialist laboratories for analysis with a view to confirming the strength of the structure.

In addition to confirming the construction of the building and the nature of the materials used, it is also necessary to confirm the condition of framing since this will be relevant to the strength. Obviously, if an engineer is to be asked to check the suitability of a building by calculation on the basis of the information given as to the loads, spans and materials used, any such calculations will be valid only if the main structural elements are in good condition. Samples taken may or may not be representative of the structure as a whole.

In many old buildings, ironwork or steelwork is buried in the walls in a manner which provides only limited protection from the elements and corrosion may be severe, especially on the weather sides or at points where leaking gutters or other sources of dampness have subjected the walls to constant saturation over many years. The older concretes, consisting of breeze and lime mortars, contain a high sulphate content which will attack adjoining ferrous metals. Roof leaks may cause deterioration to steel roof joists and the upper parts of a steel- or iron-framed structure. Steel columns set into basement construction, or steel feet set into foundations or footings, may be subject to considerable corrosion over the years from dampness inherent in such areas where tanking may have been omitted or become porous. Silver sand for rendering or in a concrete mix and containing a high proportion of china clay fragments and mica is particularly suspect. The effect of weathering is to wash out the china clay content causing the mica to flake away, and the surface of the render or concrete then becoming very porous causes the reinforcement under to rust and crack or even throw off the cover. Readers are recommended to study *BRE Digests* 263, 264 and 265 which deal with the protection, diagnosis, and assessment of deterioration and repair of reinforcing steel in concrete.

In connection with concrete construction there have in recent times been a number of reported failures of concrete elements due to chemical attack or chemical deterioration. In April 1975 the Building Research Establishment published a current paper titled 'High-alumina Cement Concrete in Buildings' (CP 34/75), in response to the collapse of two roof beams in a school in Stepney in February 1974.

The results of investigations published in the 1975 paper indicated that most high-alumina cement (HAC) concrete pre-stressed beams used in buildings more than a few years old is highly converted and chemically changed or likely to become so. The strength of highly converted concrete is substantially reduced.

A considerable margin of safety is, however, provided for in most pre-cast concrete beamwork and slabwork. Proof loading tests in the field and experience in practice resulted in the BRE proposing that for all practical purposes the risk of failure of pre-cast beams or slabs using HAC concrete was very small for spans of up to 5 m.

Accordingly, if HAC concrete is suspected to have been used in a building with spans of 5 m or more, investigation should be made to:

(a) Confirm if in fact HAC was used, and
(b) determine whether the loss of strength due to chemical conversion may be significant for the strength of the structure.

Such an investigation could be undertaken using a simple pull-out test to assess the strength of *in situ* concrete, as suggested in a Building Research Establishment Current Paper published in June 1977 (CP 25/77).

There are several other ways in which concretes can suffer chemical attack or deterioration which could necessitate advising special tests. A concrete mix can also be less than ideal, or variable, and thereby causing a loss of strength. Good building practice is not always observed on site, and concrete foundations laid in wet trenches or mixes which are incorrectly or unevenly proportioned can frequently be traced.

In the event of soil conditions indicating a danger of sulphate attack, special sulphate-resistant concretes should have been used but this is not always so and is generally unlikely in the foundations to older buildings. Deterioration is also possible if the concrete is in contact with other material which contains a high sulphate content, such as certain types of clinker breeze. Chemical attack from chlorides is also possible and occasionally encountered during a survey.

In addition to the possibility of chemical attack or chemical deterioration of the concrete itself, a possibility also arises of corrosion in the reinforcement. Both types of deterioration will be more likely and rapid in damp conditions, often being found to occur together for similar reasons. The amount of protection given to reinforcement in the past was frequently insufficient. Once the concrete cover protection given to the reinforcement begins to crack and soften, then wind and weather can begin to attack the reinforcement itself. Swimming pool roofs are a known problem area as they often have large spans of pre-cast concrete construction situated in a warm, humid atmosphere, and subject to high levels of condensation and chemical attack from chlorine. They may also become subject to weather penetration at defective jointing or on flat roof surfaces.

Before 1977 some concrete work incorporated calcium chloride as an additive to speed up the hardening process. This material absorbs water and forms a corrosive agent which rusts reinforcement bars and forces off the encasement; the combination of spalling encasement and rusting reinforcement may be highly damaging. Testing similar to that advised for HAC is required to confirm the presence or otherwise of this additive.

Occasionally it may be found that woodwool slabs have been used as permanent formwork to reinforced concrete, and this is a potential threat to the strength of the concrete because alkalis and sulphates which may be leached out of the slabs can react with the concrete; such reactions may be especially severe if HAC is present and in damp conditions. In addition, any permanent formwork may hide voids where the concrete has failed adequately to encase the reinforcement because of insufficient vibration during casting.

Chapter 13

Reports on flats and other dwellings in multiple occupation

We hear every sound they make in the flat above; and some sounds they don't make as well.
Ground floor tenant

Frequently a surveyor's report is required on a flat, apartment, maisonette or other unit of accommodation which is part of a building divided laterally as well as vertically. Such property will normally be leasehold, this factor alone requiring special treatment (see Chapter 16). Very occasionally a 'freehold' flat or apartment will be encountered in England and Wales but the equivalent of a 'freehold' will be the rule rather than the exception in Scotland where different law applies.

If a freehold flat or apartment in England or Wales is to be surveyed, the client should be advised to discuss the implications of tenure with his solicitor. There are certain technical objections to 'flying freeholds' under English law as it now stands, because of the difficulty of enforcing positive covenants against the subsequent purchaser of a flying freehold who has not himself had any direct contractual relationship with the adjoining owners. In certain circumstances under English law, action to enforce covenants of repair and support can be more difficult between adjoining freeholders following subsequent transfers of title. This is an over-simplification of a complex problem which has been solved in England and Wales by the practice of granting long leases on flats and apartments rather than selling with a freehold interest. Commonly, 99-year, 125-year or 999-year terms will be encountered, the latter being an over-optimistic figure to apply to the life expectancy of the structure, especially in the case of some post-War speculative flat developments which will be fortunate if they see the end of a 99-year term!

There are two important points affecting flats and apartments which have significance:

(1) The design of the building with particular reference to sound-proofing, and
(2) the means of escape in case of fire.

These are of profound importance to the client if he is to enjoy quiet occupation and physical safety. The survey report should always set out to cover sound-proofing as far as possible and if a noise problem seems likely, the client should be warned.

An elderly couple retiring to a ground floor apartment and hoping to end their days in tranquility will be bitterly disappointed to find that every sound made by a young family in the apartment above can be heard, perhaps late into the night.

Fireproofing between units and the means of escape in the event of fire are vital matters. The standards to apply would be those of the current Building Regulations and also those which would be required before a fire safety certificate would be issued for a new building. If an existing building should fail to meet such standards, the client must be warned and recommendations made. Often, it would be impossible to meet modern requirements in an older building without the full co-operation of all flat owners, and this would be unrealistic. In such circumstances, all the surveyor can do is advise and warn and then leave it to the client to decide whether or not to proceed with the purchase.

Types of flat

In large conurbations, especially in London, there is a ready market for converted flats which began life as conventional houses or other structures and which have been subsequently sub-divided, often to a poor speculative standard. Caution must be exercised in reporting upon such property as there are several potential pitfalls, both physical and legal involved, about which the client will need to be advised.

Generally speaking, in England and Wales there are three main types of flat or apartment development:

1. Those in the form of simple low-rise structures, either purpose-built or converted, consisting mainly of two-storey buildings similar in appearance to two-storey dwellinghouses where separate units of accommodation are provided on each floor and where each unit has its own exterior entrance door. There may be a shared front porch or perhaps one doorway in the front elevation and one at the side. Such accommodation, in estate agents' parlance, is generally referred to as 'a pair of maisonettes' (in the London area at any event). Generally, garden areas are also divided and each unit, together with its garden is held under a separate long lease. Commonly each leaseholder is liable for the interior repair and decoration of his or her own unit. For carrying out repairs to the exterior or structure of the building, a variety of arrangements may be provided, these depending upon the date of the leases since conveyancing fashions have changed over the years, although generally speaking such arrangements fall into one of two broad types. Each lessee may be liable for his or her own part of the building, having no responsibility for any other part. A lateral division of responsibility is provided for the internal structure, this generally being the base of the first floor joists with a proviso that the staircase to the upper unit is included with that property. Alternatively, lessees may be jointly responsible for repairs to the foundations, exterior, structure and roof so that in the event of a repair being required, agreement would have to be reached on the need for and the cost of the repair. Each party would then contribute towards the cost in proportion to their holding.
2. Next is the modern purpose-built block of apartments, generally of post-War origin and with communal grounds, staircases and entrance halls. Occasionally services such as porterage, hot water and central heating are also provided on a communal basis. In such cases there will generally be a liability for each lessee to

maintain the interior of his or her own unit and contribute a service charge for the maintenance and redecoration of the exterior, upkeep of the structure and roof and towards the communal services. Responsibility for arranging the communal services may vest in the freeholder who will then collect a ground rent, service charge and (usually) the insurance premiums due from the lessees, and arrange for the necessary periodic redecoration and upkeep of the exterior and structure of the building, its grounds and the communal services.

Alternatively, the responsibility for maintenance could vest in a separate body which may be a residents' association with a chairman, secretary and treasurer, being subject to rules of procedure and with published annual accounts. Such an association will balance accounts by levying on members a service charge which is sufficient to cover the outgoings. The effectiveness of a residents' association will depend not so much upon the specific rules governing proceedings as on the quality of the residents who may be persuaded (or more usually cajoled) into serving. A well-run residents' association which maintains carefully the communal areas and grounds and ensures a high standard of maintenance and decoration of the buildings is the ideal. Occasionally, indifference on the part of residents or clashes of personality within an association will produce an unhappy effect, some members being anxious to maintain high standards and others clamouring to keep down costs. The standard of maintenance will then suffer considerably.

3. The third type is the older mansion block in larger cities, originally built for letting by private landowners or institutions and having been subsequently subject to 'break-up' operations involving the selling-off of individual units on long leases. Often, original tenants remain in such blocks so that a mixture of tenures is present, some residents having bought long leases and others occupying flats under regulated tenancies protected by the Rent Acts. In such cases either a freeholder will be liable for exterior and structural repairs with a right to recover service charges, or the freeholder would have created a residents' association of some type and be in the process of devolving responsibility for such matters.

Service charges

In preparing a report on a flat or apartment held on a long lease, the surveyor should first read the lease (see Chapter 16), and if the lease provides for a service charge to be levied, he will wish to look with particular interest at the supporting provisions. There are four main requirements for a reasonable service charge provision, these being:

(1) The period of payment should be given, i.e. whether quarterly, half-yearly, yearly or on some other basis.
(2) The items of maintenance, repair, decoration and upkeep, together with all services intended to be covered, should be set out clearly.
(3) The manner in which service charges are apportioned between separate units should be fixed. Probably a number of identical flats in a block will pay the same amounts but flats of different sizes may need to be differentiated by, for example, rateable value, and other modifications may be needed in the interests of fairness (e.g. the ground floor lessees should not pay for lift costs).

(4) The manner in which the maintenance accounts are to be kept and certified should be made clear.

Commonly, where a service charge is provided for in a lease, the freeholder will wish to ensure that all possible liability is devolved upon the lessees and that no residual liability for extraordinary items of expenditure remains with the freeholder. As a consequence, those parts of the provisions dealing with requirement (2) above will often be very widely drawn and embrace all conceivable heads of expenditure. There may even be provision for additional matters to be added in the future.

There is a long history of actions in law and statutory intervention as a result of disputes which may arise between lessors or residents' associations on the one hand and individual lessees on the other over the reasonableness or otherwise of service charges. In *Finchbourne Ltd.* v *Rodrigues* ([1976] 3 All ER 581) the Court of Appeal held that a term should be implied into a service charge clause that costs recoverable by the lessor from the lessee should be 'fair and reasonable' in the circumstances, and also that where the lessor and the managing agents for the property are effectively one and the same, the managing agents will not be sufficiently independent to certify the service charge under a provision for certification.

Section 91a of the Housing Finance Act 1972 was introduced in an attempt to assist lessees and was subsequently modified by Section 124 of theHousing Act 1974 and Schedule 19 to the Housing Act 1980. This provision provides that a service charge shall only be recoverable from the tenant of a flat for the provision of chargeable items to a reasonable standard in line with *Finchbourne Ltd.* v *Rodrigues* (supra), and also that 'to the extent that the liability incurred or the amount defrayed by the landlord in respect of the provision of chargeable items is reasonable'. Provision is also made that in building works costing more than £250, at least two estimates must be obtained by the landlord, one at least of which is from a contractor wholly unconnected with the landlord or the managing agent. In respect of expenditure exceeding £2000, there is a procedure for the landlord to consult with the tenants except in cases of emergency and only then to obtain estimates for the work.

Section 90 of the Housing Finance Act 1972 is designed to enable tenants to obtain information about service charges even if their leases conferred no such right. It may well be that in order to complete his report that surveyor will need to inspect the management accounts. It is unusual to find that a prospective purchaser or his surveyor or even his solicitor have a statutory right to do this but the vendor of a long lease will have such a right, either by virtue of the provisions of the lease itself or by virtue of Section 90. If the surveyor is denied access to this information by the vendor, or if it is suggested that up-to-date accounts are not available, then this must raise serious doubts about the present state of management accounts and the matter may need to be referred back to the client's solicitors for further instructions.

If an inspection of the management accounts has not been possible, the surveyor will be unable to express any view on the reasonableness (or otherwise) of the service charge currently payable, or the likelihood that a substantial future increase in the service charge may be possible because of past under-provision for some items.

When an inspection can be made this should preferably be of accounts over a period of more than one year. Ideally, the last three years' accounts should be scrutinised. In order to forecast future trends, these accounts should be considered in the light of the need to maintain some reserve for periodic decorations, often necessary at three-yearly intervals, this causing a sudden leap in the service charge for one year if an adequate float has not been built up in the two preceeding years. Similarly, special attention should be given to checking the provision for capital replacement of items such as lifts and fixed plant which may have a well-defined life-span. If there are fixed-term contracts for cleaning or gardening and if these are about to expire, a large increase in such costs may arise if an alternative contractor has to be found.

An inspection of a single flat in a block of flats for a prospective purchaser must, of necessity, include not only the flat in question but also the building as a whole since a sudden large increase in the service charge could arise in respect of a defect in the building quite unconnected with the flat under review. In our experience this will often arise in the case of major structural defects to foundations and roofs. It is essential for the client to realise that he may be proportionally liable for this type of defect even if it is not related to the flat he proposes to buy. Similarly, a prospective mortgagee will wish to know about such matters and will expect the building as a whole to have been inspected by the surveyor in addition to the specific flat used as security.

The RICS Practice Note, 'Structural Surveys of Residential Property' states that 'Particularly onerous repair liabilities may exist quite independently of the subject property, such as where a lease or agreement imposes a liability to pay a proportion of the total estate repair costs', and 'To advise fully the surveyor must endeavour to establish the extent and nature of the repairing liabilities under the lease, the client's potential responsibility for executing repairs and also his liability to pay for repairs executed by others'.

If a block of flats suffers from a serious structural defect, the purchase of one of the flats, even where unrelated to the defective area, may be unwise unless all the implications are fully understood. It may be, for example, that a foundation defect exists and that this should be remedied by the National House-Building Council Certificate procedure, or works may be covered partly by the subsidence and landslip provisions in the building's policy. In such a situation, there may be a number of parties involved in a liability dispute including the lessees and their solicitors, the original contractor, the NHBC, the building insurers (possibly under individual policies on the flats) and the local authority who passed the work originally. There may also be a residents' association, and an owner of adjoining trees, the roots of which could have contributed to the defect.

All surveyors will be aware of problems associated with flat roofs, especially those of poor construction dating from the nineteen-fifites and nineteen-sixties. Many such roofs were used on blocks of owner-occupied flats and the roof coverings are now nearing the end of their useful life span. Renewal will often be a question not merely of stripping off existing built-up felt or asphalt and re-surfacing. Frequently it will also involve repairs to the decking and supporting construction involving major expenditure on the works and on protection of property and occupiers for the duration of the works.

A major item of expenditure such as renewal of a flat roof covering, presents particular problems to a residents' association or freeholder collecting periodic service charges. Ideally, a contingency fund should have accumulated to pay for this work but this will rarely be found to be so. It may be that the nature of the remedial works required will have to be agreed (itself not an easy matter) and then estimates obtained and contractors instructed on the basis that a sudden large increase in the service charge will have to be made to cover this item.

The chairman of a residents' association in such a situation will feel like the messengers of old who were praised if they brought good news but put to death if the news was bad. The owner of a flat in such a block may actually decide to sell and move just to avoid problems of this type which may be approaching and the purchaser will need to be warned about such circumstances.

Tenure in Scotland compared

In Scotland a different law applies to the sale of flats and apartments. Scottish law is based upon the original feudal tenure modified by statutes, with all rights to land originally derived from the Crown. Buildings and landed property are classified as 'heritable property' and being either 'corporeal' if land or buildings, or 'incorporeal' if merely rights of land or buildings. In these respects the system is similar to that operating in England and Wales. One difference is that a system of charges may be levied, similar to rent charges on freehold land in England and Wales, and termed 'feu duty', normally running in perpetuity with the land, the duty being paid by the owner or 'vassal' to the person or 'superior' who owns the right to receive the duty. Occasionally a superior may have a right to acquire the vassal's interest by virtue of a clause in the title which, in effect, gives him an option to purchase, generally at a price equal to any other offer which the vassal may have received for his interest. Such a right to pre-emption normally arises only on the first sale of the vassal's interest and not subsequently. A similar situation arises in England where an original freeholder may impose restrictive covenants on subsequent purchasers of the freehold interest, although a right to buy back the freehold is less usual.

A wide range of feuing conditions may be imposed on vassals by the superior and may generally be enforced, not only by the superior but also by other vassals who hold parts of the same original holding. This is similar in many respects to the estate covenants which may be imposed by freeholders of estates in England and Wales whereby a series of mutually enforceable covenants may apply to the estate as a whole. This is a particular feature of some residential developments built between the Wars in the higher price ranges where obligations may arise to maintain private roads, open spaces and the like with limitations on the type of alterations or uses permitted.

In English law there must be privity of contract between two parties before action may be taken, but in Scotland a vassal or 'feuer' may take action against another without there being privity of contract between them provided that the aggrieved feuer is personally affected by the breach of feuing conditions and that the superior has not himself permitted the breach specifically.

Against this background of mutually enforceable feuing conditions, which arise irrespective of whether or not there is a direct contractual relationship, it has been possible for property in Scotland to be sold as 'flying freeholds' subject to the feu duty and to the conditions. Scottish law also permits servitudes (the equivalent of English easements) in the form of rights of support, protection and light.

During the course of inspecting a flat or apartment in Scotland the surveyor will need to familiarise himself with the feuing conditions set out in the title and consider whether or not these are adequate and suitable. In so far as potential liabilities may arise for the maintenance and repair of either the structure as a whole or other parts of the building separate from the specific flat concerned, these may need to be investigated and the position explained to the client.

Conversions

Apart from general distinctions of tenure and various types of flats and apartments which may be encountered, there are two broad divisions of type which need to be identified. These are (a) those flats or apartments which have been purpose-built, and (b) those which are conversions. The surveyor should make a particular point of confirming in all cases which of these two situations applies since this is relevant to the advice which may be given and may be significant to a prospective mortgagee or client proposing to raise a mortgage. Institutional lending policy on converted flats is often very different from that applied to purpose-built flats.

In most cases the converted flat will be fairly obvious. An original Victorian or Edwardian villa in a city suburb may have two entrance doors in the porchway and a plasterboard and stud partition wall dividing the original hall. The nature of the original house and the extent of the conversion works will be self-evident in such circumstances.

Faced with such a conversion, the surveyor should see if the staircase to the upper flat has the necessary degree of fire-resistance and that the partitioning and undersides of the staircase are suitably fire-resistant, at least up to the standards of the current Building Regulations or London Building Acts. Similarly, if the upper floors are simply suspended timber floors, these will have required additional fireproofing to meet regulations. The reason is to ensure that a fire in the lower flat will not spread rapidly to the flat above and that in the event of fire, the occupants of the flat above may have a protected means of escape down the stairs. Over two storeys, the requirements become more stringent and alternative escape routes in the event of fire are necessary.

Many converted flats have never been subject to any scrutiny by a building control officer or district surveyor. The reason for this is that they have been 'converted by stealth'. Probably a house was first used as accommodation for two families. Later, various modifications were perhaps undertaken, culminating in sub-division of the accommodation and splitting of the services. If the change of use to two units of accommodation is of long-standing and if internal alterations are purely internal, no reference to the local planning department may have been made. Finally, the tenants leave and the owner, much impressed by the current level of property values for converted flats, will decide to sell the house in two parts by creating two separate leases. At this stage, one of the purchasers commissions a survey and finds that there are wide-scale breaches of the Building Regulations or the London Building Acts. If the fireproofing between units is affected, the building may actually be dangerous. The surveyor will often find partitions of plywood or hardboard masquerading as plasterboard. Often various defects such as rising damp, decay to timbers, defective ceilings and roof problems will have been dealt with in a highly unsatisfactory manner and a variety of defects may have been plastered and decorated over.

Occasionally it may be difficult to confirm initially whether or not a particular property has been converted, and some enquiries regarding its history or exposure of the structure could reveal the truth.

Chapter 14

Reports on new buildings

Where there is a contract to build and sell a house or to sell a partly-built house when it is completed, the law makes a three-fold implication: that the builder will do his work in a good and workmanlike manner; that he will supply good and proper materials; and that it will be reasonably fit for human habitation.
Hancock v *B. W. Brazier (Anerley) Ltd. (1966)*

National House-Building Scheme

The National House-Building Council's *Registered House-Builders' Handbook* is essential reading for any surveyor dealing with new houses and flats. This is a first class and easily understood guide to NHBC standards which covers all the main topics likely to arise and is written in a simple straightforward manner.

Should any new residential property fail to meet the standards laid down by the NHBC then this should be commented upon in the report. Even where a NHBC inspector has passed the building minor technical breaches of the *Handbook* requirements will often be found as, due to insufficient staffing, the NHBC cannot inspect every part of every new house during every phase of construction.

The procedures for taking instructions and carrying out the inspection, also the preparation of the report, will generally be the same as those for older buildings, but certain special considerations apply to new property.

First, the client will have a contract with the builder or developer and will need to know whether or not the requirements of that contract have been fulfilled. Even if the contract is vague about the standard of construction and finish to be provided, the law makes certain stipulations. Where the property is residential, the requirements of the NHBC should be met unless no NHBC certificate is to be issued (which nowadays is an unusual situation and one which would call for special advice to be given). In the case of a 'second-hand' house, the contract between vendor and purchaser will be one which will give the purchaser little remedy against the vendor covering defects in the property being conveyed, although a property less than ten years old may enjoy the benefits of the residue of a ten-year NHBC certificate in respect of certain types of major structural defect.

Secondly, because the structure is new no advice can be given to the client about how the building may have performed for a period of time. A second-hand house which is a few years old will normally start to exhibit signs of structural distress if there is some fundamental fault in its structure or in the underlying subsoil. Generally, it is recognised that such major faults almost always occur during the first five years of a building's life.

Because the structure cannot be subject to an extended period of observation and therefore will not have proved itself stable by the passage of time, the surveyor will normally make enquiries over the original design and will have to inspect working drawings, plans, engineer's calculations and so forth, in order to assess the quality of that design.

Normally, the builder or developer would make available any plans and calculations for the surveyor's inspection. If permission to scrutinise such details is refused, it is felt that the surveyor might well then decide to refer the matter back to his client on the basis that in such circumstances he cannot prepare an adequate report. A telephone call to the district surveyor or building inspector is often advisable. It is surprising to find how often a notionally completed building has still not been finally passed under the Building Regulations or London Building Acts due to some breach of these Regulations or other problem of design or construction. Clients should be advised not to complete a purchase until all necessary final inspections have been undertaken and the building is finally approved.

Planning and other permissions

Another important point to consider in any new building is that almost all new construction in the United Kingdom is subject to the requirements of various permissions and consents and buildings erected without all the necessary permissions and consents may be illegal or unlawful. Clearly, before a client buys or leases a new building and before a mortgagee lends money on the security of a new building, the fact that all necessary consents have been obtained must be confirmed.

In the first instance, it is the client's solicitor who is responsible for finding out whether or not the new building exists legally and lawfully and that there are no breaches of the law. As has been mentioned before, however, it is the surveyor who actually looks at the property – the solicitor will rarely see the property he conveys for a client so the advice which the surveyor can give his client or his client's solicitor will prove to be important.

Basically, there are four types of consent which may be required for new buildings:

1. Permissions under the Town and Country Planning Acts, applying in most cases but perhaps not in the case of certain types of small extensions to existing buildings or to exempt buildings such as those used for agricultural purposes.
2. Permission under building control codes, quite a separate system from planning and governed by the Building Regulations 1976, Building (First Amendment) Regulations 1978, and Building (Second Amendment) Regulations 1981, in England and Wales outside Inner London. In Inner London, the London Building Acts and London Building (Construction) Bye-laws 1972 apply. In Scotland, the Building Standards (Scotland) Regulations 1971 to 1979 apply. In Northern Ireland, the Building Regulations (Northern Ireland) 1977 and the

Building Regulations (Northern Ireland) (Amendment) Regulations 1979 apply. Building construction legislation is currently subject to a major review.

3. The consent of a landlord or freeholder of leasehold property; of an original freeholder in England and Wales who holds the benefit of restrictive covenants; or, in Scotland, the superior to a title who holds the benefit of feuing conditions. Examples may be found where titles include old restrictive covenants against redevelopment at higher densities or different types and such conditions may be removed only by applications to the Courts or Lands Tribunal. Specific insurance cover may sometimes be available against the possibility that an old restrictive covenant could be enforced and building works may then proceed with the benefit of such insurance cover. If title insurance is relied upon, the surveyor should obtain details and confirm whether or not the amount of cover is adequate since it will often be found insufficient to compensate fully a purchaser in the event of a restrictive covenant being enforced.

4. The consent specific to the particular type of building having regard to particular local or national legislation. Special rules apply to filling stations and garages which require petroleum licences and if a petroleum licence is refused or revoked, this could have a disastrous effect on the value of the premises. Similarly, fire safety certificates are required for hotels, public buildings and the like. It is important to confirm that a new building meets all such requirements, including projected changes of legislation which may arise in the future. Offices and shops are governed by the Offices, Shops and Railway Premises Act and factories by the Factories Act. In the case of buildings where people will be employed, the Health and Safety at Work legislation may apply to certain aspects of new building design.

If a new building is not residential then the surveyor will consider whether or not the design complies with all existing and projected local and national legislation to which it will be subject, having regard to the purpose for which the building was designed and the purpose for which the client proposes to use it, taking into account any potential change of use.

The fact that planning permission and approvals necessary under building control legislation have been granted does not ensure good design. The fact that a new building may have been inspected periodically by a building inspector or district surveyor does not ensure good standards of construction since such inspections, by their very nature, can only be 'spot checks'. Neither will the fact that a new house may have been inspected by the NHBC indicate good standards of construction, or even that all NHBC requirements have been met, since these inspections also are only spot checks.

Therefore, when reporting on a new building, the surveyor should not accept anything at face value, neither should he rely upon the past supervision or inspection by others as an indication that a particular item is satisfactory. He can only report properly on those matters which he can see or discover for himself.

Foundation design and subsoil

The first subject for his personal investigation is the nature of the supporting subsoil and the foundation design. In this connection, the architect's or builder's design drawings as approved by the local authority will at least show the intentions.

Consideration should then be given to the question of whether or not a design is suitable for the indicated subsoil conditions and enquiries made to discover what subsoil samples were taken and whether or not any trial bores were made on the site and to what depths. It may be that results of a laboratory examination of soil samples can be made available. If not, and if the position seems doubtful, it may be that the surveyor himself will need to recommend that his client commissions an analysis of the subsoil. In recent years, however, most local authority building control departments have required a note to be made on the submitted drawings to the effect that the foundations will be designed to meet site conditions rather than requiring an explicit detail on the drawings.

The reason for this emphasis on the foundations and subsoil under a new building is that if a building has not proved itself by performance over any extended period of time, the danger, albeit remote in most cases, is that the foundations may be inadequate or the subsoil unstable. From a client's point of view, the whole point of instructing a surveyor in the first instance is to receive advice regarding just such matters and a report which merely states that the building has not been subjected to any extended period of observation and that no advice can be given on the suitability of the foundations will seem distinctly unhelpful to a client. He will then wonder whether the exercise of instructing a surveyor was really worthwhile.

Certain obvious warning signs which should place a surveyor on his guard over a foundation design would include the following:

(1) Any known history of mining in the locality.
(2) Any known history of sand, gravel or chalk extraction or filled gravel pits etc. in the locality.
(3) Sites with steep slopes, retained by embankments or retaining walls, or where adjoining structures or highways show signs of landslips.
(4) Any indications of tipping or landfilling in the locality.
(5) The presence of shrinkable soils, especially near vegetation.
(6) Any possibility of coastal erosion.
(7) Signs of structural distress to older buildings in the locality.
(8) The presence of trees in very close proximity to the building.
(9) Adjacent flat, marshy or poorly-drained land.

Another useful indicator is to make a check on the identity and qualifications of those responsible for the foundation design. Generally, it is to be hoped that consulting engineers were employed to report on soil conditions, prepare structural calculations and designs and that qualified architects or surveyors were responsible for working drawings and layouts. Often, however, drawings are prepared by 'in-house' personnel employed by the builder or developer.

Occasionally drawings will be found carrying no indication as to the name or qualifications of the draughtsman. No hard and fast rules can be given for the acceptability or otherwise of designs prepared by unqualified or unknown personnel since they may well be experienced and competent. However, the lack of any outside professional involvement in structural design can be an indication that it was felt necessary to avoid payment of professional fees and cost cutting may then also be evident in the design or the construction work itself.

It is sometimes helpful to talk to the men working on a building site if this is possible and it is surprising how much can be learned from such casual conversations. They will give an indication of the loyalty of the workforce and the efficiency of the employer in providing adequate supervison. They will often readily discuss problems which they have encountered on site, difficulties with the local authority or faults and poor deliveries of materials. An overall impression of the general standard of care being taken with the building work can be gauged. On no account, however, should members of a workforce be 'quizzed' on the progress, administration and finances of a contract. Great care should be exercised in carrying out this suggestion and then only with the backing and full knowledge of the contractor.

Inspecting the building

Having completed all the investigations which are possible and are required by the client in respect of subsoil and foundation design, the surveyor will then proceed with his inspection of the building. This inspection will follow the same lines as the inspection of any other building using the surveyor's own normal routine. If the building work is incomplete, it is suggested that a list of all unfinished items be prepared and included in an appendix to the report with a note that the surveyor, if required, can confirm that such matters have been completed at a later time.

At each stage of the inspection, all defective work and deviations from good building practice should be noted. In the case of a residential property a check should be made for breaches of building control legislation applicable to the locality and any lack of conformity with the standards laid down in the NHBC's *Registered House-Builders' Handbook*. In the case of non-residential property, the check should be for breaches of building control legislation and any other lapse from the specific requirements of that particular building type.

Surface finishes must be checked with particular care, especially in the case of a residential property. Clients buying new houses are doing so for many reasons, but one requirement will be that the decorations will all be new. The clients will then expect that redecoration will not be necessary for several years, this clearly being a saving compared with the typical situation in a second-hand house where most buyers expect to have to redecorate in accordance with their own tastes soon, if not immediately, after moving in. Experience shows that purchasers of new houses tend to complain most over problems of final finishes to walls, ceilings and woodwork and by lack of care when installing fixtures and fittings. It is necessary therefore to apply a stringent standard to a new house where these matters are concerned, as compared with a second-hand house where most clients will accept a lower standard knowing it is their intention to improve to their own tastes. Havng said this, however, clients should be told that a builder's initial finish is not as durable as later-applied finishes may be, especially in the case of new painted softwood.

During the course of a new building inspection, an opportunity arises for the surveyor to consider the overall quality of design from the client's point of view and to comment unfavourably where necessary. In commercial and industrial structures the durability of finishes is important in view of the considerable wear and tear which may arise in connection with the client's trade or business. Floor finishes in commercial and industrial structures are very important from the point of view of hardness, freedom from dust, ease of cleaning and non-slip surface. Often, hazardous floor finishes or potential dangers in a building will be encountered which may possible give rise to claims from injured employees or visitors. Clients will expect to have been warned of such problems by their surveyor in advance.

Security in a new commercial or industrial building may be poor and a client may have to undertake protective improvements before being able to obtain insurance cover, especially if warehousing is involved or valuable goods stored. Often new factory and warehouse space is built and let, or sold, as a shell on the basis that the purchaser or tenant will undertake his own fitting-out. The provision of adequate security, fire safety precautions and fitting-out to comply with local and national legislation will have to be allowed for by the client and the advice of the surveyor in budgeting for these costs may be relevant.

The quality of fittings provided in new speculative buildings may be poor. In dwelling construction there is a wide range of qualities available in items such as sanitary ware, kitchen units, fenestration and door and window furniture. The temptation for the builder or developer is to use fittings which are superficially attractive but less durable, especially in the case of sanitary ware. A client may see a new and attractive bathroom and be impressed by the appearance of the sanitary ware and fittings, without being aware of the distinction between acrylic, steel and cast-iron baths, or the variations in enamel thickness, or the tendency for acrylic to flex in use and suffer surface deterioration from abrasion. At the present time for example, it is possible to buy baths at prices which, for the most expensive, are ten times the cost of the cheapest with very little difference in superficial appearance.

The internal planning of new accommodation is important. In residential construction it is necessary to consider whether or not the rooms will be of suitable shape and size to accommodate normal furniture satisfactorily and if furniture can be conveniently moved in and out. For example, to be usable bedrooms must be of a size and shape to accommodate a bed while leaving adequate access for bed-making and space for the door to be opened. (This may seem obvious, but there are many instances of small bedrooms being virtually unusable for this reason).

Suitable access for reading electricity and gas meters and provision for the storage of rubbish bins are necessary. External meter boxes are clearly preferable and should be located in front of any lockable side gates so that access from the highway is always free. Similarly, rubbish bins should be kept out of sight but convenient for use and for emptying. Correct planning of water-closets and bathrooms is necessary to ensure adequate room for the convenient use of appliances and door opening. Convenient kitchen layouts must avoid excessive movement being necessary from one area to another in kitchen operations; a layout of worktop – cooker – worktop – sink – worktop – fridge/freezer is preferable, unbroken by doorways or traffic-ways.

Special attention should be given to staircase and balustrade design, this often being poor. Widths should be sufficient to allow for furniture removal; handrails should be adequate and extend for the full length of the flight; good lighting is necessary, and balustrades should be provided with gaps such as to prevent the smallest child from falling through or becoming jammed. The Building Regulations demand that the space between balusters should be such as to prevent the passage of a 100-mm diameter sphere.

Chapter 15

Reports on older buildings

Built in the old Colonial day,
When men lived in a grander way,
With ample hospitality;
A kind of old Hobgoblin Hall,
Now somewhat fallen to decay,

With weather stains upon the wall
And stairways, worn and crazy doors,
And creaking and uneven floors,
And chimneys huge, and tiled and tall.
Longfellow

As there is little call to concern ourselves in this chapter with buildings dating from before the Early English period, first a word concerning the broad geological considerations which led to the use of differing designs and materials in various parts of the country from that period onwards.

When stone was the principal building material used in church and cathedral construction, for example, materials in areas devoid of roads, such as the fens, had to be conveyed on horseback and in some districts, transported by sea or river. From the earliest times, therefore, bearing in mind the primitive or absent transport, local materials have been used as close to the site of origin as possible. The limestones of Portland, granites of Aberdeen and Cornwall, Bath stone – all were first used locally, but as transport became more efficient, local distinctions disappeared and even in the Middle Ages, stone began to be brought from a distance such as the Normandy Caen stone used in Canterbury Cathedral.

However, for less grand buildings, locally-available materials were used principally in domestic construction right up to the 20th Century.

The modern type of brick, for instance, came into use around 1300 AD, having lapsed since Roman times, and the earliest brick building which survived into the 20th Century is Little Wenham Hall in Suffolk (1260 AD). The predominance of brick for domestic construction dates from the reign of William and Mary and, broadly speaking, it is still the most economic material for external facings to properties of all sizes.

Half-timbering as in Lancashire, Cheshire and the West Midlands dates largely from the 14th to 16th Centuries, terra-cotta in Essex was used in the early 16th Century, and in chalky districts a great many medieval buildings were constructed in flint, still common in Norfolk, Suffolk and parts of the South Coast.

The variety of structural materials encountered in the older buildings is therefore perhaps even greater than that of 20th Century construction.

In both ecclesiastical and secular building, the earliest periods to concern us are:

1189–1272 Early English style
1307–1377 Decorated
1377–1558 Perpendicular

All these three periods represent the Gothic style in Great Britain and, in the main, survive as ecclesiastical buildings of primary concern to those who carry out quinquennial surveys of churches and are largely of academic interest only to the general practice surveyor.

Of greater interest to surveyors is the Renaissance period which commenced at the start of the 16th Century after the Wars of the Roses and during the suppression of the monasteries (1536–1540). These events resulted in a revival of architecture, the conversion of some ecclesiastical buildings into mansions, the endowing of grammar schools and, during the prosperous Elizabethan period, a great increase in the building of country houses such as Longleat House, Wiltshire, and Haddon Hall, Derbyshire.

The Jacobean period saw such mansions as Holland House, Kensington and Bolsover Castle, Derbyshire, completed during the reign of James the First. These and the preceding 'Elizabethan' mansions were principally of brick or stone but timber construction was still employed in Cheshire, Lancashire and Shropshire. Many of the Oxford and Cambridge colleges have buildings belonging to this period such as Emmanuel College, Cambridge, and Jesus College, Oxford.

The Anglo-Italian period was introduced during the reign of Charles the First who employed Inigo Jones (1573–1652) to design complicated structures of classic grandeur. Sir Christopher Wren (1632–1723) also came within this period and we are familiar with his works but, although a genius in construction, he did not have the decorative flair displayed by Inigo Jones.

From here there was a logical progression to the 18th Century styles which split naturally into two periods:

1702–1714 Queen Anne
1714–1820 Georgian (the reigns of the first three Georges).

During the former period, Castle Howard and Blenheim Palace were designed by Sir John Vanbrugh in the lavish Anglo-Classical style, although minor domestic architecture during Queen Anne's reign was generally plain and functional with much brick used in construction – a wonderful period for domestic design.

In the latter period, Robert Adam (1728–1792) was probably the most famous exponent of the Georgian revival, as witness Adelphi Terrace, London, and Keddleston Hall, Derbyshire. Columns, vaulting and sprawling plans again became fashionable with strong emphasis on façades. This prompted the Classical Revival with ambitious pseudo-Greek models as in the Bank of England (1788) and St George's Hall, Liverpool, by H. L. Elmes (1815–1847).

An upsurge of spiritual activity in the Church then brought us to the Gothic Revival in the 19th Century with Augustus W. N. Pugin (1812–1852) as the apostle of ecclesiastical work in this style. The most impressive buildings of this time are, however, the Houses of Parliament designed by Sir Charles Barry with Pugin's help, and the New Law Courts designed by G. E. Street (1824–1881) who was a pupil of the famed Sir Gilbert Scott. Further notable buildings of this period include Keble College, Oxford, Truro Cathedral and the Manchester Town Hall.

About this time commenced the 'Free Classic' movement which attempted to use the best of classical design and construction without slavish reproduction, for example, Norman Shaw's New Zealand Chambers in Leadenhall Street, London.

Although Sir Gilbert Scott, who designed the Home and Foreign Offices between 1860 and 1870, is probably the best-known architect of those times, Norman Shaw, W. E. Nesfield (Regent's Park Lodges) and Philip Webb (Lord Carlisle's house in Kensington) had the greatest influence over domestic-scaled design.

True double-hammer beam with hammer posts tenoned into outer ends of hammer beams

Double-hammer-beam arrangement with false upper tier. The upper arch brace is carried to the back of the hammer beam

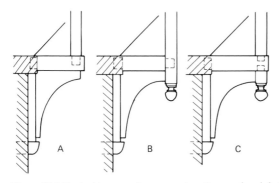

A: True hammer beam with vertical tenon
B: Pendentive hammer beam with much weaker horizontal tenon
C: Pendentive hammer beam with advantage of strength from vertical tenon, and decorative pendant

Figure 15.1 Typical hammer-beam construction used mainly in churches and cathedrals. Detailed knowledge of this type of construction is essential before an accurate assessment of strength may be made

This then brings us up to the 20th Century and the substantial and well-founded works of architects such as Sir Edward Lutyens RA whose Castle Drogo in Devon, completed in 1930, was the last great country house to be built in Great Britain. Here, however, experiments in materials – particularly the use of asphalt for flat roofs, and damp-proof membranes in solid granite walls – has led to new disaster and involved the present owner, the National Trust, in much expensive remedial work. His more traditional domestic buildings, however, such as 7 St James's Square, London, and Heathcote, Ilkley, Yorkshire, are well-found and, in addition, a delight to the eye. Other early 20th Century architects of note in the domestic field were Clough Williams-Ellis whose brainchild was the eccentric and fanciful village of Portmeirion on the North Wales coast, and Percy Scott Worthington with his Cheshire 'stockbroker belt' magnificence.

Traditional methods of design and construction

Now to deal with the types of design and construction and their main characteristics up to the present time.

The buildings themselves are even more varied and sometimes more temperamental than the occupiers; some inspire love, others hatred, but they are never dull. A few brief personal notes and opinions on typical differing types are now given to complement the foregoing short history. This is not intended to be a complete treatise on defects to be found in old buildings but just a guide to the faults one may anticipate:

Elizabethan and Jacobean

Depending upon the part of the country in which these buildings are to be found, one can be very badly caught out on occasion by historic mansions and country cottages.

Generally, walls are not plumb and vary in construction from timber lath and plaster via porous brickwork and eroded freestone to distintegrating cob. Roof timbers are often propped with tree branches from which the bark has not yet been stripped. This is indeed fertile ground for furniture beetle infestation and, depending upon geographical situation, properties of this age and type are most prone to this defect. As a great deal of oak and hardwood was also used in their construction, they are unfortunately also liable to death watch beetle infestation.

It goes without saying that floors which are laid in either stone flags or herring-bone brickwork on earth are very damp indeed and the walls are usually prey to rising damp and, in a great many cases, actual damp penetration. In the case of cob-walled cottages, however, the cob *must* be damp otherwise if it is too dry, the walls will disintegrate into piles of dust, having then no moisture content to make the earth filling cohesive.

Queen Anne, Georgian and Regency

These are generally attractive in appearance but often of flimsy construction. Solid walls are frequently not thick enough to keep out the dampness caused by driving rain, one example being the 150-mm-thick soft ashlar stonework used in the external walling of classical terraced housing, particularly in the Bath area. In these cases, the stonework is often battened off internally and covered with lath and plaster. Sometimes, even the lath and plaster is omitted and hessian used instead, or perhaps again battened and covered with hessian and paper to conceal damp plaster.

In the above periods, one has to watch out for lead flats, parapet gutters and valley gutters which, if not properly maintained, are often found to be laid on rotted boarding. Generally roofs are slated, low-pitched and not underfelted, but possibly have been parged in the past, the parging by now having entirely dropped off leaving the roof covering liable to penetration by driving rain and snow.

Again, no damp courses are present and therefore rising damp is likely to be encountered and, unlike earlier properties, there is a very good chance that dry-rot

King post

Queen post

Mansard

Figure 15.2 Early timber trusses, variations of which will be commonly encountered in older buildings

may be found in the timbers, ventilation usually being inadequate. However, one bright spot is that roof timbers are usually sound with kingpost or queenpost roof trusses, although again liable to furniture beetle infestation depending upon geographical location.

More often than not, floor joists are laid directly on to the earth and almost always sub-floors remain insufficiently ventilated.

Later Victorian and Edwardian

These are usually well-found, ugly, solid buildings but often, particularly in the case of those having stone facings, having too much fussy detail which collects pollution of all kinds, creates maintenance problems and very often weathers badly. Later buildings in this category may have slate damp-proof courses in the walls but the normal troubles found in construction carried out during this period are dry-rot, particularly in cellars, and furniture beetle infestation in roof and floor timbers. Once again, walls were built solid during this period but generally more substantial than in earlier properties.

This, in some cases, can create damp penetration problems due to lack of a cavity, particularly if the exterior rendering, applied originally as a waterproofer, has passed its useful life and become off-key and porous, as is often the case in the West Country.

The nineteen-twenties

These are generally good sound buildings, some with cavity walls, damp-proof courses (often slate) and well-constructed pitched roofs of good quality slate or clay tiles. Generally very little trouble is experienced from buildings erected during this period provided that they have been well-maintained during their lifetime. However, flat roofs were often covered in asphalt which by now is sure to have passed its useful life span in spite of maintenance. Wall ties which were not galvanised may now have rusted through, especially in exposed situations, leaving two separate single-brick leaves in a rather unstable wall. Tile coverings may be approaching the end of their useful life.

The nineteen-thirties

On the domestic scale, houses built during this period were very often flimsy, 'jerry-built' and, being the age of the speculative house, they were very often of poor construction, and a quick turnover for large profits was the order of the day. During this period, bituminous felt damp courses were used and now, 50 years later, these are often found to have perished, become brittle and broken down. Again, investigation will sometimes reveal that the early metal ties in the cavity walls can have rusted through after such a period of time since some of the original supposedly galvanised metal cavity ties had not been properly treated. Walls are then left in the state of two separate unconnected leaves of brickwork, often unstable.

Unseasoned roof timber was occasionally used which resulted in warping and distortion plus the possibility of furniture beetle infestation since generally roof timbers were not treated and there was a high proportion of sapwood present.

The nineteen-fifties

Buildings erected during this period were generally simple, solid, built to a budget and on the whole unattractive, but reasonably soundly constructed. There were, however, felt damp-proof courses which, as stated above, have a limited life, there was no cavity insulation to the walls, most ground floors were of concrete, because of restrictions on the use of timber, and many of these had inadequate damp-proof membranes. Floor coverings often consisted of Magnesite composition, early thermoplastic tiles or woodblocks. Magnesite composition has a very limited life and will disintegrate after a few years of heavy use; the early tiles were brittle and broke easily, particularly across the corners; woodblocks, again often of largely unseasoned hardwoods, are liable to attack by various forms of rot. Flat roofs were the fashion and if constructed of timber, very often by this time will have had their problems. Many flat roofs were then covered with asphalt which was unvented, interstitial condensation problems were not considered important at that time due to lower internal heating requirements and therefore by now problems will have occurred in timber roofs covered with boarding and asphalt which are not ventilated and which contain no vapour barriers. Wet-rot to exterior woodwork, especially sills and exposed fenestration, is frequently found.

The nineteen-sixties

During this decade, 'experiment', often wasteful of resources, was the order of the day. New and untried designs, methods and materials were being used. Among designers there seemed to be a strange lack of knowledge about the principles of building construction and many of the new methods which were not tested by time have since failed, sometimes quite rapidly and with disastrous results. This applied particularly to the various novel forms of roof construction which were used.

Once again, domestic construction was becoming 'jerry-built' and flimsy, as in the nineteen-thirties and the use of felt and chippings finishes to flat roofs was probably at its zenith. The motto during this period appeared to be 'live now – pay later' as those who still have to live with high-rise and curtain walling realise only too well!

The nineteen-seventies and eighties

Both design and construction appear to have improved very gradually over this period. More effective damp-proofing arrangements have been employed, the use of vapour barriers and the problems encountered by condensation were better understood, energy conservation was more fully considered and thermal insulation requirements are higher.

The message concerning the false economy of using flat roofs appears to have been driven home and more pitched roofs are now being employed on all types of buildings. However, now, in the nineteen-eighties, energy conservation methods and the super-insulation of buildings have often had an adverse effect on structure and finishes caused by interstitial and surface condensation problems, lack of ventilation, and a reduction in natural lighting – the result of over-emphasis.

It is worth mentioning that an eminent architect had notices printed which stated baldly, 'All flat roofs leak'. He made each one of his assistants pin up a copy of this notice over his drawing board, a primitive but effective method of performance feedback.

Enlarged section at BB

Sections   Plans

Internal elevation

Figure 15.3 Nineteenth-century flue construction. During inspection it is wise to count the pots and trace the flues within the building

In this country the object of a roof should not be to hold water but to obtain the swiftest run-off possible, and to this end perhaps the steeper-pitched tiled or slated roofs are the best answer.

Local characteristics

Having briefly considered the history and problems of buildings of all ages, the time has now come to consider their purely local characteristics and the influences exerted by environment.

When carrying out structural surveys, one can often learn a great deal about how design and construction should fit in with the local environment from both the geographical and climatic point of view. For example, in the Big Apple Restaurant which occupies the 110th floor of the World Trade Centre in Manhattan, attention was drawn to the fact that the management were very worried about cracks which had appeared in the plastered internal finishes to walls and ceilings. Structural failure was suspected by the occupiers but the real inference should be obvious – do not use plastered finishes near the top of a 400-m high building. The amount of 'sway' on this building is bound to make any plastered or rendered finish break down sooner or later.

Again, a textile factory was visited in an exposed situation some 2000 m up in the Colombian Andes where complaints had been made about water seepage through the concrete flat roof over the single-storey office block. This had resulted in much efflorescence and also in small stalactites hanging from the ceilings in many of the rooms. On further investigation it was found that the 225-m-thick reinforced concrete roof had no means of built-in waterproofing whatsoever, neither had it any waterproof covering. The rainfall, heat and humidity in the Andes being what they are, these penetration problems came as no surprise. In addition, the lack of thermal insulation gave the office occupants a hard time under the equatorial sunshine and the answer was finally achieved by superimposing a low-pitched, deep-eaved, corrugated asbestos sheeted roof over the concrete flat, so shedding the water rapidly away from the building and providing a satisfactory degree of insulation from the fierce heat of the sun.

As a contrast, on an inspection of a four-storey dwellinghouse in Turkey on the shores of the Bosphorus, it was found that this property, which was some 120 years old, was constructed entirely of 225-mm brickwork clad on the outside with cedar weather-boarding. The roof was of simple pitched-and-gabled construction covered with red clay pantiles and having very deep overhanging eaves which protected the wall surfaces below from the wet winter weather. Joinery to doors and windows was also in cedar but of a harder and more durable variety than is normally used in this country. None of the woodwork was painted. In spite of this property's repulsive appearance and seemingly flimsy construction, it had stood the rigours of the last 120 years very well indeed and showed no signs of an insect infestation, rot, structural or settlement faults in spite of the fact that one side of the building was literally in the water and the basement contained a boat house from which, under cover, one could step comfortably directly into the kitchen.

The lesson from these examples is that should one see a building constructed of materials which are not indigenous to that particular location and of a design which is not traditional, then one must begin to look very seriously for potential defects. Buildings, of traditional construction using local materials are very often the product of up to 300 or 400 years of experience in performance of such designs and materials for a particular locality. In such cases, practical feedback on performance has probably been handed down over the generations.

To take just a few examples from this country:

(1) *Cornwall:* In West Cornwall, walls which appear to be of solid granite in large blocks often consist of two thin slabs of granite laid on edge with a dry earth filling rammed down between. Although the granite slabs may not be more than 150 mm thick, the total wall thickness is then perhaps upwards of 600 mm, which is excellent both from a thermal insulation point of view and for a measure of protection from damp penetration but absolute hell if one wishes to make an opening in the wall, as one could easily be left with two granite skins and no filling!

The roofs often comprise random 'peggy' slates, the cast-offs from Delabole or other local quarries, fixed with oak pegs and over the years covered with layers of cement slurry. This is extremely effective in preventing driving rain from entering the roofing, but the slurry eventually causes the roof to become a homogeneous slab liable to crack in inconvenient places and suddenly return to earth, in whole or in part.

In central Cornwall, the local stone which is often used unrendered, is of a soft slatey variety which is often laid on the wrong bed. In more than one property it has been possible to scoop stone out of the surface of such walls with a forefinger, and very often the only solution to prevent the wall from disappearing altogether is to cover it with expanded metal, render and roughcast – a favourite treatment for decaying cob walls as well.

It is known that during the nineteen-twenties and -thirties several hundred houses built in Cornwall included Mundic blocks in their construction. These blocks were manufactured from the waste from the East Wheal Rose tin mine at Newlyn, and they contain arsenic, lead and antimony. In time, such blocks suffer complete loss of strength due to reaction of the concrete and sulphides of these metals to form gypsum. Houses built in Mundic blocks can suffer sudden deterioration and even collapse.

(2) *Devon*: West Devon walls, particularly in the Plymouth area, are usually of local stone (limestone in the case of Plymouth) which has been rendered and painted externally. These walls rely on the integrity of the rendering and external paintwork for their weather-proofing qualities. Rising damp is generally prevalent and if the building happens to catch fire, the limestone is calcined and the load-bearing walls may have to be demolished. Roofs are generally of grey Delabole slating or similar, but laid to even courses.

In East Devon, the traditional construction is cob and thatch. These cob walls vary in width, sometimes being almost a metre thick in places. Again, such walls rely on the integrity of the external rendering which, if allowed to crack or disintegrate, allows the weather to penetrate the cob which very soon turns to mud.

Conversely, if one attempts to insert a damp-proof course of any kind into a cob wall, there is a tendency for the cob to dry out which means that in the long term one could be left with a pile of dust rather than a wall! Excellent from a thermal insulation point of view, however, and curiously enough not much trouble from rising damp, rot or other like ailments. The thatched roofs seldom have gutters but have a generous eaves overhang, the thatch slowing down the run-off of rainwater and the eaves overhang throwing it well clear of the cob walls. One must not be alarmed by the lumpy and out-of-plumb appearance of most cob walls, but beware of external cracks.

(3) *Somerset*: Somerset is the county of red clay tiled roofs – usually pantiles, double Roman tiles or the Bridgwater interlocking variety. Generally the clay tiles are laid to a reasonable pitch of around 40° and shed the water very quickly but one must beware of pantiled roofs. Very often these are ill-fitting and not underfelted, and one can find some alarming timber structures supporting these Somerset roofs, very often heavily infested with *anobium punctatum*. Clay tiles are now of course being replaced by concrete tiles of various forms.

Wall materials vary from local brick to local stone and there are some particularly attractive stones used such as Bath, Doulting and Ham, all with rich colours but often rather friable and, in some cases, with poor weathering qualities. These stones are easily worked and are very often used for the ornamental dressings in some of the buildings, the more local limestone random rubble being used for the general walling with freestone dressings to windows and door openings.

There is a particularly hard stone in South Gloucestershire/North Somerset known as 'pennant' which is often used for paving slabs but can also be used for walling, but beware of internal wet spots since some pennant stone walls may be porous in places in spite of the hardness of the material.

Properties in the Bath area have previously been mentioned but be reminded of substantial-looking terraces and crescents which on further investigation are found to have deceptively thin walls and are particularly liable to damp penetration, dry-rot, wet-rot and similar ailments which occur when weatherproofing is inadequate and ventilation is insufficient.

One could ponder on traditional methods of construction in various parts of the country for a considerable time. For example, the traditional Lancashire construction of solid millstone walls with outward-sloping joints and millstone flagged pitched roofs; traditional Cheshire construction of half-timbering with timber lath and plaster infilling painted outside and again flagged roofs; Berkshire and the Home Countries, often hand-made brickwork with solid brick walls and some half-timbering with tiled roofs; Edinburgh with its gaunt, begrimed stone buildings; Aberdeen with its durable granite; North Wales with its slate; Essex and Suffolk with timber framing and tarred weatherboarded walls – the list is inexhaustible.

Once again it must be stressed that the surveyor should be very aware of traditional materials and traditional methods of construction for that particular locality in which he is working. This awareness can only be obtained through experience. It is the surveyor's task to study historical building methods perhaps more than new forms of design and construction since more often than not it is the older properties which will demand his attention and on which most of his time will be spent.

Referring to the use of traditional materials, as stone is one of the most widespread in use for the older buildings, a few notes on the weathering properties of the commoner building stones may be useful to the surveyor:

1. *Bath stone:* A variety of types from cream to light cream with a more open texture than Portland stone and of poor weathering qualities in industrial atmospheres. This stone is mined, it is very easy to work, and is capable of being easily cleaned.
2. *Beer stone:* Fine-grained white limestone from the East Devon coast, not very durable for external use but found in many South West churches and, in particular, Exeter Cathedral. The quarries have had to be re-opened to replace the badly weathered stone of that particular structure.
3. *Clipsham stone:* Coarse-grained light brown limestone from near Rutland used in Houses of Parliament restoration and in the Oxford area.
4. *Darley Dale:* Light grey to buff fine-grained Derbyshire sandstone with excellent weathering qualities but very difficult to clean.
5. *Doulting:* A coarse, crystalline Somerset limestone coloured grey to light brown and containing shell fragments. Unsuitable for city or industrial atmospheres or for fine detailing as then likely to disintegrate on arrises.
6. *Forest of Dean:* A blue/green/grey Gloucester sandstone with fine grain, used for monumental work and paving as well as for facings and structural work as it weathers very well.
7. *Ham Hill:* A beautifully-coloured rich yellowy-brown Somerset limestone containing shells but soft and unsuitable for use in built-up areas. Cleans well.
8. *Hopton Wood:* Creamy Derbyshire limestone containing fossils and similar to marble when polished but unsuitable for external use in city atmospheres.
9. *Kentish rag:* Grey-white limestone much used in London and the South East. Cleans well and used largely for rubble walling.

10. *Portland stone:* A Dorset limestone, almost white and probably the best limestone for use in city atmospheres as it weathers, giving a 'light and shade' effect. Encountered in large buildings of many towns and cities and particularly suitable for classical detailing.
11. *Wootton (or Runcorn):* Found in Cheshire and South West Lancashire, and generally a durable, fine-grained red sandstone much used in external works but weathers badly in marine atmospheres.
12. *York stone:* A brown Yorkshire sandstone with a fine grain and mainly used for pavings, sills and dressings externally. Very durable but not easy to clean.
13. *Granites:* These vary in texture and quality, the best probably being found around Aberdeen and on Dartmoor (Devon). Very hard and durable, it varies from pink through grey to brown. Used in engineering works as well as building. Beware of the brown granite from West Cornwall, however. This type can be porous and have poor weathering qualities as it is in the first stages of deterioration into china clay.
14. *Slates:* Obtained from various parts of the country, a variety of slates used in thin-bedded courses and varying in durability. Much used in the Lake District, Isle of Man, Wales, central Cornwall and the borders of Dartmoor. Should be laid with horizontal joints sloping *outwards* to prevent damp penetration.

Buildings of special interest

Many of our older buildings are of special architectural or historic interest, and this fact must be borne in mind when any old building comes under survey since special controls and restrictions could be involved. Grants towards the costs of repairs and maintenance may be obtainable but in many cases no alterations of any kind may be carried out without planning consent.

The Secretary of State for the Environment is required under Section 54 of the Town and Country Planning Act 1971 to compile or approve lists of buildings of special architectural or historic interest, to notify this fact to owners and occupiers concerned, and to register the building as such in Part 10 of the local land charges register. When this has been done and a building is included in a list, then 'listed building consent' must be obtained under Part IV of the Town and Country Planning Act 1971 before any person may demolish or carry works for the alteration or extension of that building 'in any manner which would affect its character as a building of special architectural or historic interest'. Section 55(6) of the 1971 Act dispenses with this requirement in the case of works urgently necessary for reasons of safety or health, but notice must still be given to the Royal Commission on Historical Monuments (England and Wales) in such cases if demolition is involved and to the local authority in any event.

Section 58 of the 1971 Act states that a planning authority may serve a building preservation notice which then 'lists' that building for six months together with all the ancillary restrictions involved.

Section 277 of the 1971 Act deals with 'conservation areas' and the local authority must, under the terms of this Section, give public notice of any planning application affecting property within that conservation area in addition to which any demolitions require consent under the Town and Country Amenities Act 1974, Section 1.

Local authorities may serve the owner of a listed building with a repairs notice to ensure the preservation of that building, or may even acquire such buildings compulsorily, compensation being reduced if deliberate dereliction of the building has been allowed by that owner. In some cases, a local authority may carry out repairs and then recover the cost and it is at this stage that the precise condition of a listed building becomes vitally important in the surveyor's report to his client.

In the case of a listed building, advice should also be included in the surveyor's report on the possibility of obtaining a repair grant. Such a grant would be in addition to any other normal house renovation grant to which reference will shortly be made. The Society for the Protection of Ancient Buildings would give further advice on this or any other related subject.

A local authority may contribute towards the repair and maintenance costs of a listed building under the provisions of the Local Authorities (Historic Buildings) Act 1962, including the upkeep costs of garden and outbuildings in some cases. In addition to a grant, interest-free loans are sometimes given, but a grant may be recovered by the local authority if the building is sold within three years.

Outstanding historic buildings may receive repair grants under the terms of the Historic Buildings and Ancient Monuments Act 1953 and this should be mentioned in a survey report if thought to apply and subsequently confirmed.

It must be remembered, however, that listed building consent does not convey immunity from building regulation and planning permissions which must be sought where applicable.

Grants

Continuing on the subject of grants, a prospective purchaser may be very interested in the possibility of obtaining one of the many home improvement grants now available, the relevance of which should be explained in the report, if favourable conditions exist. Such grants fall into four separate categories:

1. *Improvement grants:* These grants are related only to older houses and are for major improvements, associated repairs and replacements and for providing additional homes by conversion. In the case of an old house in poor condition up to 70% of the grant can be for repairs and replacement, although 50% is more normal. At present, these grants apply only to houses with a rateable value of £225 or less (£400 in the London area) except in the case of disabled owners or in housing 'action areas'. Such grants are given entirely at the discretion of the local authority without there being any statutory rights on the part of the applicant. Flats are also eligible for improvement grants, but certain conditions have to be met in all cases and, after improvement, the property must have a minimum life expectancy of 30 years, be in reasonable repair, have all standard amenities and comply with the following requirements:

   (a) Freedom from damp,
   (b) adequate natural lighting and ventilation,
   (c) sufficient artificial lighting and electric power,
   (d) efficient drainage,
   (e) stable structural condition,
   (f) satisfactory layout,
   (g) cooking and preparation facilities,

(h) adequate heating,
(i) fuel and refuse storage, and
(j) roof insulation (separate grants available).

In addition, grants may be approved for the conversion of, say, a large Victorian house into flats and this possibility may form part of a client's brief in a structural survey. Grants for conversions at present range from £5500 to £9800 (£7500 to £13 300 in the Great London area).

2. *Intermediate grants:* Intended to cover the cost of basic improvements to homes by providing missing standard amenities such as bath or shower, lavatory basin, sink, hot and cold water supply and WC. These grants are mandatory with a fixed sum in respect of each item listed above up to a present total of £1900 (£2500 in Greater London). These grants are subject to the local authority being satisfied that a house is fit for human habitation, and repairs claims can also be associated with the grant to bring the property up to a satisfactory standard.

3. *Repairs grants:* These are in respect of major structural repairs to roof, walls, floors, foundations or any other essential structural item and apply to pre-1919 houses. Minor maintenance and items such as re-wiring or replacement of fixtures and fittings do not qualify. Rateable value limits are as for improvement grants and the house must be in reasonable repair on completion. Such grants, like improvement grants, are discretionary, although if notice under Section 9 of the Housing Act 1957 has been served on the owner (i.e. a 'repairs notice') a maximum repairs grant must be given by the local authority. The maximum grant amount is £4000 (£5500 in Greater London).

4. *Special grants:* Where houses are in multiple occupation, the owner may obtain a special grant to cover the cost of providing the standard amenities as described in 2. above and, in addition, the provision of means of escape in case of fire. These grants are discretionary except in the case of a notice served under Section 15 of the Housing Act 1961 or Schedule 24 to the Housing Act 1980 when they become mandatory. Self-contained flats without shared facilities qualify for improvement or intermediate grants in the normal way. The maximum amount of a grant for the means of escape in case of fire element only is at present £6750 (£9000 in Greater London).

In addition to the above, grants are available under the Homes Insulation Scheme 1982 in respect of loft insulation and also insulation of hot and cold water tanks and pipes where no insulation already exists. An application is made to the local authority and, when approved, the work has to be carried out and a certified claim submitted within four months.

When carrying out a structural survey on an older property it is important to remember the above potential benefits to the client as they depend to a large extent upon the facilities available in a property, the structural condition and the state of repair. Once again, when carrying out works in connection with the above grants, Building Regulations approval will be necessary in many cases, and planning approval in the event that considerable alteration, extension or change of use is involved with the works.

Principal defects

Finally, probably the most damaging features in old buildings for which the surveyor must keep a keen watch are principally:

1. *Brickwork:* Ground movement due to clay, made ground or changes in groundwater levels.

   Thermal movement due to fluctuations in temperature and differential expansion between varying materials.

   Drying shrinkage where calcium silicate (sand/lime) bricks have been used.

   Deterioration from intense heat and sudden cooling as in the case of a fire.

   Roof spread due to incorrectly-designed pitched roofs.

   Sulphate attack from soil or bricks themselves.

   Corrosion of embedded metal, such as ties, beams and reinforcement, causing expansion.

   Defective mortar which is too weak in mix, or use of imperfectly-slaked lime.

   Frost damage in areas of severe exposure such as parapets, retaining walls and brickwork below damp-proof course.

   Salts in brickwork causing efflorescence and subsequent spalling and disintegration after crystallisation.

2. *Structural timbers:* The various types of fungal decay and insect infestation have been fully described beforehand, but very old buildings containing structural elm, chestnut, walnut and oak are particularly prone to infestation by death watch beetle (*xestobium rufovillosum*). Very old structural timbers, most probably having been exposed to previous fungal attack, are the most likely to fall victim to death watch beetle infestation which can lead to severe structural weakness and eventual collapse. Organic, solvent-based liquid treatments containing insecticide have in the past not proved to be fully effective, and on hardwoods a spray application is normally insufficient on such non-absorbent surfaces. Insecticide smokes are generally accepted as the most effective method of eradication and must be used during beetle emergence in late March and early April.

   It must be borne in mind that many of the visible exit holes in affected timbers may be hundreds of years old and the only certain method of assessing the position and extent of the infestation is to make a beetle count over one emergence period as beetles fall to the floor on emergence, usually under the area of infestation.

   The beetle life-cycle is usually four to six years but can be up to 15 years and consequently perhaps up to ten annual treatments with Lindane or Dieldrin-based smoke may be necessary at the emergence periods.

3. *Stonework:* Main defects in structural stonework may be caused by the following:

   Fractures caused by rusting iron cramps and ties (bronze and copper should be used in preference).

   Frost action causing cracking and spalling by freezing and expansion.

   Atmospheric pollution, particularly that causing decay in limestones due to acid action and destruction of the protective skin which forms over a stone surface.

   Incompatibility of stones, for example, association and juxtaposition of limestone with standstone in polluted atmospheres.

   Vents, shakes and soft beds causing inherent defects in the stone which affect weathering qualities.

   Incorrect bedding where structural stone has not been laid on its natural bed.

   Careless quarrying involving excessive blasting and incorrect use of tools.

Crystallisation of salts formed when wet stone dries out and consequent damage by expansion.

Seasoning – not allowing the moist 'quarry sap' to dry out before using the stone.

Living agents of decay such as ivy (which secretes acid), ferns, wallflowers, buddleias but *not* lichens and moss which are not generally harmful.

Damage caused by fire, particularly in the case of the calcining of limestones, a condition that was observed during the 1939–1945 air raids on the UK.

Defective maintenance of rainwater pipes, gutters, copings and pointing causing damp penetration and reducing the life of the stone.

From the text of this Chapter, the surveyor may conclude that structural surveys of old buildings – particularly churches, country houses and public buildings – is a specialist field, but if due consideration is given to the types of construction and materials used, as described in this Chapter, then a logical appraisal of such a building on these lines will bring the desired results.

Chapter 16

Reports on leasehold properties

> The managing director read the lease, and could not understand Clause XIV. Then he read the accompanying solicitor's letter regarding Clause XIV and could not understand that either. So he asked for a letter from them clarifying their first letter and could not understand that....
>
> *Extract from client's letter of instruction*

If a client is contemplating taking either a new lease or an assignment of the existing lease of a property, certain special considerations apply to the advice to be given, taking into consideration the particular position of the lessee (the tenant) under the law of dilapidations.

Lease of houses

A number of different possibilities may arise. In Manchester, Cardiff and certain other localities, dwellinghouses have been sold traditionally on a leasehold basis, generally for a 99-year or 999-year term. The reasons for this are essentially historical and arose because the landholdings in these areas were in the hands of certain families. Initially, the idea was good since after 99 years and the expiration of the leases, the general redevelopment of an area might have been contemplated and the ground landlords would have retained some control over the properties for the benefit of all concerned. Unfortunately, the results in practice were that leasehold dwellinghouses tended to fall into an increasing state of disrepair as leases began to run out because the lessees were unable or unwilling to improve them.

As a result of pressures for reform of the leasehold system, the 1967 Leasehold Reform Act was passed which gave leaseholders with certain types of long leases of houses (but not flats) the right to buy the freehold, or the right to a specially-extended term at a moderate ground rent subject to proving the required period of owner-occupation and certain other conditions.

Unless the lease term is short (say less than 30 years) it is felt that it would be unusual in practice for the ground landlord of a leasehold house to take very much interest in its condition, and it would be most unlikely that a schedule of dilapidations would be served except in unusual circumstances. In most cases the report on such a leasehold house will follow the same lines as would be the case with a freehold property.

Perhaps the main point which could be made to a client contemplating buying a leasehold house would be to suggest that he might acquire the freehold as well. He could do so by asking the vendor to serve the necessary Notice of Leaseholder's Claim and transfer the property with the benefit of that Notice. If this is not done, the purchaser cannot take advantage of the Act himself until he has first served out the necessary term of occupation. The client should be advised to consult his solicitor on this point. In the long run, a freehold house is a far better investment.

Where the lease of a house is running out and has only a short time to remain, then the necessity for a schedule of dilapidations may well arise. Shorter leases of houses will be encountered in some fashionable London districts, and rights to enfranchise under the Leasehold Reform Act may be different or may not exist, depending upon the rating assessment of the property concerned. A careful reading of the lease in such circumstances is recommended before giving the appropriate advice.

Leases of flats

Leases of flats and apartments are the rule rather than the exception in England and Wales for the reasons discussed in Chapter 14. An almost infinite variety of forms of such leases will be encountered in practice. However, the surveyor will find that these generally fall into one of two basic types: either there will be a lateral division of responsibility within the structure of the building with each leaseholder responsible for his own part of the structure and having no liability for other parts (mostly encountered in cases of small two- or three-storey buildings in flats, either purpose-built or converted), or the lessee will be responsible for the interior of his own unit and share responsibility for the exterior and structure as a whole with other flat owners. In the latter case, arrangements for the proper maintenance and upkeep of the exterior and structure may simply be on an *ad hoc* basis as the need arises. Alternatively, this may be the responsibility of the freeholder who would then recover costs from the lessees, or commonly, may be undertaken by a management company or residents' association.

It will be seen in such cases that a lessee may have a potential proportional liability for parts of the building, or even parts of other buildings on the estate some distance away from his own property. Particularly onerous repair liabilities may arise in the case of flats in older mansion blocks in the inner cities.

Common practice is for such a mansion block to be acquired by a speculator, and for individual flats to be sold off on new long leases with a ground rent and service charge for the maintenance and repair of the exterior, roof and common parts. Initially, in order to sell the leases, the freeholder will wish to keep the service charges low, perhaps artificially low. Once the units are all sold, however, there is no such need and when the true state of repair of the structure begins to become known, large increases in the service or supplementary charges may be levied to cover the cost of repairs which should have been dealt with at the outset during refurbishment and prior to sale.

Before undertaking an inspection of a flat in such a mansion block, the surveyor should be quite sure that his survey will be sufficient to gauge whether or not any exception service charge increases may be due. If this is to be done, it will be clear that the inspection cannot be confined merely to the one specific flat. The significance of this is discussed more fully in Chapter 14.

In all cases of surveys of leasehold residential property, the RICS Code of Practice advises that the surveyor should read the lease before undertaking his inspection. He must endeavour to establish the extent and nature of the repairing liabilities under that lease, the client's potential responsibility for executing repairs and also his liability to pay for repairs executed by others. If the lease is not available, the surveyor must set out clearly the limitations inherent in his advice.

If no copy lease is available, the client's solicitor should be approached and asked to confirm the nature of the repairing convenant which may be assumed. The surveyor may then, on receipt of such instructions in writing from his client's solicitor, refer to this in compiling his report.

The Code of Practice suggests that when taking instructions, in addition to the procedures recommended for freehold property, the surveyor should insist either on having a copy of the lease or on having advice on the nature of repairing liabilities. He should then confirm instructions in the manner recommended for freehold property, indicating also the extent to which he proposes to inspect other parts of the property or estate in order to advise on unacceptable or unusually heavy repairing liabilities outside the demised premises.

Leases of commercial premises

Dealing with leases of commercial premises, the recommendations for procedure could be similar to those for leasehold residential property in that it is highly desirable for the surveyor to read the lease before he undertakes his inspection and to have it available for references as he compiles his report. He may then consider:

(a) The repairs or other works which are required for the purposes of the client's business occupation and necessary to comply with the various local and national regulations, and

(b) the future repairs or other works which may be required in order to comply with the repairing convenants of the lease.

In the case of (a) above it is necessary to ascertain the nature of the client's business, how he proposes to use the premises and the staff which will be employed. In respect of (b), the surveyor will have regard to what the lease says and the current relevance of the law of dilapidations.

Section 18(1) of the Landlord and Tenant Act 1927 sets out certain principles in the assessment of damages for breaches of repairing covenants. It provides that the measure of damage for breach of a covenant to keep premises in repair, or leave premises in good repair when quitting, cannot exceed the diminution in the value of the landlord's reversion occasioned by these breaches. A limit is therefore imposed on the amount of damages which may be recovered by a landlord. These are assessed by valuing the premises as they are and as they would be if the covenants had been complied with, the measure of damage being the difference between these two figures. The cost of undertaking remedial works may be the same thing as the difference in value, on the assumption that a purchaser of the lessor's interest would reduce any price offered by an amount equal to the cost of remedying those defects. The cost of undertaking works may, however, be an amount quite different from the measure of damages in some cases. It is possible for there to be considerable breaches of repairing covenants by a lessee and for the landlord to have no right to compensation at all (for example if the landlord is proposing to redevelop the property in such a way that condition is immaterial to market value).

The Courts have held that the cost of undertaking works is *prima facie* evidence of the diminution in the value of the reversion, which assumption can be rebutted by evidence that damage to the lessor's interests may be better assessed by some other means, such as 'before' and 'after' valuations. In *Drummond* v *S. & U. Stores Ltd.* (1980) 258 EG 1293, *Estates Gazette*, 27 June 1981, p 1293) it was held that in the absence of clear evidence as to the damage to the reversion, the cost of undertaking necessary works was the broad measure of the diminution of value and the landlords were awarded the bulk of the cost of repairs. The landlords in this case were also awarded three months' loss of rent as part of the damages, being the estimated time reasonably necessary to leave the premises empty while the works were done, and also, as the landlord in that case was not registered for VAT, that VAT on the cost of repairs would also be recoverable.

The surveyor advising a client on a commercial lease should have uppermost in his mind the possibility of either an interim or final Schedule of Dilapidations being served on his client and should warn the client about all matters which could give rise to the service of such a schedule or a claim for diminution of value. Substantial sums may often be involved in such cases. One means of protecting a client at the commencement of a lease is to arrange for the lease to state that the lessee will not have to hand the demised premises back on expiration of the term in any better condition than they were in at the commencement as evidenced by a Schedule of Condition. An agreed Schedule of Condition is then prepared by the lessee's and lessess's surveyors, signed and attached to both lease and counterpart lease.

During the course of taking instructions to inspect a leasehold property, the surveyor should ascertain whether or not a Schedule of Condition exists which indicates the condition of the premises as at the beginning of the term. If such a Schedule exists, then it would be advantageous for the surveyor to have a copy and to take this with him when he carries out his inspection. The condition of the property as described in the Schedule of Condition may then be compared with the condition found on inspection.

If a building is to be inspected when a client proposes to take a new lease, and if that building is old or in poor repair, then the surveyor may recommend that a Schedule of Condition be prepared and agreed with the prospective lessor prior to exchange of the lease and counterpart. This may be especially important where a modern form of full repairing lease is being granted on a building which is old and which may suffer from signs of structural distress, past foundation movements, period roof construction and other matters potentially expensive to rectify. In general, the lessee's liability is for repair, and where a defect can be repaired then the liability is not to renew or rebuild, nor will there be any liability to make a building better than it was previously. In practice, however, there is considerable room for argument as to the extent of repairs which may be required.

Perhaps a roof covering is in poor condition and should be stripped off and renewed if it is to be made satisfactory. However, a repair in the form of overhaul and patching of the covering may suffice in the short term. There could be considerable room for disagreement between lessor and lessee as to the extent and nature of there pairs in such a case. A Schedule of Condition detailing the condition of the roof covering at the commencement of the term would provide a standard against which any repairs or renewals may be judged adequate or otherwise.

It may be that a property suffers from dampness. Generally, there is no liability for the lessee to provide damp-proof courses or other works where none previously existed, although in such circumstances he will be liable to deal with the effects of dampness if these have caused deterioration of the interior. If damp-proof courses were in good condition at the commencement of the lease term but failed and became porous during that term, then a liability to renew damp-proof courses could arise. In such a situation it may be difficult to confirm all the facts and if a Schedule of Condition is discovered which clearly shows that the property had a damp problem when the lease began, then this could be of considerable benefit to the lessee's case. Conversely, if a Schedule of Condition indicates that the property was dry and the damp-proof courses were in good condition at the commencement of the term, then this would assist the lessor in requiring remedial works to be undertaken at the lessee's expense, or in obtaining damages for diminution of value.

On occasion, a building may suffer from structural movements of one kind or another. In old buildings such matters rarely arise overnight. More often than not they are part of a continuing process with crack damage, bulging and leaning walls and other manifestations having appeared very gradually over a long period of time. Rarely could a lessee be found liable to undertake a structural repair such as underpinning, but there could arise a liability to provide buttresses to leaning walls or tie bars to stiffen the structure. An orginial Schedule of Condition is helpful in such cases if it accurately describes the structural condition of the building in detail as existing at the commencement of the lease term.

In addition to the repairing covenants in a lease there will also be other covenants, some not directly relevant to the survey but others which may affect the inspection and preparation of the report.

There will generally be a 'user clause' in the lease indicating uses which may be unacceptable and those which may be permitted. For example, a client who wishes to use premises for purposes other than those acceptable in the lease must first obtain the lessor's consent for the change of use. If the lease provides that such consent may not be unreasonably withheld, then the lessor, in determining whether or not to grant consent, is subject to a test of reasonableness which may be challenged. If in the lease there is no provision as to reasonableness the lessor may or may not grant consent for a change of use at his discretion. Clearly, prior to any exchange of contract to acquire a lease, a client must obtain a determination in such cases.

There may be objections to a specific retailing use which conflicts with other retailing uses in adjoining premises which are owned by the same lessor. A lessor who owns a number of retail premises in the same shopping district will wish to ensure a balance of different types of retailing in the area for two reasons, one being the need to present a broad range of retailing outlets to make the centre attractive and profitable, and the other being to limit competition between shcp units selling identical products or services which could otherwise make one, or both, competing units unprofitable.

Objections to use may arise out of the nature of the uses themselves since dust, noise, smells or other problems could arise to the annoyance of the lessor or other adjoining lessees. Certain specific trades will often be particularly referred to in a lease as being unacceptable. These will often include panel-beating, fish-and-chip shops, heavy industry in a light industrial area, or trades such as glue factories or fertiliser storage which could cause offence.

There will generally be some mention of 'assignment' in the lease. A lease with an absolute bar on assignment cannot be sold and is of value only to the lessee in possession as it has no value as a mortgage security. Where assignment is permitted with consent, the law holds that such consent may not be unreasonably withheld, even if the lease omits to state this, so that assignment to a lessee of comparable standing will normally be permitted subject to the lessor providing a Licence to Assign, generally on payment of a small fee to his solicitor.

Covenants in the lease barring structural alterations to the buildings demised are generally found. Such covenants will generally refer to the need for specific permission to be given by the lessor for any alterations to the premises, but an absolute bar on alterations may be provided as an alternative.

A lessee who wishes to undertake alterations to business premises which will constitute improvements and which may increase the value of the premises may, if he wishes, serve notices under the 1927 Landlord and Tenant Act. This is often overlooked, with the consequence that a lessee loses any rights to compensation for improvements or additions to the landlord's property when he vacates. Advice about 1927 Landlord and Tenant Act procedures needs to be given at the outset before improvements are made and should be dealt with at the planning stage.

Chapter 17

Reports for prospective mortagees

If language is not correct, then what is said is not what is meant; if what is said is not what is meant, then what ought to be done remains undone
Confucius

Mortgagees are primarily concerned with ensuring that the security they take for the purpose of the mortgage will be readily re-saleable at a price which will allow for the repayment of any monies due and cover the incidental costs involved, including the costs of sale.

Institutional mortgagees will also wish to ensure that their actions are seen to be in the public interest and they will want to foster the goodwill of their mortgagors and consumers generally. With this in mind, the main building societies and banks now release copies of their surveyors' reports to the mortgagors.

It should be mentioned at this stage that the mortagor grants the legal mortgage in return for the loan and is the borrower (and purchaser). The mortgagee takes the legal mortgage, grants the loan and is the lender. It is not uncommon for the terms to be wrongly transposed and it is important to use the correct nomenclature.

Reports for prospective mortgagees may take the form of pro-formas or be the traditional typed reports on the surveyor's own paper. Such reports may or may not include a full structural survey but they will inevitably include some comments on the condition of the structure since it is not possible to value a property without first forming an assessment of its general condition.

If the property is in poor repair the surveyor will be expected to give the mortgagees some guidance on the significance of this and the conditions which should be applied to any loan. Such conditions may take the form of retentions from the advance money pending completion of essential works and a further surveyor's inspection, or may simply require an undertaking from the mortgagor to complete the works within a specific period of time.

The advice to be given on repairs required will be dependent to some extent upon the amount of advance involved. Generally, low-percentage advances involve low risk levels for the mortgagees and in many cases the requirement for repairs will not be critical. In such circumstances, a written undertaking from a mortgagor of good repute to complete the works within a specified time would seem adequate.

High-percentage advances involve higher risk levels to the mortgagees, and experience tends to indicate that the risk of default by a mortgagor tends to be higher in the earlier years of the mortgage term when the outstanding balance of capital is at its highest. In such circumstances, it may be necessary for the mortgagees to retain part of the agreed advance and to release this against certification from the surveyor when essential repairs have been completed. Local authorities are especially vulnerable in this respect because they provide mortgage advances to house buyers in circumstances where the percentage advances are high (sometimes as much as 100%) and the security is often an older building in poor repair.

The mortgage transaction is achieved by means of a mortgage deed in which the mortgagor agrees to terms controlling the repayment of capital and interest and may also agree to certain requirements for the maintenance and repair of the property used as security over the period of the loan, also the insurance of the building against specified perils. The mortgagor retains the right to recover the property title free from the encumbrance of the mortgage, on payment of the amount due plus costs and penalties if the loan is redeemed early. The right of the mortgagor to redeem the loan is known as his 'equity of redemption'.

Virtually all mortgages the surveyor has to deal with will be mortgages granted by a charge on the property expressed by way of a legal mortgage. Since 1925, this has been the principal method of lending money to a property owner against the property security and is the only legal form of mortgage apart from a much less usual procedure for the grant of a lease to the mortgagee with provision for cessation on redemption. Occasionally, an equitable mortgage is encountered which may be a contract to enter into a legal mortgage if required, or a verbal agreement accompanied by the deposit of the title deeds or lease of the property with the mortgagee. This latter procedure is occasionally adopted by bank managers when granting small loans to achieve security without the need for a full legal mortgage. It does not confer a legal interest in the property and is not suitable for larger-percentage long-term advances, such advances invariably taking the form of a legal charge.

The security for the loan lies in the ability of the mortgagee to take possession of the property and sell it to recover the loan together with incidental costs. There are a number of ways in which a mortgagee may take steps to protect his position if the repayments under the mortgage deed are not being met. No mortgagee likes to take such steps and institutional mortgagees such as banks and building societies will go to considerable lengths to avoid such procedures. They may give the borrower an extended time to pay or a capital repayment 'holiday' to see him through a difficult time. Only as a last resort will they take steps to obtain possession of the property, especially in the case of residential owner-occupied homes. Such events in respect of homes mortgaged to building societies and banks are in fact very rare indeed. Local authorities tend to be lenders of last resort in some sections of the residential property market and the incidence of default by local authority borrowers is rather higher, as is the incidence of default by borrowers on the security of property investments and commercial premises.

Generally, the procedure adopted when all else fails is for the mortgagee to apply to the Courts to take possession. A mortgagee in possession will normally be able to require the borrower and his family to vacate if the property is an owner-occupied house and will also be able to obtain vacant possession in other cases where the borrower, or borrowing company, is also the occupier. The property would then be sold in the open market for the best price obtainable at the time. Any surplus left over after the loan, incidental expenses and accumulated interest have been paid must be paid to the mortgagor. If the property is subject to tenancies and the tenants are protected by virtue of the Rent Acts, Landlord and Tenant Acts or Agricultural Holdings Acts, then the mortgagee takes legal possession subject to the subsisting tenancies. The existence of tenancies may therefore substantially reduce the re-sale value of the mortgage security. When a surveyor inspects the security he should look out for any signs of tenancies about which the mortgagee may be unaware and suggest, if appropriate, that the existence or otherwise of tenancies be confirmed.

An alternative procedure would be for the mortgagee to apply to the Courts for a foreclosure order which would have the effect of extinguishing the mortgagor's equity of redemption and transferring the property to the mortgagee. For technical reasons this procedure is less frequently used than the procedure for the mortgagee entering into possession, but in certain situations foreclosure can have advantages.

Another alternative procedure is for the mortgagee to take possession but with a view to managing the property, collecting the income and paying any outgoings. The net income could then be used to reduce the mortgage debt and pay the interest charges with any arrears. In modern times, such a procedure would not normally be used for vacant property unless the premises concerned proved difficult to sell in the open market but were potentially lettable. These circumstances could arise with certain types of commercial or industrial premises, premises affected by planning blight or having other problems which would be a disadvantage to the potential purchaser but not to a potential tenant. In the case of residential property the effects of rent controls and security of tenure conferred under the Rent Acts in the United Kingdom will generally make any letting by a mortgagee in possession uneconomic if the property is vacant.

It may be that a mortgagee in possession will take over premises which are tenanted, either because the premises were already let and the loan was granted on the security as an investment, or because the tenancies have been created after the grant of the loan. Generally the mortgage deed will provide that the mortgagee's consent is required for any letting of the property which secures the loan, but lettings may be undertaken unlawfully without the mortgagee's consent. In such situations it is more likely that the mortgagee in possession will not seek to sell the property immediately since the value may be very low either because of the existence of tenancies or the climate in the property investment market may be unfavourable. It may then be advisable for the mortgagee in possession to manage the property and use the income to pay off the debt as well as meeting the interest due.

In valuing a property for mortgage purposes the surveyor will then need to consider two matters. First, the re-sale value of the property should be sufficient to cover the amount of the loan plus incidental costs. If this is not so, then the mortgagee will suffer a loss. In certain circumstances where the loss suffered is due to the surveyor's valuation being too high, the surveyor himself may be held to be negligent. Secondly, in the case of premises which are tenanted, or are to be tenanted, the surveyor may need to consider whether or not the net rental income from the property will be adequate to cover the repayments. Clearly it would be unwise in most cases for a mortgagee to advance money on the security of a property investment in circumstances where the income from the investment is less than the mortgage repayments.

Certan types of property represent good security for mortgage advances. Owner-occupied houses with vacant possession and in good condition are good security since there is a broad market for such houses in most localities in all save the most dire economic circumstances. Residential investments are a less satisfactory security especially as the net income will rarely be sufficient to cover the repayments on a substantial percentage advance. In modern times, much of the value of such investments lies in their potential for future vacant possession and such values are prone to the effects of general economic circumstances, interest rate changes and changes in legislation.

Commercial, industrial and other types of building will have market values and potential rental incomes which will vary greatly in different localities and in different economic circumstances. The more specialised or remote such a property is, the greater will be the degree of risk of a fall in value. Some types of older industrial building may become unsaleable or unlettable in time if a suitable alternative use cannot be found. The implications of such a situation for the mortgagee will clearly be very serious.

In making a valuation of a property for mortgage purposes, the surveyor should follow the ordinary principles of good practice. Since this book is not intended to cover the principles of valuation, it is not proposed to discuss techniques. However, there are certain matters which will have to be confirmed during the course of the survey of a building for a prospective mortgagee because the information is needed in order to prepare a valuation.

The first of these matters to be ascertained is the condition of the building. Although the survey may not be a full structural survey and the inspection may be abbreviated, nevertheless it is not felt that any building can be valued unless the surveyor has inspected it inside and out, however superficially, and formed some view as to its condition. Clearly the possibility of serious defects in a building, especially an older building, has to be considered and if such defects are present they will need to be taken into account in formulating a valuation. If such defects are suspected but cannot be confirmed in the time available or without special exposure, then a provisional or conditional valuation may have to be issued and the prospective mortgagee will then have to consider whether to pursue the matter any further in the light of the percentage loan applied for.

It is usual for the valuation report in many cases to contain caveats or conditions having regard to the possibility of concealed structural defects, high-alumina cement concrete in widely-spanned commercial structures, and similar hidden problems. In many such cases the mortgagee will require the mortgagor to obtain a technical assessment of possible structural problems of this type as a pre-condition of any advance. This is a useful way of safeguarding the mortgagee's and mortgagor's positions since any such matters which come to light will be of interest to them and may be crucial.

Measured surveys

The second matter to be assessed is the physical size and shape of the building so that it may fairly be compared with other similar buildings for valuation purposes. This will generally require a measured survey to confirm the floor areas, clear spans, ceiling heights and usable frontages. In 1979 the Royal Institution of Chartered Surveyors and the Incorporated Society of Valuers & Auctioneers jointly published their Code of Measuring Practice. It is recommended that the practices set out in this Code be adopted wherever possible. The Code recommends that gross internal area (GIA) as defined should be used for industrial and warehouse space, although agency practice in many areas is to use gross external area (GEA) when dealing with new industrial and warehousing buildings. The Code also recommends measuring procedures for shops and residential buildings.

The purpose of an accurate measured survey is to enable the surveyor to retain in his records details of properties valued so that details of similar properties may be compared on a like-for-like basis. As long as the basis of measurement is the same, the basis of comparison will be valid and the statistical records kept for valuation purposes will be correct. With industrial and warehouse space, we would commend the use of GIA as being the fairest means of comparison, especially if older properties are being compared with more modern buildings. The usable floor space in an older building with thick walls and other obstructions may be proportionally less than the usable space in a modern structure with clear spans and thin walls. A comparison of GEA in such circumstances may be misleading.

In addition to the two foregoing important matters which have to be resolved when surveying a building for a prospective mortgagee, there are also a number of other incidentals arising during the survey which may be significant. The surveyor may see evidence of tenancies, rights of way, shared access or other complications which could be significant to the mortgagee and which should be mentioned in the report. The mortgagee may also require a pro-forma report to be completed, in which case the surveyor will need to check the questions in that report and confirm that they can be answered fully from the notes he has taken on return to his office.

The mortgagee may require a plan to be prepared showing the curtilage of the property, main plot dimensions and other means of identification such as the distance from the nearest road junction and the north point. The purpose of an identification plan is to compare the property inspected with the title plan to ensure, among other things, that the surveyor has actually inspected the correct building (the possibility of the wrong house being inspected is not as far-fetched as it may seem, especially on a new estate) and that his valuation does not include any property or land which is not part of the holding.

Having completed the survey of the building for the prospective mortgagee, the surveyor will then have to compile his report. The report may be a full structural report, or something rather less, on the surveyor's own paper; alternatively it may be completed using a pro-forma report form. In addition to the necessary description and the valuation for mortgage purposes, the surveyor may need to advise the mortgagee on questions of lending policy, either in respect of a specific property or in a general sense.

General lending policy

General lending policy is concerned with the nature of the properties upon which the prospective mortgagee may feel able to lend and the duration of the loans; the terms controlling the frequency of capital repayment and the rate of interest; and the percentage advance considered suitable in the circumstances.

A trustee, clearing bank or building society lending at relatively low interest rates over long periods will expect near-absolute security for loans. They will, quite reasonably, expect that in the event of a mortgagor's default, they will suffer no loss and the proceeds of sale will cover not only the original advance but also some margin for accumulated interest and costs. Traditionally, an advance of two-thirds or three-quarters of valuation would normally be the maximum loan in respect of good, readily saleable security. Something rather less than this, perhaps 50% or less, may be considered suitable in respect of poorer security. The margin is intended to cover not only accumulated interest and costs in such circumstances, but also the possible vagaries of the market for certain types of property. If the market for a property is doubtful then it may be that no advance at all can be contemplated by an institution at low interest rates and the prospective mortgagor may have to produce some other security. Alternatively, he made approach a lender prepared to accept a greater risk which will undoubtedly involve a higher interest rate on the loan.

During the post-War period, the building society movement has tended to advance rather higher percentages on owner-occupied dwelling-houses with loans of up to 90% or 95%. To enable them to do this, they will normally require some additional collateral such as a mortgage guarantee from central or local government, from an insurance company or a charge on another property or on a life insurance policy.

A surveyor may be called upon to advise a prospective mortgagee on loans being made at higher than normal interest rates on the security of properties which may be declined for this purpose by clearing bank or building society. In this situation it is as well that the lending policy of the clients be clarified at the outset and that the surveyor is able to exercise his judgment in the light of that policy so as on the one hand to protect his client's interests and on the other hand to allow sufficient flexibility for a suitable agreement to be reached.

Mortgagees who advance money at higher than normal interest rates will normally have to accept that the quality of the security offered or the status of the borrower is lower than may be ideal. The higher interest rates which they may charge are intended to reflect this additional risk. Such lenders may be prepared to advance money on the security of residential investment property where the net income is lower than the mortgage repayments, relying upon the borrower's ability to finance the balance from some other source. They may be prepared to lend money on the security of vacant sites, or sites with buildings which are destined for redevelopment where there may be little or no income generated from the property, relying upon the borrower's ability to redeem the advance when redevelopment has been undertaken. They may be prepared to advance money on the security of unusual buildings which are in secondary or remote locations or buildings suffering from defects of one kind or another.

In carrying out a survey for such a mortgagee the surveyor cannot necessarily apply all the principles of lending policy which would be applicable to those mortgagees who charge more conventional lower interest rates. Each situation has to be considered on its individual merits, having regard to the fact that if all principles of good lending policy were to be applied then the institution concerned would be unable to compete with other institutions offering terms at lower rates. On the other hand, if an imprudent lending policy is adopted, the end result may be a spate of defaults should there be a downturn in the property market.

Local authority mortgage

Local authorities make advances on the security of residential property and, in most cases, the intention of providing this service is to enable house-purchase to be contemplated by sections of the community who would otherwise be unable to become owner-occupiers. Local authority mortgagors tend to be younger, seeking to buy houses in the cheaper price ranges with fairly large percentage loans. Whereas a bank or building society may limit advances to 75% or 80%, the local authority may lend up to 100% of valuation, and whereas certain types of building, such as older houses, converted flats and the like, will be rejected by a bank or building society as security, the local authority may be prepared to accept such property as security for an advance. Many surveys of properties for local authorities are carried out by surveyors who are employed for the purpose by the authority as staff surveyors. Occasionally the local authority will employ an outside surveying practice to do this work.

A feature of surveys for local authority mortgages is that the property being inspected is often older and in poor condition. In the larger conurbations, the building may comprise a converted flat or apartment. In some localities the local authority may be the only potential lender in the market so that the saleability of older houses, converted flats and apartments in some districts will depend almost exclusively upon the funds which the local authority has available at the time. Since the money for local authority lending is subject to the effects of national economic policy, there will be times when funds and mortgages are granted fairly freely and other times when funds are 'tight' and the availability of council mortgages may dry up altogether.

In carrying out a survey and preparing a report on an older house in poor condition, or a converted property, the surveyor should consider whether it would be reasonable to impose conditions which could make the property more saleable in the future by making it potentially mortgageable to a lender other than a local authority. Converted flats, for example, may lack adequate soundproofing or fire-resistance between units but if these matters are dealt with, perhaps at fairly modest expense, the converted unit may be more mortgageable and therefore more saleable in the future, especially in times when council loans are difficult to obtain.

Leasehold interests

The property being offered as security for an advance may be leasehold. Residential property held on a long lease will not normally be suitable for a long-term advance by way of mortgage if the unexpired term is 30 years or less. If a term of more than 30 years is available, the repayments of capital should be so made that all capital outstanding is progressively reduced until the mortgage is redeemed when the lease still has at least 30 years to run. The reason for this is obvious – a leasehold interest is a wasting asset which will fall in real value during its life. The effects of monetary inflation will mask the fall in value for a time but once the end of the lease is in sight, the fall will be rapid. When the lease expires, the value for mortgage purposes will be nil.

If an advance is made on the security of a short leasehold interest in a residential property, the risk to the mortgagee is high because in the event of default by the mortgagor, there may be considerable delay caused by the legal procedures for obtaining possession. While this delay occurs, the value of the security may be falling. With freehold security, the mortgagee will at least normally know that increasing property values and inflation will be on his side should he find that delay is incurred in proceeding with a remedy for default.

With commercial and industrial premises, a mortgage advance is often made on the security of a lease where the period available before the lease expires, or the remaining period before the next rent review, is quite short. Such leases may have only a very speculative value. In times of economic boom it may be that substantial premiums will be obtainable for such leases, partly reflecting the profit rent (that is the difference between the rent payable and the open market rent which would be obtainable) and partly elements of goodwill, tenants' improvements, fixtures and fittings and temporary scarcity. In times of economic depression, no premium may be obtainable and tenants may be glad to able to vacate by making a straight assignment of the lease without premium. While a mortgage advance may be secured by a legal charge on the lease in such situations, the real security for the advance will not be the value of the lease but will be the ability of the borrowers to repay. If the borrowers are in difficulties, perhaps during a period of economic depression, the fact that a mortgage is secured by the value of the lease may be worth nothing to the mortgagee.

A highly cautious lending policy is therefore recommended where a short leasehold interest is involved. The surveyor should ensure that all the lease covenants have been complied with, especially covenants on usage and repair. He should carefully read the lease to confirm whether or not there are any unusual covenants which could limit the re-sale value of that lease; tight restrictions on uses, in particular, may make a lease unsaleable and therefore potentially unmortgageable. If the building is in poor order, and especially if the condition is such that a Schedule of Dilapidations may be served, the property may need to be put into good repair as a condition of any mortgage advance, and probably as a pre-condition of some, or all, of the advance being released.

When surveying a leasehold property for a prospective mortgagee it is suggested that the surveyor should make a point of reading the lease. The only exception might be in the case of residential property where normal lease terms may be assumed for the purpose of the mortgage valuation and where the mortgagee's solicitors will be able to confirm this and refer back to the surveyor if unusual terms are found to apply. In many cases a building society or bank valuation will have to be undertaken on this basis and a provisional valuation given without the surveyor having seen the lease.

Insurance

A report for a prospective mortgagee will often include advice as to a suitable amount of insurance cover and the mortgage deed will normally provide that the building is to be insured in the joint names of the mortgagee and the mortgagor.

In addition to insurance against fire, there is a wide range of other perils against which cover may be recommended, including impact damage, explosion, storm, tempest, flood, burst pipes and tanks, subsidence, landslip, ground heave, public liability, plate glass, trade fixtures and fittings and loss of rental income or loss of profits. Not all such perils will arise in every case. Subsidence, landslip and ground-heave cover is normally available for residential buildings but not in other cases. Plate glass and consequential loss cover will apply to certain types of commercial premises.

The insurance should cover all buildings used as security for the advance unless they are not significant to the re-sale value. The sum insured should be adequate to cover the cost of reinstatement in the event of a total loss. If the sum insured is excessive, the mortgagor will be penalised by having to pay excessive premiums. If the sum insured is insufficient then difficulty could arise in the event of a claim not only for a total loss, which rarely occurs, but for a partial loss. The insurers may, in a case of obvious under-insurance, average the claim by paying only in proportion to amount of cover as it relates to the full reinstatement value. For example, if a building is insured for £100 000 and its true rebuilding cost would be £200 000, the insurers may be prepared to pay only 50% of any claims made for insured perils.

In the case of building societies they will generally act as agents for the insurance company who insure all their mortgage securities, often under a single block policy. The surveyor undertaking an inspection of a building for a building society or other institional lender may need to provide an estimate of the reinstatement cost for insurance purposes and also advise the lenders of any obvious insurance risks which they should then relay to the insurance company.

In low-lying or coastal areas, property could be subject to flooding, and often enquiries have to be made where a building is low-lying in order to ascertain whether or not there is a flood risk. In such cases the insurers may refuse to provide the cover for flood damage or may require additional premiums. Properties with thatched roofs or other types of potentially flammable construction may be subject to premium loading. Buildings located at potentially hazardous points adjoining road junctions or fast sections of highway may be prone to impact damage. Certain types of construction could be prone to storm damage, especially lightweight structures in exposed locations. Subsidence, landslip or ground heave cover may be restricted where a building already shows signs of existing or past structural distress.

It is a rule of insurance law that the parties must disclose any matters which could be relevant to the degree of risk and it is incumbent upon a surveyor who notes any such matter to bring it to the attention of the mortgagee in his report so that the insurers may be suitably advised.

The amount of insurance cover assessed by reference to rebuilding costs current at the time should be periodically reviewed and it is good practice to provide that the sum insured be altered annually in line with changes in building costs. Most insurers of buildings have some procedure for automatic adjustment of the sum insured along these lines. If no such procedure applies, it is suggested that the mortgagees should themselves undertake to review the amount of insurance cover each year to safeguard their position.

The Building Cost Information Service of the Royal Institutional of Chartered Surveyors publish an annual *Guide to House Rebuilding Costs for Insurance Valuation* on behalf of the British Insurance Association. This guide refers to costs of demolishing and clearing away an existing structure and rebuilding it to its original design in modern materials and with modern techniques to the same standard as the original property but to comply with Building Regulations and other statutory requirements. This information is essential where reinstatement costing advice is to be given.

Second and subsequent mortgages

In additional to the provision of first mortgages, it is possible for financial institutions or individuals to lend on the security of second mortgages, or even third or subsequent mortgages.

Clearly, the degree of security for second or subsequent mortgages will be less than that afforded by first mortgages. The second or subsequent mortgagee will be able to recover his amount owing only after the amounts owing to the first mortgagee have been satisfied as far as this is possible out of the proceeds of sale. In effect, the mortgagees have to take their turn in the queue if a mortgagor defaults and the property used as security is sold. It may be that a second or subsequent mortgagee will find it difficult or impossible to recover his debt if the amount owing under the first mortgage is substantial and if there are accumulated costs and interest charges also owing to the first mortgagee.

Having regard to the higher risks attaching to second or subsequent mortgage advances, the interest rates charged are generally higher and the terms for capital repayment often of shorter duration. If a surveyor is asked to survey a building to be used as security for a second or subsequent advance by way of mortgage, then he should find out the amounts of capital outstanding under any first or former mortgages so that he is aware of the amount of the borrower's equity in the property and the extent to which any further mortgage advance will be covered.

If the degree of cover for the second or subsequent mortgage is poor then great caution should be exercised in preparing any valuation and in making any recommendations, bearing in mind the particular need to safeguard the future re-sale value of the security in the light of the state of repair of the premises and all other circumstances.

Chapter 18

Specimen house reports

For if the trumpet give an uncertain sound, who shall prepare himself to the battle? So likewise ye, except ye utter by the tongue words easy to be understood, how shall it be known what is spoken?
St Paul

This Chapter gives specimen copies of reports (the first being on a house in North London, the second on a house in the West Country) which may be typical of structural survey reports prepared by general practice surveyors.

In putting these forward as specimen reports, we realise that other surveyors have their own procedures and forms of drafting which differ from the examples given. Some readers may be critical of the style and content and, since all report styles are subject to gradual change and improvement, in the future these layouts may seem dated just as does the layout of reports prepared some years ago compared with modern practice. The increasing use of word processors for this purpose should have an effect on style and content of reports by streamlining the drafting process.

It would be impossible to attempt to standardise the layout for such reports but the format recommended in the RICS Practice Note should be followed. These reports were prepared for specific clients in accordance with their particular requirements.

In order to facilitate the drafting of reports standard report clauses may be used since even for buildings which differ considerably in use and construction, there are clauses which could be commonly used. For example, dealing with drainage:

'*Manhole covers* – We recommend that all manhole covers be lifted, cleared, greased and re-set to provide an airtight fit'.

or with construction

'*Joinery* – Standard painted softwood architraves, skirting boards and other interior joinery are provided'.

or with condition

'*Structure* – We can report that there are no signs of unusual movement or settlement to the main walls and the underlying structure would appear to be stable'.

Such specimen clauses amplified and structured to meet the individual surveyor's requirements could be suitable for programming into a word processor but must be used with discretion and continually reveiwed and updated in the light of current practice and experience.

Specimen report on dwelling-house

SEARCH & PROBE

Chartered Surveyors

R.E. Search, FRICS   I. Probe, FRICS

> Crumbling Chambers,
> 1a High Street,
> Weathering,
> London, NW1.

A. Client, Esq.,
100 Concerned Street,
Worrying,
Hants.

Dear Sir

re 48 SUBURBAN ROAD, LONDON NW1

We thank you for your instructions to prepare a report on the above property in accordance with the terms set out to you in our letter of 1st June 1982 confirming the nature of our instructions and the extent of the proposed survey. The property was inspected on 10th June 1982 during a period of warm dry weather with the interior occupied and we have to report as follows:

GENERALLY

1.   This report shall be for the private and confidential use of the client for whom it is prepared and should not be reproduced in whole or in part or relied upon by third parties for any use without the express written authority of the surveyors.

2.   The inspection did not include any parts of the structure which were covered, unexposed, inaccessible or below ground, and we are therefore unable to report that such parts are free from defect.

3.   Direction 'right' or 'left' are always taken as if viewed facing the property from the highway at the front.

4.   All measurements and dimensions are approximate or nominal only and should not be used where accuracy is required.

5.   If further clarification of matters raised in this report is required or additional advice regarding the property, please do not hesitate to let us know.

6.   All property owners are advised to ensure that their property is insured from the moment of exchange of contracts, for a sufficient sum against all usual perils including fire, impact, explosion, storm, tempest, flood, burst pipes and tanks, subsidence, landslip, ground heave and public liability.

SITUATION
7.   The house is situated on the north side of Suburban Road facing south so that the sun will shine towards the front of the house for the main part of the day and the prevailing weather will tend to drive towards the front and left side from the south west. For these reasons you may expect to find that the paintwork and woodwork will need attention more frequently at the front.

8.   We understand that Suburban Road is an adopted highway and that no road charges, either capital or periodic in nature, are payable and your solicitor should confirm this.

9.   It is understood that the house is freehold with an unencumbered absolute title and your solicitor should confirm this. He should also confirm whether it is subject to any unusual restrictive or other covenants and whether you would be liable for specific boundary fences, drains or other matters if you buy the property.

10.   The property is located within the area of the Greater London Council and the London Borough of Brent.

11.   We understand that the property lies within an area designated for residential purposes on the district and structure plans for the area. Your solicitor should confirm this and confirm that the property is not a non-conforming user.

12.   We have not made any searches or enquiries regarding Notices, Orders, Planning Schemes or other matters likely to affect the propety and we assume and recommend that your solicitor will deal with these in the usual way.

13.   The plot is rectangular with a frontage to the highway of 11 metres and an overall depth of about 30 metres. The front garden is about 6.5 metres deep and the rear garden about 14 metres deep. There is a driveway and pavement cross-over to the highway at the front.

14.   The site where the building stands slopes upwards from the highway at the front with a gradient of about 1 in 10. The house is located on high ground with views from the front towards the south.

15.   The subsoil in this locality, as indicated on the geological survey map for the area, is a stiff bluish-grey clay being London clay of Eocene origin. We must emphasise that we have not made any trial bores or other site investigations to confirm the nature of the subsoil under the house so we are unable to describe or comment upon actual conditions. From our own local knowledge, however, from

excavations made in the adjoining road, we would expect to find the geological survey map information confirmed.

16.   Clay soils of this type normally provide a good foundation base when stable and have a high bearing capacity. They suffer a disadvantage, however, in that they are subject to volumetric change with changes in water content resulting in seasonal shrinkage and swelling of the soil near the surface. When clay shrinks it undergoes a significant and irregular reduction in its bearing capacity. When it becomes wet again it swells, causing a heaving-up of the ground.

17.   It is important that foundations on shrinkable clay rest in the soil below the level to which seasonal changes may be significant in the most extreme conditions for which provision might reasonably be expected to be made. Foundations to older property tended to be laid rather shallower than would nowadays be recommended. On the assumption that the subsoil is shrinkable and that the foundations to the house are of the traditional shallow type (neither assumption having been confirmed by exposure), we would make the following three recommendations.

18.   First, as a general rule, trees and bushes should not be permitted closer to the main walls than their mature height. Trees with a known high rate of root suction, such as poplars, willow and elm, are best avoided altogether in a garden setting on this type of soil. This is recommended because the leeching effects of tree roots can hasten and exacerbate the drying out of the subsoil during periods of dry weather, thus causing the subsoil to shrink at foundation depths and below and resulting in damage to structures.

19.   No trees are presently closer to the house than this distance and this situation should be maintained.

20.   Secondly, we recommend that the ground immediately around buildings with shallow foundations on clay be covered with paving for a width of 1 metre and not used as dug soil or for planting. This paving will assist in retaining moisture in the ground around foundations by reducing surface evaporation.

21.   It is suggested that some building up of the ground against the front elevation, and ground cover, would be advisable in this respect. The ground cover around the other elevations is satisfactory.

22.   Thirdly, it is important to maintain the rainwater pipes and gullies around the building, and the underground drains, in good condition and flowing freely since a point discharge of either stormwater or waste water into the soil immediately around foundations can cause damaging subsoil erosion and other effects. There is at present no access to the storm drains and we do not know where these run or what condition they are in. A number of storm gullies are provided for rainwater pipes and the paved areas.

23.   It is suggested that a point be made of checking the storm drains during a period of heavy rain to ensure that they flow away freely. Blocked storm drains should be rodded and if necessary re-laid so that they function correctly.

24.   For further comments on the drainage system please see later in this report.

25.   The driveway has a fairly steep upward slope from the highway which could be a problem in icy weather. The driveway concrete surface is at present worn and frost damaged.

26.   Close-boarded fences are provided as boundaries to the rear garden. No effective boundaries or gates are provided at the front.

DESCRIPTION
27.   The property comprises a two-storey detached house being one of a number of similar privately-owned houses erected in this locality in the inter-War period.

28.   The house is generally of conventional appearance and construction for its age.

29.   From the construction used we would estimate that it was built in about 1935.

30.   Some modernisation of the interior and renewal of services have been carried out in the past. The basic structure is original and has not been extended.

ACCOMMODATION
31.   On the first floor
LANDING with trapdoor to roof space
Airing cupboard.
FRONT RIGHT BEDROOM 1.   (3.30 m × 4.30 m)
FRONT LEFT BEDROOM 2.   (2.50 m × 4.10 m)
REAR LEFT BEDROOM 3.   (4.00 m × 2.25 m)
REAR RIGHT BEDROOM 4   (3.35 m × 3.00 m)
(plus cupboards)
BATHROOM   (1.70 m × 3.20 m) with bath, basin, bidet and WC

32.   On the ground floor
PORCH
HALL with meter cupboard
FRONT LIVING ROOM   (3.30 m × 4.20 m)
REAR LIVING ROOM   (4.00 × 3.30 m)
(plus bay)
KITCHEN   (3.60 m × 3.30 m)
INTEGRAL GARAGE   (2.40 m × 4.90 m)

33.   Outside
Front and rear gardens with STORE SHED.

CONSTRUCTION

34.   The main exterior walls are of solid 225-mm brick construction, having been rendered with a roughcast at the rear and sides and painted, and having a front elevation of painted roughcast panels and planted timbers at first floor level (in 'Tudor' style) and an elevation of brown facing brickwork at ground floor level at the front.

35.   Solid walls of this type are no longer permitted for residential construction, having been superseded in this locality after about 1938 by cavity walls, and nowadays cavity walls with an inner skin of insulation block would be used as these provide better thermal insulation and resistance against weather penetration. If you buy an older house with solid walls you should appreciate that its performance in these respects will not be as good as modern cavity construction.

36.   It is important with solid wall construction especially to ensure that the exterior elevations are maintained in good condition as a first barrier against the weather and that particular care is taken to avoid leaks or spillages from gutters, downpipes and overflows as dampness can penetrate directly to the inside.

37.   Having said this, it will also be appreciated that if you are interested in buying a pre-1938 house in this area, solid-wall construction will be the rule rather than the exception.

38.   The damp-roof courses at the base of the main walls are covered with a rendered cement plinth externally and cannot be seen from outside without removing some of this (which we have not attempted at this stage). Where seen the damp-proof courses to main walls, internal walls and sleeper walls appear to comprise a mixture of slates and bituminous felt strips but these have not been generally exposed for inspection in all areas.

39.   We are unable to confirm at this stage the nature of the lintel construction over openings in the main walls. However, concrete lintels of some kind appear likely. Occasionally timber lintels have been found to have been used in older houses in this locality and these are less satisfactory in solid wall construction since they deteriorate in the presence of dampness.

40.   The internal walls appear to be a mixture of brickwork and blockwork with brickwork used for the main spine walls and blockwork used for the lightweight partitions, including some eccentrically-loaded partitions which are mounted on the floors at first floor level. We cannot confirm the nature of the internal wall construction in all areas without exposure and we have not attempted this at this stage.

41.   The main roof has a covering of double-lap, machine-made clay tiles on feather-edged boarding, supported by a framework of sawn softwood timbers. The roof slopes are not felted with sarking felt, felted roofs having been general practice in this locality only since about 1938. As a consequence the roof will be less weathertight than a modern felted roof and the roof void is very dusty. The main roof is of hipped rectangular layout with two short hipped projections at front and

rear and one lower gable-end projection at the front which is finished in rendered blockwork and has non-structural timbers as a facing.

42.   The roof timbers comprise 100 mm × 50 mm rafters and joists at 400-mm centres with central 175 mm × 75 mm purlins to each roof slope; 175 mm × 75 mm and 175 mm × 50 mm hip, ridge and valley boards; five 175 mm × 50 mm vertical purlin struts; eight 100 mm × 50 mm angled purlin struts (strutting being taken from the main spine walls); and four 100 mm × 50 mm binders. The layout and dimensions of the roof timbers are normal for construction of this type although slightly more complex than usual, and all roof forces are satisfactorily resolved in the design.

43.   There is a ground-floor rear bay roof, also of machine-made clay tiles on a timber framework and of conventional hipped design. No access is provided into the void for the bay roof and we have not inspected within this area. If the opportunity arises it would be a good idea to have conditions in this roof void checked. At present we cannot describe or comment upon the construction which is hidden.

44.   Roof water drains via cast-iron gutters and rainwater pipes.

45.   There is a single-flue boiler chimney stack at the rear of the house. Another stack did exist on the left side but this has been removed and the roof tiled over at this point. There are also three flue vents provided which originally would have served gas fires but which are now redundant. Lead flashings and zinc soakers are provided to the stack and flues where seen.

46.   Ceilings are of lath-and-plaster construction and original. The life of lath-and-plaster ceilings depends upon the quality of the original job and the degree of exposure to dampness from roof and plumbing leaks and the amount of stress from flexing and so forth. Generally a life span of between 50 and 100 years is typical and it follows that the existing ceilings will reach a point where problems may be experienced. The plaster key was sound in the areas tested during our inspection but will not always remain so.

47.   Floors are of suspended timber construction with the upper floors being of butt-jointed boarding on 175 mm × 50 mm joists at 400-mm centres where seen and the ground floors being butt-jointed boarding resting on 100 mm × 50 mm joists at 400-mm centres on sleeper plates and honeycombed sleeper walls where seen. The sub-floor area varies slightly in depth, being deeper at the front of the house (following the site gradient to some extent). A series of air vents is provided at the base of the main walls to ventilate the sub-floor void and it is important to keep these vents clear.

48.   Fenestration comprises outward-opening painted softwood casement windows having leaded lights to the front and with leaded lights and coloured glass to the hall and stairwell windows. These are original except for the kitchen rear window which is a more modern type and replaces the original unit in this room. Timber sills are fitted inside and out.

49.   Standard painted softwood architraves, skirting boards, panel doors and other interior joinery are provided, the doors having been modernised by flush-facing in most cases. A glazed sliding door is provided to the front living room, probably not original.

50.   The garage is located beneath Bedroom 2 and has a concrete floor with screed finish, set down lower than the main ground floors. The interior walls of the garage are rendered in a cement rendering. The ceiling is of plaster.

51.   Two important factors should normally be covered in the design of an integral garage. First there should be a reasonable standard of fire-resistance between the garage and the remaining accommodation in case of a petrol fire. Generally the ceilings should be lined with fire-resistant material, such as asbestos cement sheets or dense plasterboard, and fire-stopped. Secondly we would mention that the heat losses through the floor of the room above will be considerable unless steps are taken to insulate the floor, and 100 mm of fibreglass quilt tightly fixed to the undersides of the floorboarding would be recommended for this purpose.

52.   We are unable to say whether a good standard of fireproofing and thermal insulation is provided but on current evidence this would seem doubtful and a check on both matters would be recommended.

53.   We do not know if any insulation is provided over the ceiling to the rear bay but we would suspect not and would suggest that 100 mm of fibreglass quilt or equivalent be laid between the joists over this ceiling if the opportunity presents itself, as this will reduce heat losses from the rear living room.

54.   25 mm of fibreglass quilt is laid in the main roof space over the ceilings. This is a fairly low level of insulation by modern standards and could usefully be increased by further layers of quilt to 100 mm in depth which is the optimum recommended at the present time. (You can, of course, always add more). Quilt should be tucked down neatly between the joists leaving a gap under the tanks which themselves should be covered and well lagged, together with all exposed pipework (including overflows).

55.   Certain steps can be taken to improve insulation to the main enclosing walls if you wish, which are solid as already mentioned, and subject to considerable heat losses to the outside. One method would be to line the exterior walls inside with 3 mm polystyrene as a backing to wallpaper and this will compensate to some extent for the lack of cavity construction. It has a disadvantage in that the wallpaper will dent if knocked.

56.   The garage has a steel up-and-over door, and power, lighting and water supplies are provided in the garage.

57.   Cupboards are provided in the porch and hall and a range of painted whitewood cupboards and a breakfast bar are fitted in the kitchen. Fitted cupboards are also provided in Bedrooms 1 and 4.

58.   Sanitary ware comprises a modern bathroom suite of bath, basin, WC and bidet, and a double-drainer, double-bowl sink unit is provided in the kitchen. The house appears to have been modernised and the fittings renewed within the last ten or fifteen years. Generally the kitchen fittings are again becoming somewhat dated and you will no doubt wish to examine the various fittings to confirm whether these meet your requirements.

CONDITION
Main walls and structure

59.   We carried out a careful examination of the wall surfaces inside and out. We also tested walls selectively for dampness.

60.   We can report that there were no signs of unusual movements or settlements to the main walls and the underlying structure would appear to be stable.

61.   Tests for dampness were made on a warm dry day with the interior occupied and ventilated. Results obtained under different conditions could be different in some circumstances.

62.   We can report that there were no signs of any general damp problem in the house but evidence was found of certain local areas of dampness, indicated by high test readings and staining to decorations, and these are discussed below.

63.   We would preface our remarks regarding local damp areas by saying that it is understood that the house had been empty until quite recently for a period of about 20 months and that we are told that it has been left unheated and closed up for this period. The present owner has apparently only recently resumed occupation.

64.   In the rear living room we found a damp stain to the left side wall about mid-height, adjoining the front wall light, and about a square metre in extent. A reading of 10 (out of a possible maximum of 10) was obtained on testing, indicating that the wall plaster is wet and that deterioration of plaster and decorations at this point will occur. This appears to be local rain penetration due to defective guttering and the condition of the exterior elevation at this point. The source of dampness should be traced and eradicated and the wall plaster and decorations made good when the wall has thoroughly dried out.

65.   Also in the rear living room we found slight staining to the wallpaper at the base of the walls in the rear bay and rear corners. Test readings of 1 to 3 were obtained locally but in most parts the wall plaster was quite dry. The exterior ground clearance is adequate and there is no evidence of general failure of the damp-proof courses so that, again, some local penetration appears responsible, probably from the splashing from leaking gutters on the paving at the base of the wall. The fact that this wall faces north means that following heavy rain it will dry out more slowly than would be the case at the front of the house.

66.   In the front living room there was a patch of soft and loose wall plaster on the right side of the front wall under the window sill. A reading of 4 was obtained at this point. Again, local rain penetration is responsible and the source of dampness

should be traced and eradicated and the wall plaster and decorations made good when it has dried out.

67.   In Bedroom 4 there was a damp stain to the wall on the right side corresponding in location to the base of the boiler chimney-stack and outer wall corner. The source of this dampness should be traced and eradicated and the wall plaster and decorations made good.

68.   At the time of our inspection the vendor was having the exterior walls, facing timbers, woodwork and ironwork prepared and redecorated. The work had only just begun so that it is not possible for us to comment on the standard of finish to be achieved. It will be appreciated that the exterior painted elevations need to be prepared and painted with a weather-resistant finish which will also allow the surfaces to breathe if a suitable long-lasting result is to be obtained. Considerable attention to the gutters and rainwater pipes is needed. All gutters need clearing out and all falls and joints should be checked. Having regard to the age of the guttering we would suggest that an all-uPVC gutter and rainwater pipe system might be preferable in the long run to obviate the need for this maintenance item in the future.

Roofs and chimneys

69.   We inspected within the accessible roof void and we examined the roofs externally from ground level using binoculars and at selected points using ladders.

70.   The clay tiles used on this roof were suffering from surface lamination and there were a number of soft cracked and slipped tiles. This problem is a feature of certain types of machine-made clay tiles due to efflorescence of dissolved salts in the tile clays (salts crystallising and breaking up the surface) and also to frost damage, especially on northern slopes.

71.   The present condition of the roof covering is unsatisfactory and requires attention. Two possible courses of action are open to you. First, you could have the roof stripped and re-covered in new tiles on battens and sarking felt over the existing timbers. We would recommend this as being the best long-term solution. The present covering is now about 50 years old and a life span for this tile of between 40 to 60 years is generally considered reasonable. Re-covering the roof slopes would be a considerable expense.

72.   The second possible course of action would be to have the roof slopes overhauled and all cracked, soft and slipped tiles replaced and a general check made on the detailing around stacks and flues so as to make the roof fully weatherproof. Further periodic roof inspections and overhauls from time to time in the furture would then be necessary also. This would be more economic but we would emphasis that in this situation the condition of the roof tiles is likely to continue to deteriorate in the longer term and that the question of their condition may well arise again on any future re-sale of the house.

73.   The tiles to the bay roof are of the same type and similar comments apply although at present they are in better condition than those on the main slopes, perhaps because the degree of exposure is less severe.

Joinery and woodwork

74.   We inspected the timbers in the main roof void and carried out a sample inspection of the floor timbers.

75.   The void under the stair which lies behind and over the garage is inaccessible, as is the void over the rear bay roof. The floors were covered with fitted carpets when we inspected and our inspection of the floors beneath has been of sample areas of the boarding where carpets could conveniently be rolled back without causing damage. No inspection of the kitchen floor is possible as the boarding in this room has been covered with tiles and we have not disturbed these at this stage.

76.   In the main roof void we found flight holes and bore dust of the common furniture beetle to the surfaces of the rear purlin and rear central valley board. General infestation of the roof timbers has not taken place and no roof timbers have been structurally weakened. As a precautionary measure we recommend that the insulation be lifted, all rubbish and debris removed, the timbers dusted down, and that all timbers in the main roof void be sprayed until refusal with a suitable insecticidal preservative.

77.   If you wish, this timber treatment could be undertaken on a do-it-yourself basis or by a jobbing builder, in which cases there would be no documentary evidence of treatment for production on any subsequent re-sale of the house. Alternatively you could employ a specialist contractor who will normally provide a free report and estimate and issue a warranty. If this is done, it is important that the contractor is reputable and that you appreciate that the warranty will be conditional and will apply only to the timbers treated.

78.   Having regard to the age of the house and the presence of furniture beetle in the roof, we recommend that all the floors should be exposed and checked for rot, beetle and other defects. This will involve lifting the fitted coverings and tiles in the kitchen. During our inspection we found that the floors in the front living room and rear bay were rather springy underfoot and the condition of the sub-floor joists and wall plates should be checked. There are some loose floorboards in the kitchen under the tiles and conditions under this floor should also be checked, paying special regard to the condition of perimeter wall plates and areas where dampness may be present.

79.   A full timber survey and inspection of the type recommended is best undertaken with the house empty of furniture and floor coverings, otherwise carpet fitter's and remover's attendance is necessary. If you wish, we can arrange for the necessary inspection and exposure work, or the specialist contractor already referred to, could be consulted.

80.   Some attention is required to the exterior woodwork to window frames, facing timbers and so forth and this was in hand when we inspected. We are unable to comment on the work since it has only just begun. We would mentioned that the preparation of sills and lower frame members needs particular attention and that some wet-rot is apparent to the porch outer doors which have filling repairs at the base. Filling repairs for exterior timber are not recommended. The only suitable

repair is the cutting away of soft wood well back from the point of decay and the splicing-in of new pre-treated wood by jointing and fixing with dowels.

General matters

81.   You should allow for the subsequent preparation and redecoration of the interior walls, ceilings and woodwork in accordance with your own personal tastes.

82.   Preparation of wall plaster should include the various soft and damp areas already mentioned. We also found small local areas of hollow or shelling plaster under wallpaper in Bedroom 4 to the rear right side corner, and if the wall plaster in the house is exposed the opportunity should be taken generally to probe and check the surfaces and make good as necessary.

83.   The sliding door to the front living room is slightly warped.

84.   There is some lifting ceiling paper and mould growth to the cornices in the porch, probably as a result of condensation if the house has been left closed up for a period. Some ventilation into this porch from the outside might be recommended if the problem persists, although probably the air changes involved in normal occupation will be sufficient to deal with the problem.

85.   The tiles in the kitchen are laid directly over the floorboarding, which is bad building practice, and this has resulted in cracking to the tiles at the boarding joints. The whole floor is now of poor appearance and needs re-laying. Tiles or roll vinyl flooring should be laid over a suitable plywood or hardboard backing with the joints in the back overlapping joints in the boarding to form a rigid base, in order that the needs of the surface finish are met. It is recommended that this be done after the necessary sub-floor checks have been made. (See para. 78 above).

86.   Some wall tiles in the kitchen around the boiler are loose and need attention.

87.   There is a narrow lateral crack line over the brick course above the garage door lintel, indicating that the brickwork has loosened slightly in the past due to slight bedding down of the lintel. This is not serious at present and requires no specific attention other than a pointing in of the mortar joint.

88.   On each side of the front elevation there are pathways to the rear garden with brick archways bonded to the main walls. These arches may be subject in the future to differential movement relative to the main walls as a result of local ground movements, especially if the pier foundations are shallower than those to the house (which is probable). Ideally, the archways should be separated from the main outer walls by an open joint, damp-proof course or movement joint, but no specific work of this type is considered necessary at present on current indications.

89.   The undersides of the roof soffits (the overhangs) are of laths and rendering and particular attention to this should be paid during the decoration works as this type of rendering will be soft and loose if it has been affected by dampness in the past and may need repair prior to painting.

90.   The windows are original units, in generally fair condition for their age. The leaded glass is slightly bowed in places but basically quite satisfactory for its age. The windows were being prepared and painted when we inspected and we assume that this work will be completed to a satisfactory standard and that the windows will then prove serviceable for a further period.

91.   In the longer term, you may care to consider whether you would wish to replace windows with double-glazing or other improved units. This is obviously a matter of personal preference and taste.

92.   There is a small store shed in the rear garden. We have not inspected this and you should examine it yourself and confirm whether it meets your requirements for the purpose you have in mind.

SERVICES

Electricity

93.   The service head with meter and switch boxes are located in the meter cupboard in the hall.

94.   We have not inspected any of the hidden wiring nor have we tested the electrical system.

95.   We recommend that the system be inspected and tested by a qualified electrician and a report obtained. As far as can be seen, some re-wiring has been undertaken but we suspect that this could be partial only and that some older wiring may remain which needs renewal. Pending receipt of an electrician's report we would suggest that you allow for the possibility that some expenditure on the electrical installation will be needed.

96.   Particular attention should be paid by the electrician to the immersion heater wiring and loft wiring.

Gas

97.   The service head with meter are located in the garage. As a normal routine safety precaution we recommended that the gas service, together with any fixed gas appliances included in the sale, be inspected and tested for safety by a qualified gas fitter before the house changes hands. Gas appliances should be serviced before use. Ventilation into the kitchen of the equivalent of a 225 mm × 150 mm airbrick from the outside should be maintained at all times for the safe running of the conventional flue boiler.

Water

98.   There is an underground and rising main supply pipe to a plastics cistern in the roof space. The underground pipe and rising main are lead pipes where seen. A company stopcock is located in the front lawn.

99.   For health reasons lead pipes are no longer recommended. Old lead pipes can develop leaks, especially if run in subsoil subject to movement, and nowadays,

polythene pipes are used underground for this purpose. If you are concerned about the fact that a lead pipe is used, replacement with a new polythene main would be the best solution.

100.   Where seen inside the house the main plumbing has been renewed in post-War copper pipes in 15 mm, 22 mm and 28 mm tube. Outlets run to bath, basin, bidet, WC and sink. A lead supply off the rising main serves a tap in the garage.

101.   We must emphasise that we have not inspected any of the hidden pipework, either under floors or boxed in, so we are unable to comment upon this. No specific plumbing defects to the pipework seen were noted.

102.   Hot down-services are via a copper cylinder, located in the airing cupboard, which has an immersion heater (not tested) and an indirect flow and return by primary circulation from the boiler. The cylinder is mounted on the floor but this is not ideal practice and it would be better mounted on two 100 mm × 50 mm sleepers off the floor although we do not consider it necessary to re-locate it unless other plumbing work is being done at the same time.

Central heating

103.   There is a gas-fired boiler with conventional flue in the kitchen. This has a built-in programmer and there is a wall thermostat in the hall to control the heating circulation.

104.   The system is fed from a plastic header tank in the loft with 15-mm feedpipe and 22-mm expansion pipe from the primary circulation at the cylinder. The header tank overflow is run into the main cistern which is bad plumbing practice. This should be diverted to run separately to the eaves. The header tank platform is of poor construction and a stronger platform support should be provided. The header tank should also be properly covered and lagged.

105.   Four pressed-steel radiators and one cast-iron radiator are provided to the ground floor rooms, and five pressed-steel radiators are provided to the first floor rooms plus a towel rail.

106.   We recommended that the system be inspected and tested by a qualified heating engineer and a report obtained. We noted corrosion to one joint to the cast-iron radiator which should be checked.

107.   If the system has not been drained down recently and may have been unused for a period, it is recommended that a heating engineer be asked to drain it down, flush through, chemically cleanse the system and recharge it with an inhibitor to reduce internal corrosion which is otherwise quite rapid in this locality.

108.   If you are in any doubt as to whether the system will provide heating to meet your requirements, you are advised to consult a heating engineer and ask him to carry out a test and advise you generally on the performance of the system.

Drainage

109.   No access to storm drains below ground is provided so we are unable to describe or comment upon the system.

110.   Foulwater drains consist of a private drain running at the right side of the house with three manholes, the front manhole enclosing an interceptor and cleaning eye with fresh-air inlet. The drain runs into a public sewer under the highway.

111.   Fresh-air inlets are no longer regarded as necessary where a vent pipe is provided (as in this case) and accordingly we would suggest that this be sealed off and removed. The front manhole frame is loose and should be re-set in a new cement fillet. All covers should be cleaned, greased and re-set to ensure an airtight fit. The manholes should be hosed out.

112.   The drain flow was satisfactory when we inspected. We looked through the drains using a mirror and the pipework appears straight and clear of obstruction. As a precaution we recommend, however, that the drains be tested.

113.   We have not tested the foulwater drains at this stage. If you wish, we can prepare a Supplementary Drains Test Report for you and we must await your instructions in this respect.

114.   The gullies are of the older open-grating type which are generally regarded as unhygienic, and if you wish they could be replaced with the modern sealed-trap or back-inlet type gullies which are more satisfactory.

FIXTURES AND FITTINGS

115.   If there is any possibility of doubt as to the contents, fixtures or fittings which may be included in the sale, we recommend that vendor and purchaser prepare a list and you may care to confirm the position regarding such matters as the floor and window coverings, light fittings, etc.

SUMMARY

116.   The main points arising out of our inspection at this stage are as follows:
  (i) The condition of the roof tiles necessitating either renewal of the roof covering or overhaul.
 (ii) The furniture beetle in roof timbers and the need for general timber exposure and inspection in the house.
(iii) The various points of damp penetration and poor plasterwork involving some repair and preparation prior to internal redecoration.
 (iv) The recommended reports on the services to be obtained from electrician, gas fitter and heating engineer.

CONCLUSION

117.   We see no reason why you should not buy this house, subject to the various comments and observations indicated in this report, provided that the price is reasonable. Suitably improved and repaired the house is capable of a making a pleasant family home in a popular and convenient location.

Yours faithfully,

R. E. SEARCH, FRICS

In contrast, the following report on a simple, uncomplicated and unoccupied property was made by an experienced building surveyor using the technique of direct on-site dictation on a portable cassette recorder with the survey typed straight off the cassettes through a transcriber unit and stethoscope. In this case, the sequence and general format of the report are so familiar to both surveyor and typist that a written checklist was not necessary.

Time taken from start to finish would be approximately three hours on-site inspection/dictation and perhaps four hours uninterrupted typing.

Specimen report on dwelling-house

SEARCH & PROBE

Chartered Surveyors

R.E. Search, FRICS   I. Probe, FRICS

Crumbling Chambers,
1a High Street,
Weathering,
London, NW1.

A. Byre, Esq.,
13 Lucknow Lane,
Longworthy,
Lincs.

Dear Sir
       re 24 PRINCES ROAD, WHITCHURCH, WEST HALLAMSHIRE

STRUCTURAL SURVEY

In accordance with your instructions I have atttended at the above property and carried out a structural survey and have to report as follows.

I have not inspected woodwork or other parts of the structure which are covered, unexposed or inaccessible and I am, therefore, unable to report that any such parts of the property are free from defect.

The report on services will not include electrical wiring test or a test of the water and drainage pipes, unless especially required. My opinion and observations will be based on visual inspection of the services where these are accessible.

Central-heating, space-heating and hot-water boilers have been visually examined but no definite opinion can be given that the equipment is entirely free from defect or, if not operating at the time of inspection, that they are in good working order. A separate test and report can be arranged if so required.

This report is based on the condition of the property on the date of inspection and no liability can be accepted for any deterioration in the condition of the property after this date

GENERALLY

1.   This house is at the end of a terrace of four which were built as part of an estate for the previous Local Authority some 25 years ago and have since been sold off to private purchasers.

2.   There are all main services, i.e. mains gas, water, drainage and electricity.

3.   Princes Road is a cul-de-sac with a turn-round in close proximity to No. 24 which can also be used for additional parking spaces.

INTERIOR
Roof void

4.   The roof void is accessible by means of a generously-sized ledged and battened manhole cover giving access to the roof space. The roof is of simple pitched and gabled construction and is completely underlined with reinforced roofing felt. There were no signs of any damp penetration through this roof.

5.   Construction consists of 75×50 mm rafters at 400-mm centres supported on both slopes in mid-span by 175×75 mm purlins which are strutted down to the internal partitions.

6.   Ceiling joists are of 75×50 mm softwood at 400-mm centres and receive additional support from two 100×50 mm binders running the full length of the roof space.

7.   As well as being weatherproof, the roof is very soundly constructed indeed, all timbers being in very good structural order and the only defect being evidence of furniture beetle infestation in two of the ceiling joists over the bathroom. This is very minor and would respond to spray or brush treatment with an insecticide.

8.   The party wall at the north end is of brick construction and in good order and the gable wall at the south end is of 280 mm cavity brick construction with brickwork in good condition and no signs of any structural or settlement cracks or like faults.

9.   The roof structure receives additional support by two 100×38 mm collars on either side of the struts supporting the purlins.

10.   The chimney stack passes through the centre of the roof void, is of sound brick construction, rendered for most of its height, contains a damp course at the upper level just below the ridge and, it is understood from the present occupier, has been lined for the gas boiler. There is no sign of any damp penetration either previous or current around the perimeter of the stack where it passes through the roof.

11.   The ceilings to the first floor consist of non-foil-backed plasterboard covered with 25 mm glasswool quilt insulation between the joists. In spite of the plasterboard not being foil-backed, there is no evidence of any condensation within the roof void.

12.   The expansion tank is situated close to the chimney breast and consists of a black uPVC 4-gallon actual capacity header tank fitted with ball valve and all in good working order at the time of the survey and having a white polypropylene or similar overflow passing through the roof void. It is recommended that this overflow should be wired back to the support from the strut as at the moment it is loose. The copper expansion pipe discharges into the expansion tank and the cold water supply pipe is lagged in hessian, as is the expansion pipe for the greater part of its length. The expansion tank is not covered and not lagged and it is recommended that a cover and lagging round the outside of the tank (not underneath) should be fitted.

13.   The main header tank consists of grey fibreglass set on a substantial softwood stand and is cased in fibreglass insulation and polythene sheeting, also having a hardboard cover. It was in working order at the time of the survey and it was noted that service and expansion pipes are in copper, lagged in hessian and the overflow pipe in white polypropylene or similar passing through the gable wall. All was in satisfactory order.

14.   There is electric light fitted in the roof void and all electric wiring where seen was in white uPVC-sheathed cable, modern and in good visual order.

15.   Altogether, a good sound dry roof void, but it is recommended that the furniture beetle infestation be treated as quickly as possible before it has the opportunity to spread.

First floor

Smaller front bedroom

16.   Plaster and emulsion ceiling and frieze, walls plastered and papered, woodwork enamelled, in fair decorative order.

17.   Very sound boarded floor, very firm to the tread and covered with fitted carpeting. Where seen the boarding was in good order and the staining caused by a previous leak from the radiator valve is now dry.

18.   Four-panelled standard door with anodised lever furniture, door having warped and shrunk slightly, there being approximately between 6 and 12.5 mm gap between shutting stile and lining.

19.   Modern aluminium double-glazed window in softwood frame having two top-hung outward-opening fanlights, all in good order.

20.   A further fixed steel sash in softwood frame also in good order.

21.   Built-in cupboards over staircase bulkhead, the larger having two sliding doors top and bottom, both in working order and the lower cupboard containing the circulation piping for the central heating system and an SMC Cadet circulation pump with a cut-off valve on the cylinder side only, the pump being in working order at the time of the survey. If the pump is ever removed for maintenance or replacement it is recommended that a further cut-off valve be placed on the boiler side of the pump so that the pump may then be removed without having to drain down the copper piping on the boiler side of the pump.

22.   Adjoining this at high level is the cylinder cupboard which contains a modern copper hot-water cylinder, which is understood to be indirect, with a coil so that the primary circuit from the boiler heats the water inside the cylinder through the coil, the coil heating being on the same circuit as the central heating, i.e. a sealed circuit and not capable of being drawn off. This is an extremely satisfactory arrangement.

23.   The cylinder has a lagging jacket and an immersion heater with switch inside the cupboard and neon warning light all in working order at the time of the survey.

24.   The piping where seen was in modern copper, and wiring in uPVC-sheathed cable.

25.   There are four rows of slatted shelving for airing inside the cupboard and also a 13-amp switch socket outlet served by uPVC-sheathed cable.

26.   The door is fitted with a cupboard catch and is in good working order.

27.   Finally, there is electric light with cord pull-switch and wall-switch, also modern pressed-steel central-heating radiator underneath the larger window.

Bathroom

28.   Anaglypta and emulsion ceiling, walls part-papered part-tiled, woodwork enamelled, in good decorative order.

29.   Boarded floor sound and firm to the tread and covered with fitted carpeting (two layers). This carpeting has been laid over vinyl tiling which in turn has been

laid over some form of linoleum on top of the boarding so there are in fact four thicknesses of floor covering above the boarding precluding a full inspection.

30.   It was possible to see a part of the boarding alongside the WC pan where the floor covering had been removed, and this was dry and sound at the time of the survey.

31.   There is a galvanised-steel window in softwood painted subframe, this window being in small squares glazed in small hammered glass and in good order.

32.   Fittings consist of a coloured suite with panelled vitreous-enamelled cast-iron bath with shower fitting and mixer tap, pedestal lavatory basin with hot and cold, bidet fitting with hot and cold, and low-level close-coupled siphonic WC suite, all modern and in good visual order with the WC in good working order, not leaking at junction of pan and trap.

33.   There is electric light operated by a cord pull-switch, modern pressed-steel central-heating radiator and strip lamp with shaver point alongside bathroom cabinet.

34.   The door fitted with lever furniture, and bolt is well fitting.

Larger front bedroom

35.   Woodchip and emulsion ceiling, papered walls, enamelled woodwork, in excellent decorative order.

36.   Very sound boarded floor covered with fitted carpeting with stained boarding under fitted carpeting in good order where seen.

37.   Panelled door with lever furniture as before well fitting.

38.   Two aluminium replacement windows with top-hung outward-opening fanlights, both set in painted softwood subframes, all in very good order.

39.   Centre electric light operated by a wall-switch, and modern pressed-steel central-heating radiator under front window. Three 13-amp switch socket outlets as compared with one 13-amp switch socket outlet in the smaller front bedroom.

40.   The living room flue passes through the bedroom on the staircase wall, is in good order and the circulation pipes to the cylinder are cased in where they pass up the wall alongside.

Landing and staircase

41.   Woodchip and emulsion ceiling, papered walls, enamelled woodwork, in very good decorative order. Boarded floor covered with fitted carpeting sound and firm

to the tread with two boards under window cut out where previous radiator has been removed.

42.   Fixed galvanised-steel sash in softwood subframe forming window.

43.   Centre electric light, staircase consisting of straight flight very sound and firm to the tread with short painted softwood balustrade at landing level and sound mopstick handrail alongside staircase down to the ground floor.

Ground floor

Lounge

44.   Anaglypta and emulsion ceiling, expanded polystyrene cove cornice, papered walls, enamelled woodwork, in excellent decorative order. Front, rear and party walls tested immediately above skirting with a moisture meter but no reading given, indicating that the damp course is functioning correctly and there is no rising damp in the walls.

45.   Sound solid floor covered with fitted carpeting and thermoplastic tiles under.

46.   As this property is some 25 years old it would have been built in compliance with the strict Local Authority requirements at the time and undoubtedly the solid concrete floors to the ground floor would have incorporated a damp-proof membrane.

47.   Four-panelled door with anodised lever furniture, again slightly distorted linings, possibly due to the installation of the central heating causing the woodwork to warp very slightly but door shuts properly.

48.   Aluminium replacement windows in front and rear walls as before and both in timber subframes and in good order. These windows, it is understood, were installed some three to four years ago.

49.   Baxi Bermuda combination radiant fire/convector/boiler, the boiler providing the domestic hot water and the central heating. The convector and radiant heater were not turned on at the time of the survey but the boiler was in working order.

50.   Centre electric light and 13-amp power, there being four switch-socket outlets, two of them being doubles.

51.   The Venner time-switch and controls for the domestic hot water and the central heating are situated alongside the chimney breast together with a master switch. The circulation pipes from the boiler are cased in alongside the chimney breast and one very good point is the fact that a screwed access panel has been provided at low level. Inside this access panel is a draw-off point to drain the system.

Kitchen/dining room

52.   Anaglypta and emulsion ceiling, walls part-papered in dining area and fully-tiled in kitchen recess area, woodwork enamelled, generally in excellent decorative order but grouting to tiling over worktop alongside gas cooker requires completion.

53.   Sound solid concrete floor covered with thermoplastic tiles in kitchen and entrance area, and fitted carpet over thermoplastic tiles in dining room area. Apart from two damaged tiles in the kitchen area, the floor appears to be in good order.

54.   The entrance door has been converted to a sliding door which operates satisfactorily.

55.   There are three windows, the one to dining recess being the front window to the house is a double-glazed replacement window as for the remainder of the replacement windows, the side window is a fixed two-light softwood framed sash and the rear window a standard galvanised-steel window is painted softwood frame having opening casement and top-hung outward-opening fanlight, all in good order.

56.   External walls where accessible were tested with a moisture meter no reading was given, indicating that there is no rising damp.

57.   Fittings consist of modern kitchen units with Formica type worktops and cupboards and single-drainer stainless-steel sink with hot and cold all in very good order.

58.   Plastered brick and part-glazed screen separating dining recess from kitchen in good order.

59.   Hot and cold water supplies (where seen) in copper in good visual order, grey uPVC waste and polypropylene bottle trap underneath sink, all in very good condition. Although there is evidence of previous slight seepage from one joint in the cold water tap this is now dry.

60.   There is a modern gas convector fitting in the dining area with copper supply pipe as well as gas point for the cooker. Also centre fluorescent light to kitchen, ceiling light to dining area and adequate 13-amp switch socket outlets.

Hall

61.   Woodchip and emulsion ceiling, papered walls, enamelled woodwork, in very good decorative order.

62.   Well-fitting two-panelled glazed entrance door fitted with lever furniture, Yale pattern nightlatch and mortice deadlock.

63.   Solid concrete floor covered with vinyl tiles or similar stuck down on to concrete, this in turn being covered with fitted carpeting.

64.   A further four-panelled door, with lever furniture, leading out into back vestibule.

65.   Staircase covered with fitted carpeting leading to first floor, very solid and firm to the tread.

66.   Centre electric light, modern pressed-steel central-heating radiator with copper piping in good visual order and two-way switching for first floor landing light.

Rear lobby

67.   Previously rear passage and WC but wall between old WC and passage now removed.

68.   Ceiling and beam woodchip and emulsion, walls papered, woodwork enamelled, in fairly good decorative order but papering in old WC area somewhat rough as it has been papered over the old brickwork, there being no plaster.

69.   Solid concrete floor covered with fitted vinyl and very sound and firm.

70.   Well-fitting fully-glazed rear entrance door with two upper panels glazed, lever furniture, Yale pattern nightlatch, and it is suggested that due to the glazing, a mortice deadlock ought to be fitted for security.

71.   There is a weatherboard to the bottom of the door, also a hardwood threshold and galvanised water bar, all in good order.

72.   Note that there is also a galvanised water bar to the threshold of the front entrance door. This is an excellent feature and prevents any possibility of driving rain.

73.   Centre electric light and 13-amp switch socket outlet. High-level ventilator from old WC now blocked off and fixed softwood sash forming window, this having a ceramic tiled sill in good order.

74.   Plastics hit-and-miss vent at low level over skirting to return wall is to provide an air supply for the gas-fired boiler in the living room.

75.   Ledged, braced and battened door with Norfolk latch giving access to cupboard under stairs, door being well fitting and in good order. Cupboard under stairs has brick walls on both sides also brick front partially supporting staircase. Sloping plastered soffit floor and general condition of interior of cupboard both structurally and decoratively good.

76.   Modern consumer unit consisting of mains switches, fuseboard and meter. All in good order with uPVC-sheathed cable to meter and supplies but backboard to meter (which belongs to SWEB) suffering from considerable active furniture beetle infestation which should be treated with Rentokil injection-applied disinfestation fluid or similar as soon as possible to prevent spread of the infestation. This presumably will be the responsibility of SWEB.

Interior generally

77.   Extremely well built and well maintained having been tastefully and practically modernised. All services appear to be satisfactory and the general condition of the decorations and fittings is good.

78.   The only urgent items requiring attention are the disinfestation of the two minor areas affected by furniture beetle infestation.

79.   There are no signs of any structural or settlement cracks, no dry-rot, wet-rot, damp penetration or rising damp in the external walls.

80.   One particularly impressive feature about this property is the solidity of the brick cavity walls and in particular the brick internal partition walls 115 mm thick on both floors.

DRAINS

81.   The property is on main drainage, there being combined foul- and stormwater drainage in this instance.

82.   The house drains are accessible from a manhole in the rear garden, this having a cast-iron cover and frame, the manhole being of brick construction with 100-mm through channel, two 100 mm branches (one now disused) and the whole of the channels and branches well benched up in cement mortar. Although the cover is somewhat rusted it is easily raised and the interior of the manhole is in excellent order. The through channel takes the kitchen and bathroom wastes and the first branch the WC from the first floor. The second branch is now disused, this having previously served the ground-floor WC which now forms part of the vestibule.

83.   The drains were water-tested and were found to be in excellent working order, very free-running with the 100-mm channel and branches laid to adequate falls.

84.   There is an asbestos soil pipe and vent serving the first floor WC, this having a dome wire capping to the vent pipe which is carried up above eaves level.

85.   There are two joints to the soil pipe which possibly may require remaking, the one between bend and junction in the pipe proper and the upper joint immediately below the junction of soil pipe and vent.

86.   There is a trapped gully situated in a recess in the concrete paving in the south-west corner of the building, this being a salt-glazed stoneware trapped gully with cast-iron grating taking the uPVC waste from the ground-floor kitchen sink and also the asbestos pipe which takes the uPVC wastes from bath and lavatory basin via an asbestos hopper head into which the asbestos rainwater pipe from the rear slope of the roof also discharges. All was in satisfactory working order at the time of the survey, the fixings for soil-pipe, vent and rainwater pipe all being in galvanised metal which has also been painted, with no signs of rusting.

87.   The manufacturer of rainwater goods, stackpipes, etc. is Everite and all are carried out in asbestos.

88.   The roof water from the rear slope discharges into a half-round Everite asbestos eaves gutter which is unpainted and therefore stained. The galvanised brackets supporting this gutter are in good order and the gutter appears laid to adequate falls although it was not raining at the time of the survey. However, there are no signs of any leaks of any substance but some of the joints will probably require remaking as there are signs of seepage round three of the collars, one of which has recently been stopped in.

89.   As the asbestos tends to become porous with time, it is recommended that the next time the exterior painting is carried out these gutters could be cleaned out and then painted inside and out with a chlorinated rubber paint.

90.   The front gutter is of half-round asbestos with signs of previous seepage from four of the joints. Chlorinated rubber treatment inside and out is suggested. Galvanised brackets in very good order. The rainwater discharges through a short length of rainwater pipe into the gutter of the adjoining property No. 23 from whence it runs down a rainwater pipe which discharges within the curtilage of No. 23's property.

EXTERIOR

Roof

91.   Pitched and tiled with dark brown concrete interlocking tiles and half-round concrete ridge, all in excellent order. Square brick chimney stack with concrete capping and louvred flue terminal for gas boiler, all in good order as are the lead stepped and apron flashings at junction of stack and roof.

Walls

92.   Of 280-mm brick cavity construction with non-insulated cavities and internal floor level above external ground level at all points.

93.   All external wall surfaces rendered, roughcast, and painted with Sandtex stone-textured paint with the rendering very sound, on-key, and walls entirely free from any signs of structural or settlement cracks. There are also no hair cracks in the rendering.

94.   There is a black bitumen painted plinth around the whole house, this being in good order, and all tiled sills to windows are weathered to a good angle to throw away the rainwater, and also have approximately 40 mm overhang, again to throw rainwater clear. All have been painted and are in good order apart from one broken tile to the ground-floor window on the side gable elevation.

Windows

95.   Aluminium replacement double-glazed windows fitted some three to four years ago are all in excellent order. All four windows on the front elevation are aluminium double-glazed replacements, as are the rear bedroom and living room windows on the rear elevation, again in very good order. None of the aforementioned windows will require any painting.

96.   The galvanised-steel windows are in good order. Normally with the painted softwood window frames to the fixed sashes and the painted softwood subframes to galvanised windows these do rot in some properties where they have not been properly maintained but in this case, there is no evidence of any rot to any of the fixed sashes or subframes although the bottom members of the softwood frame to the side kitchen window are in need of repainting.

97.   Generally, however, all windows are in excellent order.

Doors

98.   The external doors have been commented on previously and both are in good condition, as is the brick step to the front entrance door and the concrete step to the rear entrance. Once again, the provision of hardwood thresholds and galvanised water bars is an excellent idea.

Other items

99.   High-level vent between back door and fixed sash redundant and no longer required. Louvred vent at low level between rear kitchen window and corner, again not used and having been for previous larder ventilation.

100.   Three high-level vents, one to bedroom on rear elevation, one to bathroom and front bedroom on side elevation, all now redundant and not required.

101.   Balanced flue outlet to dining room gas convector situated alongside dining room window in good order and protected by dome wire guard.

102.   Mains electricity supply cable serving this and the adjoining properties runs up the gable wall of this house, being protected in a galvanised pipe for some 5 ft. above ground level from whence it continues in a cable to the junction box high up on the gable underneath the cement verge to the roof. From this point on electricity supplies are then run along the fascia boards to the properties.

103.   Fascia boards painted softwood in good order, painted eaves soffits in good condition as also are the tiled corbels to the gable and the pre-cast concrete canopy over the front entrance. These two tiled corbels are not so much for support as for decoration as the concrete canopy over the front door is cantilevered out of the brick wall. One good point is that it has a throated underside to the front edge which will prevent rainwater from running back underneath the canopy.

104.   There is a further cast-iron manhole cover in the front drive between gable and boundary fence on the south side. This manhole cover, however, is not concerned with the property but takes a main drain which in all probability serves the adjoining properties on the south side and then runs away in an easterly direction towards Queens Road. The maintenance of this cover, manhole and drain is
not the responsibility of the owner of No. 24 but there must be some arrangements made for access by whoever is responsible for such maintenance. This matter should be checked during the searches with the deeds of the premises and any wayleaves investigated.

OUTBUILDINGS

Garage

105.   Of pre-cast concrete unit construction with pre-cast concrete panels and frame and pitched corrugated asbestos roof with uPVC eaves gutter and rainwater pipe on one side only, rainwater pipe discharging into a uPVC hopper head connected to a soakaway and gutter in need of a stopped end just above rainwater pipe outlet.

106.   Steel-framed window at rear rusting slightly, ledged, braced and battened pass-door in fair order and galvanised-iron up-and-over door working correctly at the time of the survey through spring balances but with ironwork to bolts and balancing in need of repainting.

107.   Excellent concrete floor to garage, electric light and 13-amp power fitted together with separate main switch and fuseboard serving outbuildings.

108.   Corrugated asbestos roof supported on light angle iron trusses by now in need of repainting, and sundry small holes where bolts have been fixed through sheets in need of stopping in externally with mastic.

Garden shed

109.   This is very much a home-made structure with roof consisting of double galvanised-steel up-and-over garage door laid flat, timber framing internally, timber floor, small window and rainwater disposal by a uPVC rainwater pipe at the rear. Generally in satisfactory order for a garden shed.

THE SITE

Back garden

110.   Rear and north boundaries consist of bank and hedge and south boundary is mainly delineated by the side walls of the garage and outbuilding with the adjoining house's toolshed forming the boundary towards the rear of the garden and one interwoven panel fence, all rather dilapidated and probably in need of sorting out.

111.   Concrete flagged paths with small brick path up to garage, back door and toolshed in fair order.

112.   Concrete area outside rear entrance door in very good order indeed and more recent concrete area at front of garage door with step up from area outside rear entrance. This concrete is also in very good order.

Front garden

113.   Drive consisting of 760-mm-wide concrete path with concrete strips on either side as far as the front of the gable-end to the main building but from there to the front entrance having rough chippings on hardcore finish either side of the path. For about 4.5 m back from the path weeds require removing from either side and it is recommended that the whole of the drive on either side of the path, up as far as the fully concreted portion, should be re-covered in local stone chippings bedded in cold bitumen.

114.   Leading from the drive to the front doorthere is an 800-mm-wide concrete path, this being in excellent order.

115.   The remainder of the boundaries to the front garden consist mainly of hedge with modern interwoven panel treated timber fencing on treated timber posts separating No. 24 from No. 25's drive. No. 25's drive is at a much higher level than No. 24 and it is very likely that this fence is the responsibility of the adjoining owner.

SITE AND EXTERIOR GENERALLY

116.   In excellent order and well maintained with only minor works required. External painting very good (the present owner is a painter by trade) and no external painting (other than the ground floor side window sill) required for another three years.

117.   No subsidence, settlement or structural cracks in the main building or indeed in the paths and concrete surrounds to the property.

(Signed) ....
I. Probe, FRICS
30th February 1983.

Chapter 19

Legal considerations

> The buyer is not entitled to remedy the defect and charge the cost to the surveyor. He is only entitled to damages for breach of contract or for negligence.... So you have to take the difference in valuation.... In other words, how much more did he pay for the house by reason of the negligent report than he would have paid had it been a good report?
> *Lord Denning MR – Perry* v *Sidney Phillips & Son (1982)*

Liability in contract and tort

The chief protection against claims made for negligence in respect of professional work lies in the skill and knowledge which are acquired and maintained by continuous technical study and practical experience. The law requires a standard of care and skill which would be displayed by a reasonably competent person who has the normal skill associated with the profession in question. The law does not require all members of a profession to exhibit the very highest degrees of skill which are to be found among the most eminent practitioners, and it will not normally find a professional man liable for a mere error of judgement on a difficult point.

The standard of care required is, therefore, that standard which a Court would expect to be displayed by a reasonably competent surveyor undertaking surveys and valuations of buildings. If his professional institution issues guidelines for the conduct of this type of work and if the surveyor fails to comply with those guidelines, then this will not, of itself, leave him open to a claim for negligence. However, failure to comply with such guidelines or recommendations may make it more difficult for the surveyor to defend his position should he find himself in the unhappy position of having to do so in Court.

The standard of care required from all practitioners in a profession is, nevertheless, an exacting one. The law requires that if a surveyor puts himself forward to clients as being qualified and fitted to survey buildings, then he should in fact be so qualified and fitted, and capable of achieving reasonable standards. But if he recognises when he is unable to carry out particular instructions in cases which involve matters beyond his capabilities, then he should decline those instructions.

There is little excuse for a professional man who commits a gross error when advising his client about a particular property. A gross error resulting in substantial and avoidable financial loss to the client is a situation which should never occur. Surveyors will not commit gross errors if they have studied this volume and conducted themselves in accordance with the guidelines and recommendations of their professional institutions, and have carried out careful and thorough inspections and carefully checked their reports before dispatch.

A client may, of course, buy or lease a building, or lend money on it as security and suffer a financial loss in the future due to some unforeseen event, the nature of which no reasonably competent surveyor, carrying out specific instructions of a particular kind, could be expected to foresee. Liability in such circumstances will not arise and the surveyor may have a clear conscience that the loss suffered, while obviously regrettable, was not a matter about which he should feel responsible. The only protection for a client against events of an unforeseen nature is insurance in so far as insurance may cover the type of loss involved. It must be emphasised that a surveyor's report is not an insurance policy, and clients should not regard it as such.

It is to be hoped, therefore, that no reader who is a practising surveyor will ever find himself in the position of having committed a gross error. He may, however, find himself subject to a claim from an aggrieved client in respect of some defect in a building or advice given in a report. There may be nothing of substance in the client's claim at all, or the matter may be arguable; the surveyor may find that he has acted for a client who is a 'professional' litigant who may make a habit of engaging in legal disputes of one kind or another. The purpose of this Chapter is to discuss in a general way the present state of the law relating to professional negligence and associated liabilities in England and Wales.

Surveyors should ensure that their liability for professional negligence is covered by a policy placed with a reputable insurer and that the sum insured is adequate. Other insurances should be maintained, depending upon the nature of the surveyor's practice, covering public liability and personal and employee liability. The RICS Practice Note 'Structural Surveys of Residential Property' recommends this. The sums insured should be subject to regular review in the light of the changes in property values and building costs generally and the nature of the surveyor's practice in particular. The temptation to under-insure in order to save premium costs should be resisted.

A legal liability which may arise will do so, in English law, under the law of contract where there is either a direct contractual relationship between surveyor and client or a contractual relationship which is held to include a third party; it may also arise under the law of torts where there is no direct contractual relationship but where the law provides that a duty to care exists. The law in both areas has continually evolved since the Second World War due to the establishment of a series of important legal precedents in certain leading cases. The potential liability of a surveyor towards his clients and third parties is now much greater than would have been thought possible 40 years ago. In addition, certain limitations have been placed upon the extent to which liability may be avoided by the use of exclusion clauses, particularly by the Unfair Contract Terms Act 1977.

Important and interesting cases

In order to convey the flavour of this process of evolution a number of leading and recent cases are now summarised where the Court judgements may be of interest to surveyors, having particular regard to cases which indicate the Court's reaction to particular circumstances and interpretation of the standard of care required in specific cases. The Unfair Contract Terms Act is also discussed.

Morgan v Perry (1973) 229 EG 1737

This was a case of gross negligence heard on 16 November 1973 before Judge Kenneth Jones in the Queen's Bench Division of the High Court, and it comprised a claim by Mr Morgan against a surveyor Mr Perry in respect of serious faults which developed in a house called 'Samarkand' at Cleeve Hill, Cheltenham.

Mr Morgan had obtained a report from Mr Perry and subsequently purchased the house. The claim was therefore a claim for professional negligence arising out of a contract between the parties, it being alleged that the defendant failed to exercise reasonable care and skill in and about the survey of the house, and the preparation of the report. These allegations were found proved.

The house was built upon a steeply-sloping hillside which, in fact, was so steep that the house was of split-level construction with the living rooms at first floor level at the rear and ground floor level at the front, and the bedrooms at ground floor level at the rear and forming a basement at the front. The house had been built in 1964 and the defendant surveyed the house in July 1968, issuing his report the following day. Under 'Condition external' he reported 'the structure is sound and there is no evidence of settlement'. Under 'Condition internal' he reported 'there are some hairline plaster cracks. These are of a minor nature'. Under the heading 'Opinion' he reported 'We are of the opinion that this property is structurally sound. There should be no undue maintenance costs in the foreseeable future'.

The Judge commented that the report was a remarkable document; apart from the minor hairline cracking to plaster in unspecified locations, no defect of any kind was referred to. The defendant had given the house a completely clean bill of health and the plaintiff had proceeded with the purchase. However, while laying the drawing-room carpet the plaintiff had noted that the floor was not level. Moreover, after taking occupation he had noted certain cracks in the external walls. Lacking any expert knowledge the plaintiff, at that time, had not appreciated the significance of the sloping floor or the cracks.

In May 1969 the plaintiff applied for a mortgage, and in June 1969 a survey had been undertaken on behalf of the Halifax Building Society. The Halifax surveyor found evidence of settlement, and eventually, having failed to obtain subsidence insurance, the Halifax declined to advance any money on the security of the house. In due course bore holes were sunk and advice taken. A firm of consulting engineers reported in January 1972.

Engineers reported that the topsoil to a depth of 3.3 metres was slipping on the consolidated clay beneath. The slip was taking place in the three masses; one mass was slipping rotationally; one mass was slipping so that the garage was tilting towards the house; and a general movement down the hillside was taking place. The engineers advised demolition of the house, slope stabilisation work, special foundations and a new house, this being the only way to produce a house on the site with firm and lasting foundations.

The Court decided that it was fundamental to establish the visible condition of the house in July 1968 when the original survey took place. Twelve witnesses were called to give evidence, some by the plaintiff and some by the defendant. The original owner, and vendor to the plaintiff, was called to give evidence and the Judge found that he was less than frank with the Court regarding defects which apparently arose during his period of ownership, and some filling of cracks which had been undertaken prior to sale. Whether or not the vendor had deliberately covered up the defects, the Judge found that the effect of crack filling, replastering and wallpapering which had been undertaken was the same as that of a deliberate cover-up job with the intention of making the house saleable. The Judge decided that the defendant, Perry, did not in fact observe any defects when he carried out his survey, but he found it impossible to rely upon his evidence that no defects were observable.

The Judge found that the defendant had failed to notice repointing, or the shape and extent of various cracks, repairs to plasterwork, doors not closing properly, over-painting and so forth. He commented that, human nature being what it was, there would be instances of vendors taking steps to cover up defects, and that was at least part of the reason why a prospective purchaser employed a surveyor. Considered against the fact that the house was built on a steeply-sloping site with known potential dangers, the surveyor should have undertaken a close examination of the house, which would have revealed the slopes to the floors. Evidence was given that the highway outside the house had been subsiding for many years, and the surveyor should have looked at the highway, which would have aroused his suspicions and led him to make enquiries with the highway authority. The Judge found that the defendant committed a breach of his contract with the plaintiff and provided him with a report which was so misleading as to be valueless. Accordingly, an award of substantial damages plus costs was made.

Leigh v Unsworth (1972) 230 EG 501

A case rather similar to *Morgan v Perry*, but with a different outcome, was heard before Judge Everett QC in the Queen's Bench Division of the High Court on 21 November 1972. This comprised a claim by Mr Leigh against a surveyor Mr Unsworth in respect of faults in a house called 'Greenacres' at Swallowfield, Berkshire.

The defendant surveyed the house in April 1965 and the plaintiff subsequently purchased. The writ aginst the defendant was not issued until 5 years and 51 weeks after the date of the survey, a matter which the Judge described as regrettable, especially as a further delay then ensued before the matter was finally brought to trial, so that 7½ years elapsed between the date of the survey and the date of the trial.

The house had apparently been built in about 1960 to a very poor standard, especially in respect of the main defect which was that the outer walls rested on conventional foundations but the internal walls rested on a concrete raft supported by a backfilling of loose clay and other unsuitable material, rather than conventional hardcore. It was agreed at the trial that the manner in which support was provided for the internal walls was lamentable building practice. The issue was whether, at the time of the survey, there were present sufficient indications of the existence of settlement of the internal walls and raft, such as to make a competent surveyor advise his client of the problem.

The Judge held that the duty of the surveyor in these circumstances falls into two areas. The first is actual observation, and the inferences to be drawn from the results of that observation. The second is just what is required of him by way of information, put quite broadly, to his client. In the report the defendant had stated 'Generally the property is soundly constructed and no major defects were found.

The works of maintenance and repair are generally maintenance works due to original shrinkage and drying out'. He also stated that the chimney stacks had lead flashings, whereas in fact they had cement fillets which subsequently leaked. The report stated that 'The roof was found to be strongly framed with good-quality timbers of ample-sized scantlings' and 'the ceilings were covered with fibreglass except for a proportion of the roof which was not so treated'. The defendant clamed that the main roof was poorly constructed, in that there was a complete lack of vertical hangers, and purlins were not properly strutted having individual lengths butt-jointed and cantilevered. Further that, apart from one small area, the ceilings were not in fact insulated. the plaintiff had rendered an account for builder's charges in connection with drains tests, but, it was alleged, had failed to discover a massive leak in a drain under the building.

Having moved into the building the plaintiff discovered various defects, including the fact that the kitchen floor had sunk between 12 and 18 mm. During the course of the trial evidence was given from each side as to the condition of the premises as it had developed, which was agreed to amount to a serious settlement, and the condition of the premises as would have existed at the time of the survey. The outcome was that the Judge found that three minor errors in the report had been made: the poor construction of the roof timbers; the lack of lead flashing to the stack; and the poor level of insulation.

As to the substance of the case, which was the settlement of the internal raft and walls, the Judge found that the plaintiff's case had not been made out, and an award for the three minor matters only, plus some costs, was made. The leakage of the drains was considered to have arisen after the date of the survey, and the defendant's evidence, that the drains passed a test at the time of the survey, was accepted.

Clearly, if the three minor errors in the report had not been made the outcome of the case would have been to vindicate the surveyor, in the circumstances described. The significance of the fact that the writ was served 5 years and 51 weeks after the date of the survey lies in the fact that an action for breach of contract must be commenced within six years of the date of the alleged breach. In order to be able to defend an action for breach of contract all records relating to the matter must be retained for at least six years. In respect of actions in tort the time limit may, in effect, be longer since such actions may be commenced within six years of damage resulting to the building (see *Pirelli General Cable Works Ltd.* v *Oscar Faber & Partners [1983] 1 All ER 65, [1983] 2 WLR 6)*. For this reason it is suggested that all surveyors' records dealing with surveys and reports be retained, in their entirety, without time limit.

Hedley Byrne & Co. Ltd. *v* Heller & Partners Ltd. [1963] 2 All ER 575, [1964] AC 465

In Hedley Byrne the House of Lords introduced a new principle into the common law which was that a liability arose in tort between the maker of a statement of fact and opinion and a person who may rely upon that statement of fact or opinion, even if there is no direct contractual relationship between them. Prior to Hedley Byrne the Courts had restricted liability in tort to actions, rather than the spoken or written word, and restricted the right to compensation for damage to that occasioned by physical damage rather than financial loss.

Hedley Byrne established a new type of liability in tort as being that for the spoken or written word giving rise to financial loss where the writer or speaker and the person who relies upon the advice have a relationship of proximity or neighbourhood which gives rise to a duty to care.

Dutton v Bognor Regis Urban District Council [1972] 1 All ER 462, [1972] 1 QB 373

In *Dutton* v *Bognor* the question of liability in tort was further considered, and extended. In this case the plaintiff, Mrs Dutton, purchased a house in 1960 not knowing that it had been built on made ground, in fact an old rubbish tip. It became clear, shortly after the purchase, that the house was unstable, and the plaintiff sued the local authority for negligence and breach of statutory duty in respect of the inspection of the house when under construction pursuant to their powers under the Public Health Acts and local bye-laws (since superseded by the Building Regulations). The trial Judge found that the local authority surveyor had been negligent in not noticing evidence of rubbish in the foundation trenches before they were covered-up.

The issue in *Dutton* v *Bognor* was whether the local authority owed a duty to care to a subsequent purchaser of the house. The Court of Appeal found that they did owe such a duty to care, and the significance of this is that it confirms a position in law, which is that a surveyor undertaking his work may find himself legally liable for financial loss sustained by some person whose existence may, at the time, be unknown to him. Liability may arise towards a subsequent purchaser of a building, or a mortgagee who relies upon one of his reports originally prepared for some quite different purpose.

Accordingly it is recommended that a disclaimer against liability towards third parties should always be inserted in reports. Such disclaimers may not of themselves absolve the surveyor from liability in all situations if a relationship of proximity or neighbourhood exists between the surveyor and the person who may rely upon his report. Disclaimers are in any event subject to the test of reasonableness required by the Unfair Contract Terms Act.

Yianni v Edwin Evans & Sons (a firm) [1981] 3 All ER 592, [1981] 3 WLR 843

In the High Court Mr Justice Park ruled that there was a sufficient relationship of proximity between the surveyor to a building society and the borrowers that the borrowers could sue the surveyors in tort, notwithstanding disclaimers of liability used by the building society.

In 1975 Mr and Mrs Yianni, as sitting tenants, were offered a house in North London at a price of £15 000. They applied to the Halifax Building Society for a mortgage of £12 000 which was an advance of 80% needed in order that they could buy. The Halifax instructed their surveyors, Edwin Evans & Sons, to prepare a pro-forma report and valuation of the house in the normal way. In their offer of a mortgage advance the Halifax enclosed an explanatory booklet which included a statement that the Building Society accepted no liability for the accuracy of the valuation, and that the valuer's report was confidential information used by the Society to determine whether or not an advance should be made. It was stated that if the buyers required a survey they should instruct an indepenent surveyor, and indeed this was recommended. The Yiannis did not read the booklet, and the report by Edwin Evans & Sons did not reveal any faults. In due course the Halifax lent £12000 as an 80% advance indicating that their valuation was £15000.

It transpired that some cracks had apparently appeared in the house before it had been offered to the plaintiffs, and the then owners had discvered subsidence. Some repairs and redecorations had been carried out prior to the survey. After the purchase further cracks appeared and were diagnosed as resulting from subsidence; it was found that the end wall of the house needed rebuilding, and other walls needed underpinning. By 1978 the estimated cost of repairs had risen to £18000. Edwin Evans admitted negligence in failing to notice that the building had been subject to past subsidence, in failing to take proper steps to have reasons for subsidence investigated, and in reporting to the Halifax that it was suitable security for an 80% loan. They claimed, however, that they did not owe any duty to care to the plaintiffs, with whom they had no contractual relationship and with whom there was no liability in tort.

For their part the plaintiffs contended that Edwin Evans owed a duty of care to them since they relied upon the Halifax offer as indicating that the property was worth £15000. The Judge agreed that a relationship of proximity existed such that, in the reasonable contemplation of the defendants, carelessness on their part might be likely to cause damage to the plaintiffs.

During the course of the hearing evidence was given that perhaps only 10% of house purchasers obtain an independent surveyor's report of their own, the remainder relying on the building society surveyor or their own inspections as being sufficient indication that the property is sound and worth the price. (The writers' researches tended to indicate about 20% have their own private report.) In these circumstances the Judge held that the plaintiffs were not liable for contributory negligence in failing to obtain their own report, and the defendants were found liable for substantial damages. On the facts of this case at least the Courts have decided that a purchaser is right to place some reliance upon the building society report as an indication of the condition, and value, of the property. The implications will be important for the future conduct of building society inspections (see Chapter 11).

Donoghue (or McAlister) v Stevenson [1932] All ER Rep 1, [1932] AC 562

It will be seen from the summaries of the foregoing Hedley Byrne, Dutton and Yianni cases that the range of persons to whom a surveyor may be held responsible in tort is wide, and has progressively widened in recent years. The process by which the Courts can make new law in this way is termed the doctrine of *stare decisis*, by which points of law are determined by the Courts so as to establish precedents, the decisions of the Appeal Courts having greater weight than those of the High Court, with the decisions of the House of Lords, the premier appelate court (the European Courts excepted), having the highest stand.

In *Donoghue* v *Stevenson* Lord Atkin described the range of people to whom a duty to care is owed, under the law of torts, in the following terms: 'The rule that you are to love your neighbour becomes, in law, you must not injure your neighbour and the lawyers' question "who is my neighbour"? receives a restricted reply. You must take reasonable care to avoid acts or omissions which you can reasonably foresee would be likely to injure your neighbour. Who then, in law, is my neighbour? The answer seems to be – persons who are so closely and directly affected by my act that I ought reasonably to have them in contemplation as being affected when I am directing my mind to the acts or omissions which are called in question'.

Bolam *v* Friern Hospital Management Committee [1957] 2 All ER 118, [1957] 1 WLR 582

In this case the standard of care required from a professional man was described by McNair J. as 'The test is that of the ordinary skilled man exercising and professing to have that special skill. A man need not possess the highest expert skill: it is well established law that it is sufficient if he exercises skill of an ordinary competent man exercising that particular art'.

Rona *v* Pearce (1953) 162 EG 380

In this case the extent to which a surveyor should describe and comment upon aspects of a building and the action he should take in respect of those matters which could not be inspected or confirmed was considered by Hilbery J., who said 'It is highly important to ordinary members of the lay public that a surveyor should use proper care to warn them regarding matters about which they should be warned on the construction or otherwise of a piece of property and that they should be told what are the facts. If surveyor cannot ascertain any fact he should say he was unable to ascertain it and therefore unable to pass any opinion on it'.

Perry *v* Sidney Phillips & Son (a firm) [1982] 1 All ER 1005, [1982] 3 All ER 705, [1982] 1 WLR 1297

This case, which was a claim arising out of a negligent survey, was subject to hearings in the High Court and subsequently in the Court of Appeal. The case is of interest because of the facts, and because the issue of the quantum of damages was considered; the issue on damages being whether these should be assessed on the basis of diminution of value, or cost of necessary repairs, and the date at which damages should be assessed.

In 1976 Mr Perry bought a cottage in Worcestershire for £27 000, having first obtained a report from surveyors Sidney Phillips & Son in which the latter reported that the cottage was generally in order and a reasonable buy at the price. Subsequently Mr Perry discovered a number of defects and commenced an action for breach of contract and negligence.

In the High Court the main allegations were either conceded by the defendants, or upheld by the Judge. On the understanding that Mr Perry intended to remain in the house for the foreseeable future the High Court Judge awarded damages for (i) the cost of repairing defects which the surveyors had negligently overlooked; (ii) compensation for the inconvenience and discomfort anticipated while the remedial works were being carried out, and (iii) compensation for distress, discomfort and other consequences of living in a house in defective condition. The High Court Judge further held that repair costs were to be assessed at the date of judgement, rather than the date of the breach of contract since the defendant was unable to undertake the works at an earlier date due to lack of funds. The High Court judgement on negligence was accepted by the defendants, but they appealed to the Court of Appeal on the issue of the assessment of damages.

The facts, which were not at issue in the Appeal Court, were set out in the High Court judgement ([1982] 1 All ER 1005). The defects in the property, in respect of which a lack of care in the undertaking of the survey and preparation of the report was established, included a number of defects in the roof, a blocked doorway, lack of weatherproofing to windows, a chimney stack lacking proper support', a bowed and bulging wall, water penetration to the interior and various minor defects including a loose basin and loose wall tiles. In addition, the cottage had septic tank drainage which was unsatisfactory and not functioning correctly; the drainage system was a nuisance and generated unpleasant smells.

Unfortunately, by the time this case reached the Court of Appeal the plaintiff's circumstances had changed and he had sold the cottage; it therefore followed that it was no longer possible for the plaintiff to argue the merits of 'cost of repair' as an alternative to 'diminution in value'. The original award of damages based upon cost of repair was made only on the understanding that the plaintiff intended to reside in the house as his home for the foreseeable future.

The Appeal Court reduced the damages to a figure equal to the difference between the price paid for the house, and its true value, as at the date of the purchase, plus interest as some compensation for inflation and 'vexation'; compensation for vexation being a modest recognition of the anxiety, worry and distress arising from the physical consequences of the breach. Damages were to be assessed by the official referee. The surveyors' appeal was therefore allowed on the principle that damages are assessed on the basis of diminution in value, and as at the date of the breach. Two members of the Appeal Court were careful to emphasise that the changed circumstances prompted the decision, and that 'cost of repair' was, at the time of the Appeal Court hearing, no longer arguable. The third member, Lord Denning MR, was however prepared to venture a more general opinion of the position, and he said: 'Damages are to be assessed at the time of the breach, according to the difference in price which the buyer would have given if the report had been carefully made from that which he in fact gave owing to the negligence of the surveyor.... The buyer is not entitled to remedy the defect and charge the cost to the surveyor. He is only entitled to damages for breach of contract or for negligence.... So you have to take the difference in valuation.... In other words, how much more did he pay for the house by reason of the negligent report than he would have paid had it been a good report?'.

Lord Denning added that, while damages would be assessed at the date of the breach, they would carry interest, so that by this means some protection against inflation was provided.

The Appeal Court was not required to assess damages. However, the principle of damages for vexation was confirmed, and some indication given that such sums as may be awarded under this heading should not be large; Lord Denning referred to 'modest compensation', Oliver LJ suggested that such damages would be 'not very substantial', and Kerr LJ confirmed that vexation damages were limited and not intended to deal with 'tension or frustration of a person involved in a legal dispute.... such aggravation is experienced by almost all litigants'. Vexation damages were intended to deal only with the physical consequences of the surveyors' breach of contract.

Eames London Estates Ltd. v North Hertfordshire District Council (1981) 259 EG 491

In the event that defects arise in the construction of a building, a number of parties may be at fault, apart from the surveyor who may have inspected the building for the purchaser. Rules governing the extent of liability have been stated in a number of post-War legal actions, in addition to those already mentioned. On occasion, local authority building control, architects, consulting engineers, builders, developers and surveyors have all been found liable of breach of duty to care, breach of statutory duty, or negligence. For a broad view the reader is recommended to study the judgements in *Anns* v *Merton London Borough Council* [1977] 2 All ER 492, [1978] AC 728: *Batty* v *Metropolitan Property Realisations* [1978] 2 All ER 445, [1978] QB 554; *Acrescrest Ltd.* v *W. S. Hattrell & Partners* (a firm) [1983] 1 All ER 17, [1982] 3 WLR 1076 and *Eames London Estates Ltd.* v *North Hertforshire District Council* (1981) 259 EG 491.

In Eames the case concerned an industrial building which was designed by an architect, built by a firm of contractors for a firm of developers, and subsequently let with the freehold reversionary interest sold to investors. The building was erected partly on made ground subject to past landfilling, and some cracks appeared in 1971, but it was not until 1976 that the cracking caused such alarm that expert advice sought by the tenants.

Eventually a total of three paintiffs took action against four defendants, the defendants being the architect, the local authority who passed the foundations, the developers and the builders. Judge Fay held that all four defendants were liable to pay damages. The architect was considered to bear a high degree of responsibility, since the building, and its foundations, were his design; the fact that the local authority had passed the design was no excuse. The architect was found liable to pay 32½% of the total damages awarded. The developers were held liable for 22½% of the damages having regard to their apparent knowledge of the site conditions, and lack of suitable instruction as to foundation design. The builders were held 22½% liable, despite evidence that they had found fill material in the trenches and reported this to the architect, and proceeded only on the architect's instructions. The local authority were also held 22½% liable for failing to take sufficient steps to confirm that the foundation design was suitable.

Eames is of interest because of the manner in which liability was apportioned among the negligent parties. The developers could not evade liability by pointing to the fact that they had consulted an architect; they were still liable to ensure that the land was suitable for the foundations proposed (following *Batty* v *Metropolitan Property Realisations* (supra)). The builders were unable to plead successfully that they were acting on the instructions of the architect and building inspector from the local authority in continuing to lay foundations in bad ground.

Eames also touched upon the question of the time from which the period of six years prescribed in the limitation Act for actions in tort or contract would run in circumstances where progressive crack damage was appearing in the building. It was held that this period ran, for the purpose of an action in tort, from that time when reasonable skill and diligence would have enabled the plaintiffs to have detected not merely the symptoms (cracks) but also the nature of the underlying cause (differential settlement). In Eames the plaintiffs' case against the defendants was held to be within the necessary time limit, having regard to the evidence given as to the nature of the structural movements involved and the dates at which crack damage became apparent. Interestingly, the architect claimed to have known in 1972 that differential settlement was probably the cause, this being some time before the plaintiffs were held to have appreciated this fact; it was held, however, that the architect could not rely upon his own knowledge to defeat a claim made against him on the grounds that the claim was therefore out-of-time.

Balcomb v Wards Construction (Medway) Ltd.; Pethybridge v Wards Construction (Medway) Ltd. (1981) 259 EG 765

In the Balcombe and Pethybridge cases two claims were heard together, both being claims by the purchasers of houses against the builders and their consulting engineers arising out of cracking in newly-built houses resulting from heave damage, the buildings having been erected with shallow foundations on a London clay site where a number of trees had been removed prior to commencement of construction.

Evidence was given that, following the removal of trees, heave damage can last for many years, perhaps as many as ten years, and that the shallow foundations used at a reputed depth of 1.05 metres were unsuitable. Engineers had advised the use of foundations at this depth, suggesting that it would be deep enough to avoid damage from any change in the condition of the clay. The houses had been built in 1972, and in 1974 substantial repairs were undertaken; this did not cure the problem and it was agreed, for the purpose of the legal action, that the cost of proper repair exceeded the value of the houses.

The builders, Wards, admitted liability in contract to the purchasers and agreed the quantum of damages during the course of the trial. The consulting engineers also agreed the quantum of damages if they were liable to the purchasers or the builders, but they disputed the issue of liability. The Judge, Sir Douglas Frank, held that the engineers were liable to the builders for breach of contract in failing to exercise professional skill, and also liable to the builders in tort for breach of duty to care. The Judge also held the engineers liable directly to the purchasers in tort following *Bolam* v *Friern Hospital Management Committee* (supra) and *Batty* v *Metropolitan Property Realisations* (supra).

The Judge considered, on the evidence, that in 1971 when the engineers took soil samples and gave their advice to the builders a competent engineer, encountering London clay, would have made enquiries to discover whether or not there had been trees on the site and, finding that there had been, would have caused moisture content and plasticity tests to be made on the clay. It was considered that the results of such tests would have necessitated different advice from that actually given in that deeper and special foundations would have been required to accommodate future clay swell.

Interestingly it was held that the builders were not themselves liable for negligence; the Judge considered that the builders discharged their duty by employing engineers to advise them, in this respect differing from the Eames case (supra) where the employment of an architect was not considered sufficient to absolve either the developer or the builder from a measure of responsibility for defective construction. Having regard to the fact that Wards were not themselves qualified to carry out the site investigations the Judge found it impossible to think of any other way that they could have discharged their duty other than to rely upon the consulting engineers' advice; accordingly no contributory negligence by the builders was found, and the full burden of liability for the defective foundations rested with the engineers.

Surveyors are advised to foster a relationship with a firm of consulting engineers, and to refer to them for advice on structural matters in many situations (see Chapter 3). It is suggested that, in view of the possibility that a shared liability may arise for advice given, all requests for assistance from consulting engineers should be made in writing stating the specific services required and requesting that engineers themselves should advise on the nature and extent of any testing or sampling they require to provide complete advice and that any limitations involved be carefully explained, in writing, to the client.

McGuirk *v* Homes (Basildon) Ltd. and French Kier Holdings Ltd. (*Estates Times* 29 January 1982)

In this case a claim was made by the purchasers of a house built with mortar found to consist of only one part Portland cement to thirteen parts of sand. The very weak mortar was stated by a structural engineer, called by the defendants, to have complied with building bye-laws applicable at the time, and with BSI CP 111:1970, and the defendants denied any breach of duty.

The Judge found differently, in that the duty of the defendants was 'to build in a substantial and workmanlike manner, and not merely to comply with the bye-laws'. The house had been built in 1960 and the local bye-laws applicable at the time were those of Basildon Urban District Council dated 1958. After 1965 the bye-laws were replaced by the Building Regulations in England Wales (outside inner London), and BS Code of Practice CP 111 has been revised, so that it is thought unlikely that 1:13 mortar could be defended today on the grounds that it complied.

The defect was not discovered for some years. In 1978 it was noticed that smoke was escaping from the chimney stack through the mortar joints, and a local builder was asked to investigate. He found the mortar between the bricks being blown away by the wind and many bricks loose so that they could be lifted out. Further investigation by the plaintiff revealed that the problem was quite general and applied to all the brickwork in the house.

The house has been purchased in 1960 for £3165. The eventual award of damages for diminution in value and loss of amenity was £6684.92. Concluding his judgement Judge Leonard said that the case had been a misfortune for both sides, in that the defendants found themselves saddled with an unexpected liability over 20 years after they had sold the house, and he added 'I regard this as a misfortune for them because I think it is most improbable that anyone in authority intended an unduly weak mortar mix to be used, or suspected that it was being used. The saving in expense would be minimal. It is no part of my function to speculate on the explanation. It is enough for one to say that nothing in the case has come to light suggesting any deliberate intention on the part of the defendants to build otherwise than in accordance with the contract. No word has been said suggesting that the rest of the house was not properly and soundly built'.

It is worth emphasising that a surveyor inspecting a building under construction can undertake only spot checks on materials and workmanship. The modern practice of dispensing with an on-site clerk of works (who represents the client or purchaser rather than the contractor), and the impracticability of undertaking continuous on-site supervision, means that, no matter how frequent and diligent are the surveyor's inspections, they cannot prevent deliberate breaches of good building practice by the workforce occurring between site visits. If workmen on site wish there are many opportunities for them to undertake work badly, cover up the evidence and avoid detection. Some indication of the overall quality of the workmanship and the skill and honesty of the tradesmen on site can, however, be gleaned from meeting and talking with the workforce (see Chapter 14).

London & South of England Building Society *v* Stone (1981) 261 EG 463

Mr Stone prepared a pro-forma building society report on a house in Wiltshire and valued it at £14 850, the society then lent £11 880 to the purchasers Mr and Mrs

Robinson. The house subsided, and remedial works eventually cost £29 000. The society decided to waive their rights under the mortgage deed against Mr and Mrs Robinson and proceeded against Mr Stone for £29 000 plus costs. Mr Justice Russell did not award the cost of remedial works as damages, but adopted a lower figure of £11 880 as being the difference between the stated value, and actual value of the property at the time of the report, and further deducted £3000 from this because he considered that the society had failed to mitigate their loss by waiving their rights against the borrowers. A net award of £8880 plus some costs was made.

The judgement recorded that the surveyor, Mr Stone, was a frank and honest witness who displayed a professional approach to the allegations made and emerged from the witness box with credit. He described his inspection, lasting about an hour, during which he had not seen anything untoward.

The case against Mr Stone was that he should have noticed an important crack, even allowing for some cosmetic remedial works which had been undertaken, and that he should have detected rotational movement in an outhouse, and that he should have noted sticking doors and cracking inside the house. Prior to his survey the then owner had apparently made an insurance claim for subsidence damage, which had been resisted by the insurers on the ground that it originated before they came on risk. The house had been built in about 1961 on sloping ground and on the site of an old quarry. Records existed in the form of a surveyor's report and photographs prepared for the insurers, indicating the condition in February 1976. The inspection by Mr Stone was in May 1976, so that considerable evidence existed of a major structural fault as at the date of Mr Stone's inspection.

The reader will not need reminding by now that we have emphasised in this book the desirability of acquiring local knowledge about old quarry workings and the like, and the higher risks of structural damage likely to arise with buildings erected on sloping, as opposed to level, sites which should place a surveyor on guard.

The Judge noted that attempts had been made by the vendor to better his property and that this would have resulted in some covering up of crack damage. It was felt that evidence of past internal damage was not available to be seen when Mr Stone inspected. The Judge was, however, driven to the conclusion that the crack in the exterior of the structure, and the rotational movement in the outhouse, were available to be seen and that, for whatever reason, Mr Stone had failed to detect them. The Judge found this to be an isolated lapse on the part of a surveyor of considerable expertise and experience, but that liability was plainly established.

The Judge commented upon the nature and extent of a building society survey; that it was not a full structural survey but merely a survey for building society valuation purposes. Nevertheless, the surveyor in this instance had failed to exercise the degree of care and skill expected of a reasonably competent surveyor carrying out the type of examination that he was required to carry out on behalf of the building society.

Fryer v Bunney (1982) 263 EG 158

An action for negligence and breach of duty to care was brought aganst a surveyor arising out of serious dampness found in a house due to leakage within solid floors from defective small-bore central heating pipework. The defendant surveyor, Mr Bunney, reported that the house had been checked with a moisture meter and that no reading of dampness had been found. When the purchasers took possession they soon discovered serious dampness, which was confirmed by measuring the loss of water from the central heating header tank. It became necessary to excavate the hall floor, remove defective pipework and renew joints. The judgement went in favour of the plaintiffs and the defendant surveyor was held to have been negligent in not noticing or recording the dampness. Damages of £5346 were assessed, comprising cost of repairs and decorations, reduced value of shrunken carpets, and an amount for vexation arising out of the plaintiff's inconvenience and distress (the cost of remedying the defects being presumably equivalent to the diminution in value of the property).

Problems associated with small-bore and micro-bore pipework embedded in solid floors are well recognised. It is essential that such pipework be tested for leaks under pressure before screeds are applied; frequently this is not done. In *Fryer* v *Bunney* the evidence was that soldered joints had not been properly made, and pipes were merely a push fit (indicating, among other things, the contractor's negligence). It is also essential that lagging be properly provided to permit thermal expansion and contraction. Even well-made joints can fail if the pipework is screeded in solidly and unable to respond to thermal movements. From a surveyor's point of view such pipework is inaccessible on subsequent survey, and the only practicable tests are of moisture levels in surrounding walls and floors. Unfortunately for Mr Bunney it was held that he had not undertaken such testing to the standard and extent required in the circumstances.

Fisher *v* Knowles (1982) 262 EG 1083

The purchasers claimed against their surveyor some four years after the purchase, particularising 14 items as being alleged defects; the judge found that the surveyor had failed to warn his clients of only two matters, being some wet-rot to window frames and defects to ceiling joists.

Instructions arose because the surveyor was to inspect the house for the building society, and the purchasers approached him with a request that he also provide them with a private report and valuation. The Judge found that these instructions amounted to something more than a bare valuation report, but something less than a full structural survey. The RICS Practice Note (which was not published when the allegedly negligent inspection was made) now recommends that if something less than a full structural survey is to be carried out it is important that the true nature and extent of the obligation being assumed by the surveyor is understood by, and agreed with, the client.

The Judge emphasised that the burden is on the plaintiffs to prove that, on the balance of the probabilities, the defects were of a kind to which the defendant should have drawn attention. Making the best he could of the evidence the Judge awarded £500 damages for diminution in value of the house, resulting from the two alleged defects found to have existed at the time of the inspection and missed by the surveyor. A claim for a further 12 items was unsuccessful.

Wet-rot to softwood window frames is a known hazard, and the defendant surveyor was in the habit of testing joinery with a penknife; he considered that he would have done so in this case. The Judge found, on balance, that there had been wet-rot to the window frames, and that for some reason the surveyor had failed to detect it. He also felt that the surveyor had failed to notice defecting ceilings under a bathroom floor due to the poor fixing of a WC pan, which would have placed him on guard.

The writers would recommend that particular care be taken in inspecting exterior painted softwood for signs of rot, and also whenever possible in checking conditions under WC pans resting on timber floors, since rot to timbers from leaking seals will commonly be found.

Unfair Contract Terms Act 1977

This applies to England and Wales, but not to Scotland, and limits the extent to which a contract may attempt to exclude liability. Before a surveyor attempts to limit his liability he should confirm, by taking professional advice if necessary, that it is possible to do so having regard to the provisions of this Act. A surveyor will also have to consider if a limitation of liability is ethically appropriate having regard to the circumstances.

In Section 2 of the Act provisions are made in respect of negligence liability. The Act states:

'(1) A person (in the course of business) cannot by reference to any contract term or to any notice given to persons generally or to particular persons exclude or restrict his liability for death or personal injury resulting from negligence'.
'(2) In the case of other loss or damage, a person cannot so exclude or restrict his liability for negligence except in so far as the term or notice satisfies the requirement of reasonableness'.

In these contexts the term 'business' includes a profession.

In Section 3 the Act provides certain rules in respect of liability arising in contract, and states:

'(1) This section applies as between contracting parties where one of them deals as consumer or on the other's written standard terms of business.
'(2) As against that party, the other cannot by reference to any contract term (a) where himself in breach of contract, exclude or restrict any liability of his in respect of the breach; or (b) claim to be entitled (i) to render a contractual performance substantially different from that which was reasonably expected from him; or (ii) in respect of the whole or any part of his contractual obligation, to render no performance at all, except in so far as (in any of the cases mentioned in the above sub-section) the contract term satisfies the requirement of reasonableness'.

The 'requirement of reasonableness' means that the contract term should be fair and reasonable having regard to all the circumstances of which the parties were aware, or ought to have been aware, at the time the contract was entered into.

A distinction is made between those cases where a surveyor is acting for a client as consumer and those cases where the client is not a consumer, 'consumer' for this purpose meaning an ordinary member of the public making use of the surveyor's services in his private capacity in connection with his personal affairs. A client who is himself in business, or a company client, will not be a consumer for this purpose and as between such non-consumers and their surveyors the Act allows special bargains to be struck which can exclude any need to consider if the test of reasonableness need apply.

A member of the public buying a house is a consumer for this purpose. Whatever are the terms agreed between the surveyor and such a client they must pass the test of reasonableness. The normally-accepted and traditional practices of a profession, in respect of the nature of the inspection and the matters covered in the report, would be a reasonable basis for a contract between the parties. A substantial departure from normal or traditional surveying practices might be unable to pass a test of reasonableness.

In so far as a surveyor follows traditional and normal practices, and the recommendations of his professional institution, it would seem most unlikely that this would be held to be unreasonable.

Supply of Goods and Services Act 1982

This Act, which came into force on 4 July 1983, codifies the common law position as already described in this Chapter, and covers any contract under which a person agrees to carry out a service. The Act provides implied terms which are deemed to be incorporated into every contract for the supply of a service in that the supplier (the surveyor) will exercise reasonable care and skill, that he will carry out the service within a reasonable time and that the charge made will be a reasonable one (terms as to time and charges apply only when these matters are not covered by the contract itself). Only if the contract fixes neither the fee nor the manner of its assessment (i.e., an hourly rate for professional time) may a client challenge a charge made using the Act's provisions.

It is felt that the Act will not make any significant change in the legal liability for negligence in surveying buildings, merely that it has codified existing law by statute.

Professional indemnity insurance

As the professional man's liability at law has been increasingly put to the test over the last few decades so the insurance industry has sought to provide a constructive and effective form of protection. With the considerable growth in negligence claims made against surveyors the demand for appropriate insurance cover has risen dramatically. Understandably, as a professional partnership does not enjoy limited liability status, the need to transfer professional risk by means of an insurance contract has become a major consideration of many practices. The primary function of such insurance is to provide an indemnity to the Assured for claims made by third parties against them arising out of professional negligence or, more importantly, alleged professional negligence in the course of the firm's business.

Insurers provide cover on what is termed a 'claims made' basis. The policy is designed to respond to claims notified to Underwriters during the currency of the policy. Therefore it is not important with most policies when the event that gives rise to the claim occurs but when the actual claim itself is made. As long as this falls within the policy period, the insurance will be operative. Theoretically, the Insurers of a practice today could be asked to provide an indemnity to their Assured for claims arising out of work carried out ten or more years ago. Policies of this type are known to be 'fully retroactive' and will cover the Assured for claims arising out of the practice's work since the establishment of the business. Consequently it is important to notify Insurers as soon as possible of any circumstances that may give rise to a claim, especially if the end of the policy period is approaching.

Within the term 'Assured' Underwriters are providing an indemnity in respect of work undertaken by the partners, employees and those under contract of service with the practice. Furthermore the policy should cover past partners and also the estates and legal representatives of any deceased partner. Should the practice be dissolved then it is of vital importance to arrange suitable 'run-off' cover as the partners will still be jointly and severally liable for the past work of the firm.

It is not easy to identify an adequate limit of indemnity for any given practice; clearly it must bear some relationship to the size of the firm's operations and type of business undertaken. Very large partnerships will normally purchase indemnity limits running into many millions in order to provide themselves with full protection.

Costs and expenses in defending a claim are also provided for under the policy with the consent of Underwriters and are usually paid in addition to the indemnity limit. Naturally this aspect is of considerable importance when one considers both escalating legal costs and possible prolonged litigation in the event of a claim. Indeed this time perspective should be carefully taken into account when estimating the required limit of indemnity. What may seem to be adequate cover in today's terms may well be insufficient when a particularly complex and lengthy claim notified now is eventually settled in a number of years' time.

Many Insurers will offer a limit of indemnity on an 'any one claim' basis. Thus instead of providing cover of, say, £500 000 in total over the twelve months' policy Underwriters will respond to any number of claims during the period but the indemnity will be limited to £500 000 in respect of each and every claim.

As the demand for professional indemnity insurance has grown so the cover offered by Insurers has developed. Many policies will include claims arising out of breach of contract, breach of warranty of authority, breach of trust, conversion of property, and claims for monies had and received. In its most sophisticated form cover can be offered on a 'civil liability' basis which provides an indemnity to the Assured against claims emanating from any civil liability that the Assured may have at law in connection with the professional business of the practice. Other aspects often included under these policies are fidelity guarantee, costs of restoring or replacing lost documents, and a proportion of legal costs involved in action for recovery for professional fees.

It is quite usual for Insurers to insist that the Assured contribute a certain payment to each and every claim, and this is known as the 'excess'. Normally this is very small in relation to the limit of indemnity provided by the policy. It is hoped that this device will ensure a certain degree of caution in the Assured's activities as clearly the policy will not provide one hundred per cent cover. Therefore the Assured knows that he will still have a 'financial liability' to some extent in relation to any negligence on his part.

As with all insurance contracts the cover is governed by a set of conditions, such as the Assured's agreement not to admit liability in the event of a claim without the prior agreement of Underwriters. Again, most policies require the Assured to provide immediate notice in writing of any claims or circumstances that may give rise to a claim and provide Insurers with all reasonable assistance in defending such claims.

As with policy conditions, so policy exclusions feature in the wording, and detail those activities or types of claim that will not be covered, such as surveys undertaken by unqualified staff or losses that would normally be covered by other insurances.

It would seem that as society becomes more litigious and professionals are increasing being asked to account for their actions so the need for professional indemnity insurance becomes all the more essential. If a partnership is to continue its professional business without the possibility of suffering unacceptably high losses as the result of human error then appropriate steps must be taken to transfer the risk to a specialist insurance carrier.

Bibliography

'Shelling of Plaster Finishing Coats', Building Research Establishment (BRE) Information Sheet, TIL 14 1971

'Settlement of a Brick Dwellinghouse on Heavy Clay, 1951–1973', W. H. Ward, BRE, CP 37/74, February 1974

'High-alumina Cement Concrete in Buildings', BRE, CP 34/75, April 1975

'A Simple Pull-out Test to Assess the Strength of *in situ* Concrete', BRE, CP 25/77, June 1977

'Field Measurement of the Sound Insulation of Plastered Solid Brick Walls', E. C. Sewell and R. S. Alphey, BRE, CP 37/78, March 1978

'Foundations for Low-rise Buildings', BRE, CP 61/78, September 1978

'The Performance of Cavity-wall Ties', BRE Information Paper, IP 4/81, April 1981

'House Longhorn Beetle Survey', R. Geraldine Lea, BRE Information Paper, IP 12/82, July 1982

'Inspection and Maintenance of Flat and Low-pitched Timber Roofs', W. T. Hide, BRE Information Paper, IP 15/82, August 1982

'Considerations in the Design of Timber Flat Roofs', I. S. McIntyre and D. P. Birch, BRE Information Paper, IP 19/82, Septemer 1982

'Assessment of Damage in Low-rise Buildings', *BRE Digest* 251, July 1981 (from HMSO)

'The Durability of Steel and Concrete', Parts 1, 2 and 3. *BRE Digests* 263, 264 and 265, July, August and September 1982 (from HMSO)

'Specifications for Roofing Felt', British Standards Institution (BSI), BS 747:1977

'Metal Ties for Cavity-wall Construction', BSI, BS 1243:1978

'Guide to the Choice, Use and Application of Wood Preservatives', BSI, BS 1282:1959 (revised 1975)

'Preservative Treatment for Constructional Timber', BSI, BS 5268, Part 5:1977 (supersedes CP 98)

'Code of Practice for Trees in Relation to Construction', BSI, BS 5837:1980

'Foundations and Sub-structures for non-Industrial Buildings of not more than Four Storeys', BSI, CP 101:1972

'Structural Recommendations for Load-bearing Walls', BSI CP 111:1970

'The Structural Use of Timber', BSI, CP 112, Part 2:1971

'Roof Coverings: Mastic Asphalt', BSI, CP 144, Part 4:1970
'Small Sewage Treatment Works', BSI, CP 302:1972 1st revision. Revised as 'Code of Practice for Small Sewage Treatment Works and Cess-pools', BS 6297:1983
'Foundations', BSI, CP 2004:1972

Building Regulations, and Building Regulations (Amendments), Her Majesty's Stationery Office (HMSO)
'Common Defects in Buildings, H. J. Eldridge, Property Services Agency (PSA), Department of the Environment (DoE), HMSO, 1976
Small Claims in the County Court, HMSO
Quality in Traditional Housing (series), R. B. Bonshor and H. W. Harrison, HMSO, 1982: Vol 1: *Investigation into Faults and Their Avoidance*: Vol 2: *Aid to Design*: Vol 3: *Aid to Site Inspection*
Registered House-Builders' Site Manual, National House-Building Council (NHBC), 1974
Registered House-Builders' Handbook, 1974, and Practice Notes, NHBC
'Timber-framed Buildings', NHBC Practice Note 5 (1982), rewritten and reissued November 1982
'Suspended-floor Construction for Dwellings on Deep-fill Sites', NHBC Practice Note 6, August 1973 revised April 1974

'Structural Surveys of Residential Property', Royal Institution of Chartered Surveyors (RICS), Practice Note, May 1981 (from Surveyors' Technical Services (STS))
Buying a House? RICS 1981 (from STS)
Guide to House Rebuilding Costs for Insurance Valuation (annual), RICS Building Cost Information Service (BCIS) with British Insurance Association
'Code of Measuring Practice', jointly RICS/ISVA (Incorporated Society of Valuers and Auctioneers), 1979

Manual of Timber-frame Housing (A Simplified Method), (National Building Agency) NBA/TRDA (Timber Research and Development Association), The Construction Press, 1980
Timber-frame Housing Design Guide, Section 9, 'Structural Recommendations', TRDA, 1979
Trees in Britain, Europe and North America, Roger Phillips, Pan Books Ltd, 1978
'Building Defects', *The Chartered Surveyor* Supplement, April 1981
'Regulations for Domestic Equipment', Institution of Electrical Engineers (IEE)
Mitchell's Building Construction (series), B. T. Batsford Ltd, Vol 1: *Structure and Fabric*, Part 1, 2nd edn 1979: Vol 2: *Structure and Fabric*, Part 2, 2nd edn 1977: Vol 3: *Materials*, 2nd edn 1978: Vol 4: *Components*, 2nd edn 1979
A History of Architecture, 4th edn, Prof. Banister Fletcher, FRIBA, and Banister F. FLetcher, ARIBA, B. T. Batsford Ltd, 1901. 18th edn, Sir Banister F. Fletcher, rev'd J. C. Palmes, The Athlone Press (LU), 1975
Building Techniques (series – Science Paperbacks), Chapman & Hall, Vol 1: *Structure*, 2nd edn 1979: Vol 2: *Services*, 3rd edn 1980
Principles of Element Design, Peter Rich, George Godwin Ltd, 1977
Design Failures in Buildings (series), First Series 1972, Second Series 1974, George Godwin Ltd
The Law and Practice of Arbitrations, John Parris, George Godwin Ltd, 1974
Builders' Detail Sheets, Series 2, Northwood Publications, 1977

Building Maintenance Management, Reginald Lee, Crosby Lockwood Staples, 1976
Shaw's Commentary on the Building Regulations, Shaw & Sons Ltd, 1977
New Metric Handbook, The Architectural Press, 1979
How to Study Architecture, Charles H. Caffin, New York Tudor Publishing Co, 1937
Rebuild, R. Derricott and S. S. Chissick, John Wiley & Sons Ltd, 1982
Quality and Total Cost in Buildings and Services Design, The Construction Press, 1976
Architects' Standard Catalogues (annual) Standard Catalogue Information Services Ltd
Spon's Architects' and Builders' Price Book (annual), E. & F. N. Spon
Laxton's Building Price Book (annual), Kelly's Directories Ltd
The Enemies of Timber, The Cuprinol Preservation Centre, 1971
Alteration or Conversion of Houses, 4th edn, J. F. Garner, Oyez Press Ltd, 1975
Nothing But The Truth, John Watson, The Estates Gazette Ltd, 1971
Real Property Law, Hugh H. V. Forbes, The Estates Gazette Ltd, 1962

Related Butterworth books

Building Maintenance and Preservation: a guide for design and management, Editor: Edward D. Mills, 1980
Building Problems: Science and Solutions, Lyall Addleson, 1983
House Builder's Reference Book, Editor: M. J. V. Powell, 1979
Maintenance and Repair of Buildings and their internal environment B. D. Hutchinson, J. Barton and N. Ellis, 1975
The Conservation of Historic Buildings, Bernard M. Feilden, 1982
The Conservation of Structural and Decorative Stone, J. Ashurst, 1983
Building Conversion and Rehabilitation: designing for change in building use, Editor: Thomas A. Markus, 1979

Acts of Parliament and other Regulations

Agricultural Holdings Act 1948
Building Regulations 1976
Building (First Amendment) Regulations 1978
Building (Second Amendment) Regulations 1981
Building Regulations (N Ireland) 1977
Building Regulations (N Ireland) (Amendment) Regulations 1979
Building Standard (Scotland) Regulations 1971 to 1979
Defective Premises Act 1972
Factories Acts
Fire Precautions Act 1971
Fire Precautions Act 1971 (Modifications) Regulations 1976
Health and Safety at Work Act 1974
Historic Buildings and Ancient Monuments Act 1953
Homes Insulation Scheme 1982
Housing Acts 1957, 1961, 1974 and 1980
Housing Finance Act 1972
Landlord and Tenant Acts 1927 and 1954
Law of Property Act 1925

Leasehold Property (Repairs) Act 1938
Leasehold Reform Act 1967
Limitation Acts 1939 and 1980
Local Authorities (Historic Buildings) Act 1962
London Building Acts and London Building Acts (Amendment) Act 1939
London Building (Construction) Bye-Laws 1972
Offices, Shops and Railway Premises Act 1963
Public Health Act 1939
Rent Acts
Supply of Goods and Services Act 1982
Town and Country Amenities Act 1974
Town and Country Planning Act 1971
Unfair Contract Terms Act 1977

Court cases

Acrecrest Ltd *v* W. S. Hattrell & Partners (a firm) [1983] 1 *All ER* 17,
[1982] 3 *WLR* 1076
Anns *v* Merton London Borough Council [1977] 2 *All ER* 492, [1978] AC 728
*Balcomb *v* Wards Construction (Medway) Ltd (1981) 259 *EG* 765
Batty *v* Metropolitan Property Realisations [1978] 2 *All ER* 445, [1978] QB 554
*Bolam *v* Friern Hospital Management Committee [1957] 2 *All ER* 118,
[1957] 1 *WLR* 582
Bunclark *v* Hertfordshire County Council (1977) 243 *EG* 455
*Donoghue (or McAlister) *v* Stevenson [1932] *All ER* Rep 1, [1932] AC 562
Drummond *v* S & U Stores (1980) 258 *EG* 1293
*Dutton *v* Bognor Regis Urban District Council [1972] 1 *All ER* 462,
[1972] 1 QB 373
*Eames London Estates Ltd *v* North Hertfordshire District Council
(1981) 259 *EG* 491
Finchbourne Ltd *v* Rodrigues [1976] 3 *All ER* 581
*Fisher *v* Knowles (1982) 262 *EG* 1083
*Fryer *v* Bunney (1982) 263 *EG* 158
Hancock *v* B. W. Brazier (Anerley) Ltd [1966] 2 *All ER* 901, [1966] 1 *WLR* 1317
*Hedley Byrne & Co Ltd *v* Heller & Partners Ltd [1963] 2 *All ER* 575,
[1964] AC 465
*Leigh *v* Unsworth (1972) 230 *EG* 501
*London & South of England Building Society *v* Stone (1981) 261 *EG* 463
*McGuirk *v* Homes (Basildon) Ltd and French Kier Holdings Ltd (*Estates Times*
29 January 1982)
*Morgan *v* Perry (1973) 229 *EG* 1737
*Perry *v* Sidney Phillips & Son (a firm) [1982] 1 *All ER* 1005, [1982] 3 *All ER* 705,
[1982] 1 *WLR* 1297
Pirelli General Cable Works Ltd *v* Oscar Faber & Partners [1983] 1 *All ER* 65,
[1983] 2 *WLR* 6
*Rona *v* Pearce (1953) 162 EG 380
*Yianni *v* Edwin Evans & Sons (a firm) [1981] 3 *All ER* 592, [1981] 3 *WLR* 843

*Cases discussed in Chapter 19

Useful addresses

National House-Building Council (NHBC)
  Chiltern Avenue, Amersham, Bucks HP6 5AP
Building Research Establishment (BRE)
Building Research Advisory Service (BRAS)
  Garston, Watford, Herts WD2 7JR
Department of the Environment (DoE)
Property Services Agency (PSA)
  2 Marsham Street, London SW1P 3EB
Royal Institution of Chartered Surveyors (RICS)
Surveyors' Technical Services (STS – publishers for RICS)
  12 Great George Street, London SW1P 3AD
Building Cost Information Service (BCIS) (RICS)
Building Maintenance Cost Information Service (BMCIS) (RICS)
  85–87 Clarence Street, Kingston-upon-Thames, Surrey KT1 1RB
Royal Institute of British Architects (RIBA)
  66 Portland Place, London W1N 4AD
Institution of Electrical Engineers (IEE)
  Savoy Place, London WC2R 0BL
Incorporated Society of Valuers and Auctioneers (ISVA)
  3 Cadogan Gate, London SW1X 0AS
British Standards Institution (BSI)
  Head Office: 2 Park Street, London W1A 2BS
  Sales: 101 Pentonville Road, London N1 9ND
Her Majesty's Stationery Office (HMSO)
  Government Bookshop, 49 High Holborn, London WC1V 6HB
Society for the Protection of Ancient Buildings
  55 Great Ormond Street, London WC1N 3JA
Timber Research and Development Association (TRDA)
  Chiltern House, Stocking Lane, Hughenden Valley, High Wycombe,
  Bucks HP 14 4ND
Ordnance Survey
  Romsey Road, Maybush, Southampton, Hants SO9 4DH
Institute of Geological Sciences
  Exhibition Road, London SW7 2DE
British Insurance Association
  Aldermary House, Queen Street, London EC4N 1TU

Index